THE NEW NATURALIST
A SURVEY OF BRITISH NATURAL HISTORY

FOSSILS

The aim of this series is to interest the general reader in the wild life of Britain by recapturing the inquiring spirit of the old naturalists. The Editors believe that the natural pride of the British public in the native fauna and flora, to which must be added concern for their conservation, is best fostered by maintaining a high standard of accuracy combined with clarity of exposition in presenting the results of modern scientific research.

The text and line illustrations are here reproduced unaltered, but the process of manufacture used to achieve an economic price does not, unfortunately, do full justice to all the photographs; and those originally in colour appear in black and white.

AN ENGLISH LANDSCAPE IN COAL MEASURE TIMES

See page 86

THE NEW NATURALIST

FOSSILS

by

H. H. SWINNERTON

C.B.E., D.SC.

PROFESSOR EMERITUS

THE UNIVERSITY OF

NOTTINGHAM

Bloomsbury Books
London

First Edition, 1960
Reprinted, 1962
Reprinted, 1970
Reprinted, 1973

This edition published 1989 by
Bloomsbury Books an imprint of
Godfrey Cave Associates Limited
42 Bloomsbury Street, London WC1B 3QJ
under license from William Collins Son's & Co. Ltd.

ISBN 1 870630 93 9

CONTENTS

Part III: An Era of Transitions (the Mesozoic)

Part IV: An Era of Culminations (the Cainozoic)

* As explained on the second page, these plates are here reproduced in black and white.

LIST OF PLATES

*For most of the fossils in these plates the generic names alone are given
in the captions. Students will find the specific names, with the generic,
in the Index at the end of the book*

LIST OF TEXT FIGURES

EDITORS' PREFACE

OVER the past two centuries the word 'fossil' has undergone an evolution in meaning. Rightly applied from its Latin derivation, to anything dug up, it came first to be used for the more interesting objects so revealed—to stones of curious shape, to minerals of strange character—and so especially to those 'figure-stones' which obviously resembled living things. Here, entombed in the rocks, was the incontrovertible evidence of Noah's flood but, as successive horizons of fossiliferous beds came to be observed, there must have been other and earlier floods. In due course the pioneer geologists who made the first geological maps of Britain, notably William Smith, came to realise that the different rocks were characterised by different assemblages of fossils. Then, as the uniformitarian school of geologists, headed by Charles Lyell, demonstrated that the slow processes of denudation and accumulation which could be observed taking place on the earth's surface were adequate to explain the observed facts without invoking giant cataclysms or world-wide deluges so it was found that the youngest rocks had fossils most closely resembling animals and plants now living. The older the rocks the more the buried remains differed from living creatures.

So the word fossil has come to be restricted to the evidences of former life now entombed in the rocks of the earth's crust. Hard parts, bones or shells, may be preserved little changed; the impression of a leaf may remain whilst the substance is completely altered; a footprint made in sand now hardened to sandstone may be the only trace of an extinct animal but still comes into the category of fossil.

Britain is exceptionally fortunate in its geology. It includes samples, as it were, of rocks laid down in almost every division of geological time. It would be difficult to find any other area of the earth's surface of comparable extent which is such a natural museum. Thus an account of British fossils covers remains of almost every type and of almost every geological age. Naturally the earlier workers looked upon the different fossils as separately created species. In many rocks in Britain fossils occur in sufficient numbers at successive levels that evolution at work can be traced stage by stage and the species of the older palaeontologists merge into one another by almost imperceptible gradations.

The Editors of the New Naturalist count themselves extremely fortunate in having persuaded Professor Swinnerton to write this volume. For the past fifty-seven years he has been closely associated with a single University institution—University College, Nottingham, now the University of

Nottingham of which he is Professor Emeritus. After getting his First Class at Imperial College, London, and serving there as Demonstrator he joined the staff of the old all-embracing 'Natural Sciences Department' at Nottingham in 1902. As the College grew, fledgling departments left the nest, but for many years Swinnerton was Head of Geology and Geography till the latter became independent. Perhaps it is this broad academic background which has prevented Professor Swinnerton from becoming the narrow specialist. His detailed researches, for example on the Teleosts, have earned for him the highest honours in the geological world culminating in the Presidency of the Geological Society in 1938-40, but he always sees the detailed work against a background of the natural sciences as a whole and never divorced from field-studies—in particular in the Midlands which he knows so intimately.

We know, therefore, of no better guide for the New Naturalist reader into the fascinating world of the life of the past. In the pages which follow he not only conducts us into the past but he introduces us to very many of the men and women whose work uncovered the secrets—it is a human as well as a scientific story.

THE EDITORS

AUTHOR'S PREFACE

FOSSILS are not merely stones, not merely curiosities to be collected, enumerated and described, they have a meaning and they tell a story. The purpose of this book is to relate briefly how that meaning was uncovered and that story unfolded. In laying the foundations of this study of fossils, this Science of Palaeontology, British students have played a large part for they have always been favoured with an abundance of easily accessible material from rocks of all ages. They have therefore made great contributions towards equipping geologists for exploring the rocks in all continents, discovering economic resources and elucidating the creative processes that have controlled the development of living things upon the Earth.

While writing this book I have become increasingly indebted to many who have readily helped me both with the text and the illustrations. My thanks are due to the Librarian and Staff of the Geological Society of London who have searched out for me numerous obscure as well as ordinary references; also to Sir Julian Huxley for reading the manuscript with great care and giving me the benefit of his unique knowledge in the form of criticisms and suggestions.

For such a subject as 'Fossils' numerous illustrations are a necessity. In obtaining these I was fortunate at the outset in establishing a link with my old friend and pupil the late Sir Arthur Trueman. Years ago he himself set out to write a book on 'Fossils' but was prevented from completing it by the pressure of other duties. He did, however, assemble a number of photographs for this purpose. Professor Neville George kindly put me in touch with Mr. Andrew Ferguson who made those photographs and generously placed them at my disposal. For other illustrations I gratefully acknowledge my indebtedness to the staff of the Geology Department of the University of Nottingham, to Professor W. D. Evans, to Mr. W. Sutcliffe his photographer and to Dr. F. M. Taylor, lecturer in Palaeontology; also to Mr. F. T. Baker, Curator of the City and County Museum, Lincoln; to Dr. H. Godwin at the Botany School, Cambridge; to Dr. F. Hodson, the Department of Geology in the University of Southampton; to Dr. P. E. Kent and the British Petroleum Exploration Company; and to the Palaeontographical Society for permission to reproduce several figures from their Monographs.

A brief inspection of the plates will show how great is my debt to the Geological Survey of Great Britain, to the Director, Sir William Pugh, D.Sc., F.R.S., and to other members of the Survey who, with their usual generosity, have given me every assistance in securing suitable photographs.

My thanks are also due to the Controller of Her Majesty's Stationery Office for granting me permission to reproduce these photographs many of which have already appeared in official publications. Others appear here for the first time.

My thanks are due to Mr. Maurice Wilson for the skill with which he has interpreted suggestions made for a coloured Frontispiece. In the execution of this he has discussed details with various experts and thus produced a picture that is scientifically accurate as well as artistically beautiful.

Finally, while producing this book I have been very conscious of the wholehearted way in which the 'New Naturalist' committee and the publishers with their staff, have entered into the task of making this volume a worthy companion for the other members of the series.

H. H. SWINNERTON

Part One

PRELIMINARY
CONSIDERATIONS

CHAPTER I

FIGURED STONES

C OLLECTING shells is one of the pleasures of a seaside holiday that is enjoyed by 'children and grown-ups too'. Sometimes it develops from being a passing fancy into the hobby of a lifetime. Such may have been the case with Martin Lister (1638-1711) who, at the opening of the eighteenth century, became house physician to Queen Anne. He was also an active member of the newly formed Royal Society.

In Lister's day any object found buried in the ground such as crystals, minerals, ores, prettily coloured and curiously shaped stones, were called fossils. This term, however, was eventually confined to the shaped stones which at that time were known as 'lapides figurati' or figured stones. Some of these, found in such rocks as chalk, limestone and clay, attracted his attention because they closely resembled in shape some of his sea shells. In 1678 he published a book with three parts giving precise descriptions of the objects in his collections. The third part, dealing with sea shells, included a section on 'figured stones' which is of value even today, a value that is enhanced by a number of plates with carefully drawn figures. Lister was, however, only one of a small galaxy of English naturalists that also included Edward Lhwyd, Robert Hooke, John Woodward and John Ray who, towards the end of the seventeenth century, laid the foundations of the study of fossils in Britain.

They were by no means the first people to notice the figured stones for these were known even in classical times to both Greeks and Romans, who had seen them in the plains of Egypt as well as in the mountains of their native lands. From what little is known of their observations, it seems that they usually accepted the facts at their face value and looked upon these fossils as the remains of animals and plants; and as evidence that the sea had in past times occupied even inland areas. On the other hand there were some who, like Aristotle, gave their imaginations free play and held the opinion that the earth

FOS.—B

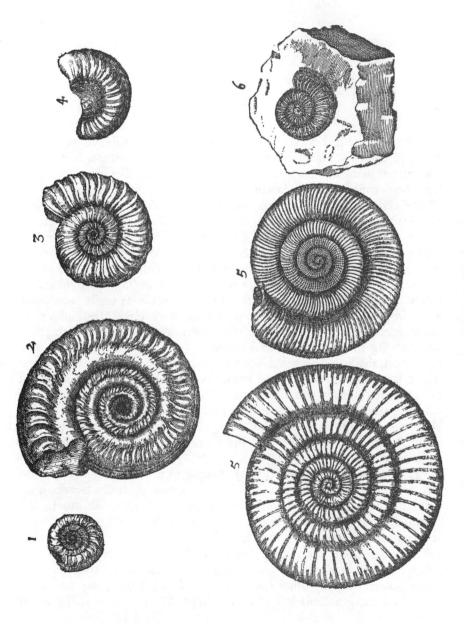

itself had 'plastic virtues' which enabled it to give birth to these figured stones. Pliny's imagination led him still further to the view that these stones fell from heaven during eclipses of the moon and were of value to mankind when suffering from sickness or from love.

Even in this highly enlightened twentieth century flights of imagination, as well as careful observation and experiment, play their part in scientific progress. It is not surprising therefore that in the centuries which preceded the dawn of modern science, when men were beginning to grope their way into and through the intricacies of nature, fact and fancy were mixed together in their various interpretations. Thus, for example, Lhwyd (Luidius), Keeper of the Ashmolean Museum, Oxford, published a good factual description with illustrations of the specimens under his charge. Nevertheless, in a letter to Ray he suggested, as an explanation of the presence of figured stones in the rocks, that mists drifting from the sea over the land carried with them the 'seed' of sea animals. These were washed down by the rain into the crevices of the rocks and caused the growth of stones resembling the shellfish, sea-urchins and the like from which they had come. There was perhaps more sense in his line of thought than in the teaching of a learned Oxford Divine as late as the nineteenth century who, according to a story told by Sir Archibald Geikie, was of the "opinion that fossils in the rocks had been purposely placed there by the devil to deceive, mislead and perplex mankind." Even in this twentieth century there are in England folk, otherwise quite sensible, who keep hidden about their persons a fossil to bring them luck; or some other object, dried potato or nutmeg, as a guard against rheumatism. Every year hundreds of sightseers visit caves in the Mendips or in Derbyshire and gaze with gullible wonder at the fantastic figures pointed out to them there in the heart of the rocks. Such modern whims and fancies are vestiges of a medieval outlook and help us to appreciate the mental atmosphere in which these early students of nature worked and thought.

Fig. 1. 'FIGURED STONES'

Reproduced from Martin Lister *Historiae Animalium Angliae* published in 1678, Plate XVI, p. 205. For improving technique in representation compare Fig. 19 (1865). Plate XIV*b* (1916) and then all the other plates, including the frontispiece. The stones here shown are now identified as follows: 1, *Arietites*. 2, *Hildoceras*. 3, *Arietites*. 4, *Schlotheimia*. 5, *Dactylioceras*, coarsely and finely ribbed species. 6, ?

It was gifted men like Lister, Lhwyd and their fellows who in this and other lands were pioneers blazing pathways for later generations to follow in the study of nature. In these pages we are concerned mainly with the study of 'Fossils in Britain' but the presence of workers in the background in other lands must be kept in mind. Though communications were slow, limited to the speed of coach and horse, new knowledge percolated to and fro and the study of fossils, today called the Science of Palaeontology, came into being. Its progress in Britain consequently reflects its development throughout western Europe.

In the forefront among foreign pioneers was the Italian Leonardo da Vinci (1452-1519) who lived two centuries before Lister. In addition to his many activities in public life and in painting, music, poetry and architecture he was an engineer. In this last capacity he was sometimes engaged in making canals and had often seen fossils in their natural positions in the rocks, and his observations upon them led him to combat the fanciful ideas about their origin which many others entertained. He favoured the view that they were the actual remains of marine animals that lived on the spot where their remains are now found and had been buried in the mud and sand brought down to the sea by rivers or pounded from the cliffs by waves. In course of time these deposits hardened into rocks and, being raised in level, became land.

In England the problem received little attention until the end of the seventeenth century when it was tackled vigorously by the band of workers mentioned above. Lister, unlike Lhwyd, was in a state of uncertainty. He was willing to concede that fossils found around the shores of the Mediterranean might be the remains of sea animals, and that certain fossil shells from Kent, shown to him by Lhwyd, were really oyster shells. But that could not be the case for some specimens found by him in many English quarries. He observed that some found in ironstone consisted of ironstone; others found in limestone and chalk consisted of limestone and chalk. To him that seemed conclusive evidence that they were produced by some plastic influence at work within the rocks themselves. Woodward, Hooke and Ray on the other hand held the same view as did da Vinci, that they were the actual remains of organisms; a view which became generally accepted by the middle of the eighteenth century.

Woodward built up a comprehensive and systematically arranged collection of fossils and compiled a catalogue. These he bequeathed to the University of Cambridge and also founded what is now known as the Woodwardian Chair of Geology. Hooke, a physician and mathematician at Gresham College, was a genius endowed with a fertile imagination that led him to make many suggestions that later work proved to be correct. Thus from the presence of fossil turtles in the rocks of the south of England he inferred that the climate there must at one time have been much warmer than it is today. He also considered that fossils had a historical value similar to that possessed by coins and ancient manuscripts.

It is not often that pranks played by students have helped forward the cause of science, but such was the case for a trick played by the students of the University of Würzburg upon their professor who was still obsessed with the plastic virtues hidden in the rocks. They carved figures of various creatures, of sun, moon and even Hebrew letters upon stones and planted them in suitable exposures about the countryside. In due time these were discovered by their professor along with genuine figured stones. In 1726 he published an illustrated account of his finds. At a later date he found a stone with his own name carved upon it. This opened his eyes to the trick that was being played upon him and he promptly destroyed all copies of his work upon which he could lay his hands. That incident hastened the decline of fanciful interpretations of figured stones, and by the middle of the eighteenth century they were forgotten.

During much of the eighteenth century progress in the biological sciences slowed down temporarily; for they had to mark time until chemistry had broken away completely from the bonds of alchemy, and had begun to give a sound insight into those processes which underlie the bodily functions of plants and animals. Similarly the study of fossils had to await the further advance in the systematic study of living organisms and of the rocks. These basal aspects of palaeontological studies must now be briefly considered.

CHAPTER 2

THE NATURE AND
ORIGIN OF FOSSILS

IN bygone days one of the housekeeper's main worries was how to keep meat and other foods stuffs from going bad. In recent years this problem has been largely solved by the introduction of refrigerators and of tinned meats and vegetables. In the former the action of destructive bacteria is prevented by low temperatures and in the other their presence is excluded by hermetically sealing the tin containers.

In nature similar methods have been used with varying degrees of success to preserve the remains of animals and plants as fossils. Thus for example in the frozen muds of northern Siberia carcasses of a large elephant, the mammoth and of the woolly rhinoceros have been found completely preserved from the furry covering of the body to the last meal taken into the stomach. Equally striking though not so impressive are the 'Bees in Amber'. In present day pine forests a resinous substance may often be seen oozing out on to the bark of the trees. Occasionally a fly, a bee or some other equally small creature becomes entangled and then engulfed in this, and is thus effectively sealed off from the action of decaying influences. Lumps of a similar kind of substance in the form of amber containing insects are found in ancient soils and peats.

The mention of peat is a reminder that it also is a preservative of no mean importance in nature. In our own islands extensive accumulations of peat have been and are still being formed in boggy areas. Portions of these are often covered with verdure which gives to the surface a false appearance of solidity and animals venturing upon it have sunk in and disappeared. Some of these bogs, drained naturally or artificially, have been extensively excavated and the peat used for fuel or other purposes. Now and then skeletons have been found, many of which belong to the so-called Irish Elk (a deer named

Megaceros giganteus) a magnificent creature whose antlers sometimes had a stretch of more than 10 feet from tip to tip.

It should be noted that in peat decaying influences are not completely eliminated, for in every instance, the flesh has disappeared and only the bones have survived. During the times of formation of the peat many corpses have lain exposed on the ground in the open landscape. Their flesh quickly decayed, their bones remained for a while longer, but they too were gradually dissolved by the rain and pulverised by frost. Under terrestrial conditions therefore, peat has proved a valuable though not perfect preservative of animal remains.

But peat is itself essentially a masses of fossil remains, for it consists almost entirely of plant fragments ranging from tree trunks and branches to leaves, seeds and even minute spores and pollen grains (Plate XXIIIa). As will be seen later the detailed study of peats has thrown much light upon the changes undergone by British vegetation during the last half million years.

In the first stages of peat formation the tissues of the plants undergo very little change and under some circumstances become almost perfectly preserved. Thus for example when calcareous water from 'petrifying springs' flows into the bog the remains become impregnated with lime which crystallises and hermetically seals the tissues. Similarly, siliceous waters from hotsprings seals the remains in chert. In both cases the minutest details of internal structure may be preserved for untold aeons (Plates Va, IXa.).

Under normal circumstances the plant substances undergo slow and progressive chemical changes leading to carbonisation and complete loss of structure as for example in coal, which is in fact fossilised peat.

Hitherto our attention has been limited to fossil formation in terrestrial or subaerial situations. It must, however, now be turned to subaqueous situations, especially in the sea, where it takes place on a far grander scale than elsewhere.

In the sea the number and variety of animal forms is vastly greater than on land. When these die their bodies come to rest on the sea floor where their flesh is rapidly consumed by other creatures or rots away. The hard parts, bones, shells and the like, last much longer and frequently are buried under mud, sand or gravel derived from the destruction of the land and accumulated layer by layer to great thicknesses. Thus covered these remains are protected from the destructive action of boring organisms and the chemical action of water. In fact, they become fossils.

In the sea the water is in constant circulation so that oxygen is transported everywhere, consequently, some creatures are able to live even in the profoundest depths. Under some circumstances, especially in epicontinental seas, circulation may be confined to the upper levels while the water in the greater depths becomes so stagnant that living things are absent and the activities of destructive bacteria are slowed down or halted. Meanwhile the upper waters swarm with jelly fishes, worms, crustacea and so forth. When these die their bodies sink down into the gloomy lifeless realms and, reaching the floor, rest undecomposed long enough to become buried under fine mud. In due time this is converted into rock and the organic remains become fossilised.

Rocks formed under such circumstances have rarely been found. The most striking example known was discovered by the great American geologist C. D. Walcot in Mount St. Stephen, British Columbia, in formations belonging to the Middle Cambrian, and therefore, over 400 million years old. Here he came upon a black shale about 4 feet thick which split into thin layers or laminae. On the surfaces of these were numerous iridescent films exhibiting the external forms and some internal details of structure of a wonderful variety of creatures. The reader who, when on holiday by the seaside, has come upon a dried up jelly fish on the beach, will easily understand why these fossils are mere films for the bodies of such creatures consist mainly of water and very little actual fleshy substance.

No such striking examples have hitherto been found in Britain. It may be that the dark shales in Wales and southern Scotland, that have yielded so many graptolites, record an approach to such conditions (v. Chaps. 8, 10 and Plate II: *1, 2*).

The majority of invertebrate fossils stored in museums and handled by workers in the field and in laboratories come from rocks formed under normal conditions out of ordinary sediments. These included all the 'figured stones' referred to in the previous chapter. A brief account of these in the light of modern knowledge will help towards an understanding of the difficulties which baffled such keen observers and collectors as Lister and others.

Some of these fossil remains have undergone little or no change since their original owners were alive. Others, however, have been considerably altered. Reference has been already made to the gradual carbonisation of plant fragments. Similar changes have taken place in such animals as graptolites and sea mosses whose supporting framework consisted of some organic chitin like substance. In the overwhelming majority of cases the framework consisted of an inorganic mineral, of calcium carbonate or less commonly of silica. These remains are often unchanged except for loss of colour; even that, however, is sometimes preserved.

In many cases the substance of the shell or skeletal element has been changed. The agency which has brought this about is water which is almost universally present in the rocks where, however, it is almost stationary until earth movements uplift the rocks to become land. Much of the water then seeps through the rocks and finds its way back into the sea. Meanwhile rain falling on the land soaks into the rocks and thus a constant circulation is established. Water is a chemical agent and first-class solvent. These properties are augmented by the gases it has dissolved from the air and by the acids it extracts from the soil and minerals from the rocks. It may be a weak agent but it thus becomes a complex one and, having almost unlimited stretches of time for action, may bring about great changes, some of which have not as yet been reproduced in laboratories.

Thus endowed water may replace the silica of sponges by carbonate of lime or the carbonaceous tissues of plants and the lime of shells and coral by silica. It may also replace the substance of shells by one or other of a variety of minerals, by oxide of iron or iron sulphide (pyrites) or less often by copper carbonate (malachite). In all these cases the fossil though transmogrified is still there.

Very often this percolating water has removed the shell or skeleton completely and left only an empty cavity. This is frequently the case for fossils in rocks that are porous, such as sandstones. Fortunately, the lining surfaces of the cavity still retains the impressions of the ornamentations and other marking of the outer and inner surfaces of the original shell or bone (Plate IV: *1-4*). These are known as the external and internal casts of the shell. Though the original has disappeared these specimens may be classed as fossils for they yield so much information about the actual organism.

On the borderline between fossils and non-fossils are the tracks or the borings made by worms and the footprints and trails made by fourfooted animals (Plates VIII*b*: *2*, and XII: *1-3*).

From all this it will be seen that though in the strictest sense a fossil consists of the actual remains, whole or fragmentary, of an animal or plant, the term must be extended to include mineral and rocks specimens which faithfully record markings impressed by an organism on its hard parts or upon its environment. Whether mineral oil, which retains a slight aura of organic origin, is a fossil suggests a problem that may be left to those who have the acumen of a philosopher or a lawyer to decide.

CHAPTER 3

A PLACE FOR EVERYTHING

'A PLACE for everything and everything in its place'. That is the motto for the good housekeeper or business man. Some people are naturally tidy. If they have a heavy correspondence they keep it all systematically arranged so that when a particular letter is wanted they know just where to find it. Systematic arrangement is also a prime necessity in the study of fossils. Even as late as the eighteenth century students in this field were floundering because they had no good system for coping with and describing their increasing collections.

The need is well illustrated by a work of great merit which appeared in 1755. It was produced by Georg Wolfgang Knorr of Nuremberg who combined the qualifications of an artist with those of a collector. After his death in 1761, the work was extended by Johann Walch, Professor of Philosophy and Poetry in Jena. Even today the excellence of the coloured illustrations strikes the eye, but the arrangement of the specimens for description seems to be almost chaotic. They were grouped together under such unrelated headings as corallites, encrinites, osteoliths, belemnites, dentalites, vermiculites and so forth. The order in which these were placed did not seem to matter in the slightest.

By that time fossils had become recognised as the remains of living things; but the problem of devising a sound scheme upon which to build up a classification of animals and plants, was only just beginning to receive the serious attention of naturalists. In Knorr's grouping those fossils which looked like corals were called corallites; like bones, osteoliths; like teeth, denticulites; like worm-tubes, vermiculites. Students of fossils laboured under the great disadvantage that their specimens were usually no more than mere fragments of organisms. Botanists and zoologists, however, were better off for they had the whole plant or animal at their disposal for examination. Nevertheless, even they floundered because, as shown by Ray, they concentrated

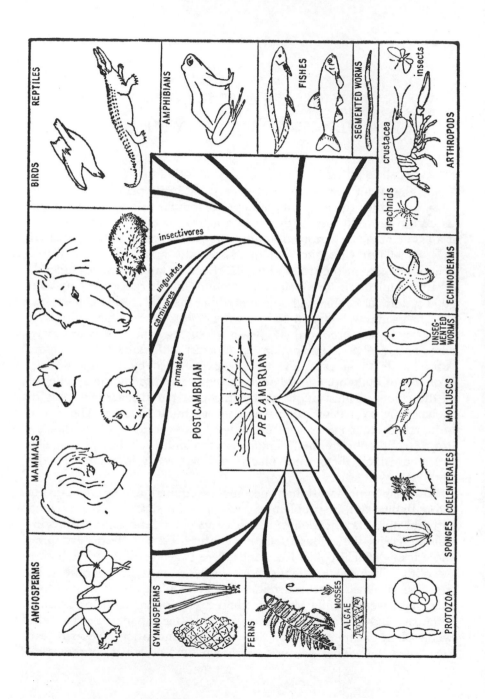

their attention upon unimportant or even accidental features such as the scent of flowers or the taste of fruit in plants; or, in animals, upon features which merely reflected the climate in which they lived or the type of food they ate. He then went on to point out that only bodily structure could provide a basis for a sound classification. The fact that all the individuals of many types of animals such as rabbits were almost identical in structure showed that they were of one kind or *species*. The fundamental feature about a species was that the offspring resembled one another and their parents. In other words, the members of a species were all genetically related. Though he did not express himself in such modern terms that must have been fundamentally at the back of his mind. At that time in the western World, the only known theory of the origin of species was that contained in the Genesis story of creation. Inasmuch as the Creator rested on the seventh day no new species had since come into being, and consequently, the number of species was fixed and unchanging. It was not until a much later date that this was disputed. Ray also noted that some groups of species resembled one another more closely than they did others. Thus for example, the rabbit and hare resemble one another more closely than they resemble the rat and mouse. The two former ought, therefore, to be put along with other closely similar species into one larger group or *genus* having the common generic name *Lepus*. The rabbit could then be named *Lepus cuniculus*; and the hare, *Lepus timidus*. By developing and clarifying the ideas of *species* and *genus* Ray prepared the ground for the next great advance in systematising the knowledge of organic nature. This was initiated by Linnaeus (1707-1778) a native of Sweden who was gifted with a flair for law and order. While still a young man he published his greatest work entitled 'Systema Naturae' in which he developed the framework of a classificatory system that was soon accepted throughout the world.

Following the teaching of Ray he adopted the *species* as his basal unit in classification. In one of the later editions of his work published in 1753, he went further, and incorporated the idea by giving them

Fig. 2. THE CLASSIFICATION AND HISTORY OF LIVING ORGANISMS

The centre represents the dawn of life upon the earth. The branching lines represent the evolving life streams as they flowed thence through the Precambrian and Postcambrian up to the Present Age. The outer zone of drawings summarises the main divisions in the classification of existing organisms.

names for the genus and species respectively. These were usually in Latin, an interesting survival of medieval time when Latin was the only universally understood language. With each new name introduced he gave a precise description of the species. Henceforth any worker who wished to publish an account of some new discovery about an animal or plant had no need to start by describing it. He had only to mention its generic and specific names and readers of all nationalities would know precisely the animal or plant to which he was referring.

On the basis of yet wider similarities between groups of genera Linnaeus instituted other and broader categories called orders and classes respectively. He thus devised a classificatory system which has proved sufficiently elastic to be expanded and adjusted to the requirements of the many advances, made since his day, in the knowledge of living and extinct forms of life. Furthermore, a similar system is used in scientific libraries for arranging books, magazines and journals. The student can therefore, without unnecessary loss of time, find the literature that will be the most helpful to him in persuing his investigation on any organism or group of organisms.

Though Linnaeus applied his sytem with considerable success to land plants and backboned animals or vertebrates, he gave only scanty attention to the backboneless or invertebrate animals. The latter are, however, of vital importance in the study of fossils and of the rocks that contain them. This is due to the fact that a very large proportion of the fossils are the remains of sea animals that were buried in the deposits from which the rocks were formed. This defect in the *Systema Naturae* was largely rectified by Chevalier de Lamarck (1744-1829).

Lamarck was born in the north of France. His father wished him to become a priest but at the age of seventeen he entered the army. After a period of brilliant active service he was passed on to garrison duty at Toulon. There along the Mediterranean coast he had ample opportunity to indulge his love for natural history. Trouble appeared in his throat which led to his discharge from the army. He then went to live in Paris where he continued his studies by taking a medical course. At the same time he eked out his small pension by working in a bank and doing hack writing. He also wrote a book on the 'Flora of France' which attracted the attention of the great naturalist Buffon, who introduced him to scientific circles and befriended him in other ways. At the age of fifty he was appointed 'Professor of Zoology, of Insects, of Worms and of microscopic animals'. In the pursuance of his new duties he carried through a series of illuminating researches on the internal anatomy, as well as the external features, of these lowly creatures. In the course of this work he was impressed by the gradation of structure as he passed from one type to another. With this basal idea he produced a classification of the invertebrates, the broad outlines of which are still largely used. Particular mention must be made of his work upon the invertebrate fossils which occur in the rocks found in the Paris region. His extensive knowledge of living forms enabled him to describe and classify these fossils with precision. Comparison between the fossils and living forms convinced him that the latter had descended from the former. He thus became a pioneer in the doctrine of evolution and meditated deeply on the causes which brought about the change. He believed that he had found a clue in the commonly observed fact that in the bodies of both men and animals some changes do in fact take place during life as the outcome of use and exercise. He assumed that the features thus developed would be passed on from parent to offspring; in other words that acquired characters could be inherited. He concluded (wrongly as we now know) that by a repetition of this process through successive generations bodily changes accumulated with the result that new species and even genera emerged. Though his systematic and anatomical work made a marked impression on the minds of other workers in kindred fields of study, his evolutionary theory passed into oblivion for half a century; for under the leadership of his distinguished countryman, Baron Cuvier, the doctrine of the immutability of species continued to be almost universally held.

CHAPTER 4

THE DELUGE

FROM the outset those who accepted the view that fossils were of organic origin were confronted by sundry new problems. When did these creatures live? How did they die? How were they buried? In order to put the discussion of these problems in their right perspective it is once more advisable to sense the atmosphere of the time. This is well reflected in the injunction given by Charles II when he granted the Charter of the Royal Society to those "whose studies were to be applied to the further promoting by the authority of experiments the sciences of natural things and of useful arts, to the glory of God the Creator, and the advantage of the Human Race."

It was within the atmosphere of religious thought reflected by these words that discussions on the origin of fossils and of species took place. For those early workers it was a religious as well as a pleasant duty to study the 'Works of the Creator'. In so far as this religious urge stimulated enquiry it was beneficial to the advancement of scientific studies. Ultimately the debt was repaid, for those studies did much to release the human mind from the ties of ancient and charming but inadequate traditions that had come down from the dawn of civilisation.

In searching for an explanation of the origin of fossils some turned with confidence to the Scriptures; to the story of the Flood. Here, as it seemed to them, was just the solution they required for their problem. Fossils were the remains of creatures that lived before the Flood. They were drowned by the Flood; and were buried in the debris that settled down from the flood waters. Scientific criticism as applied to the Scriptures, was as yet unborn. To them, therefore, the story was an authentic record of events. As the details of the story were scanty, they tried to read between the lines and for this purpose used their imaginations freely. John Woodward, for instance, described fossils as the "remains of the Universal Deluge when the waters of the ocean, being disastrously turned out upon the earth, bore along with it fishes of all sorts, shells and the like movable bodies which it left behind at its return back again to its channel."

Some of the fossils revealed creatures that were unknown; but that did not perturb them, for did there not exist great areas of land and of depths in the sea not yet explored where similar strange creatures might still be living? This explanation became known as 'The Diluvial Theory' and occupied a prominent place in discussions throughout the coming century. Other thinkers and workers turned to the study of nature herself for details about the Deluge. If indeed the story were authentic, then the Deluge must have left its traces on the landscape. It was to the landscape that da Vinci had turned two centuries earlier. There he came upon many facts that did not seem to fit in with the story. Thus fossils of marine animals, often large and heavy, were found in the rocks even near the tops of mountains. Now, according to the Genesis story, the rise of the waters was due to persistent rain. In that case the waters covering the mountains would have been fresh—but these fossils were the remains of sea animals. On the other hand, if as some thought, the sea came up on to the land carrying shells of many different kinds, then those kinds would have been mixed together and left scattered about on the surface. Da Vinci pointed out that these fossils did not lie on the surface but were buried deep in the rocks; not scattered, but congregated in definite layers at different levels. They were not confusedly mixed but were distributed, multitudes of one kind here, and of another yonder. Moreover, if the shells were to be carried up to the mountain tops they would have to float at the surface, but many of these shells were too large and heavy to float and must have stayed on the bottom of the sea all the time. These sound and weighty arguments were all committed by him to his notebooks where they remained hidden and were brought to light only in recent years.

Da Vinci's observations were apparently unknown to Ray who, two centuries later when criticising the Diluvial Theory, also appealed to evidence drawn from the landscape. He pointed out that fossils could not have been carried to the tops of mountains by the Flood, for the torrents of rain which caused it would have swept all shells downwards. He was much impressed by seeing a buried forest at Bruges "in places which 500 years ago were sea". Since the time when

FOS.—C

they grew they had become submerged and hidden under mud brought by the river. He was still more forcibly struck by the discovery of beds of cockle-shells at a depth of 100 feet in a well sunk in Amsterdam. The accumulation of so great a thickness of sediment above the shells must, he considered, have taken a very long time. There was no evidence that either the forest or the shells were suddenly overwhelmed and buried by flood. To him the length of time implied for their burial under so much sediment was inconsistent with the newness of a world believed to be only 5600 years old.

As Canon C. E. Raven has shown, these ideas did not disturb Ray's mind, because for him Nature was "nothing else but the ordinary power of God" and "loyalty to truth was loyalty to God." It was

---

PLATE I

a. THE TOWY VALLEY NEAR LLANDEILO

It was here in this landscape that Sir Roderick I. Murchison proved the presence of fossils in the rocks of the 'Transition Series' of Wales. The older fossils come from the rocks occuring on either side of the flood plain, the younger, from those in the far distance. (v. Text Fig. 3). (*H.M. Geol. Survey*)

b. THE EARLIEST BRITISH FAUNA

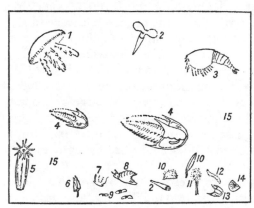

1. Jelly Fish
2. *Hyolithus*
3. *Hymenocaris*
4. *Callavia*
5. Sea Cucumber
6. *Paterina*
7. *Micmacca*
8. *Helicionella*
9. *Microdiscus*
10. *Obolella*
11. Siliceous sponge
12. Bristleworm
13. *Protolenus*
14. *Eoorthis*
15. Seaweeds

Classification of these organisms:

Animals: Sponges, 11. Cœlentera, 1. Vermes-Annelida, 12. Echinoderma, 5. Mollusca, 2, 8. Brachiopoda, 6, 10, 14. Arthropoda: Crustacea, 3. Trilobite, 4, 7, 9, 13.

Plants: Seaweeds make up much of the background e.g. 15. (*H.H.S. del*)

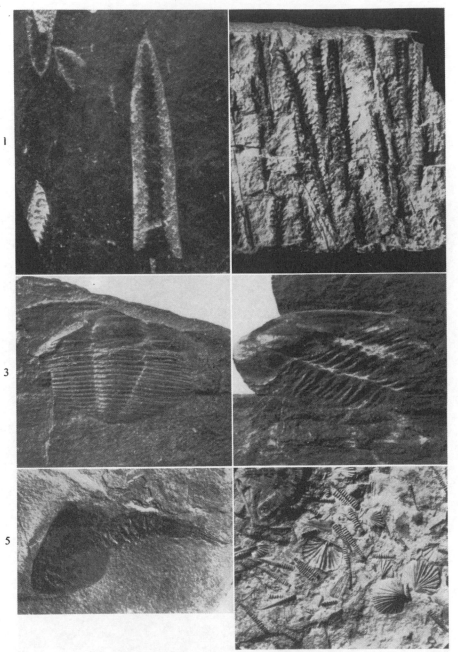

largely as the result of Ray's balanced honesty of mind and reverence of spirit that no religious controversies arose out of the scientific discoveries during the next century and a half. Indeed, some leaders of the Church adopted his viewpoint. Even John Wesley published a summary of Ray's views for the instruction and enlightenment of his followers.

Meanwhile the Diluvial Theory, by reason of its simplicity and attractiveness, retained its hold on the minds even of scientific workers. In the opening years of the nineteenth century it was, however, absorbed into a broader theory originated by Cuvier (1764-1832). This great French naturalist had found time in the midst of his multifarious public activities to do outstanding work upon the vertebrate fossils discovered in the quarries around Paris. While engaged in this work he was struck by the fact that the groups of animals, whose remains were preserved at successive levels in the rocks, differed from one another. All this seemed to him clear evidence that these faunas had lived at different periods. That being the case, each fauna must have been destroyed and subsequently replaced by another and different fauna. How had this been brought about? Observations made by him and others upon the rocks furnished him with an answer. In the neighbouring Alps the strata, crowded with the remains of marine animals, were seen heaved up to great heights, overturned, crushed and crumpled. Such a state of affairs could only have been produced by catastrophic forces which from time to time must have been let loose upon the earth. Each time of catastrophic destruction

---

PLATE II

FOSSILS FROM THE OLDER PALAEOZOIC ROCKS

1. *Didymograptus,* a graptolite from the Llandeilo beds of Abereiddy Bay, Pembrokeshire. 2. *Orthograptus,* a biserial graptolite from the Upper Llandeilo Beds of Laggan Burn, Girvan, Ayreshire. 3. *Angelina,* a trilobite from the Upper Tremadoc Beds, Garth Minnfford, nr. Portmadoc, North Wales. This has been distorted from back to front thus showing how much the rock itself has been compressed by earth pressures. 4. *Angelina,* this trilobite has been squeezed obliquely. Compare 3, which is from the same rock and place. 5. *Ceratiocaris,* a crustacea from the Upper Silurian of Lesmahagow. 6. *Tentaculites,* shell of an enigmatic organism with orthid brachiopods. Caradocian Beds, Marshbrook, East Shropshire. (1, 2, 5, 6, *M. A. Ferguson.* 3, 4, *W. Sutcliffe*)

must have been followed by a period of calm during which the earth was repeopled and replenished. Thus the Catastrophic Theory was born. It was not merely a development of the diluvial theory. The Hebrew story of the Flood, together with similar stories in the ancient legends of other nations, were taken by Cuvier as historic evidence merely for the last and most feeble of these terrible manifestations. As shown by the rocks this had been preceded by a series of other and much more disastrous upheavals.

Weighted with such authority, both scientific and legendary, the Catastrophic Theory found widespread favour in religious and scientific circles. Eventually prolonged work on fossils combined with progress along other lines of research culminated in the establishment of the principle of evolution and in the passing of this older theory into oblivion. Nevertheless, the latter had played a useful part in opening the way for the acceptance of the new theory; by loosening man's mind from allegiance to the idea of one short sharp act of Creation, and by accustoming their thoughts to a long drawn out succession of events, in the course of which new plants and animals were from time to time brought into being, extinguished and then buried. The fossil remains of these were at last felt to be worthy of study as reliable records of the history of life upon this earth and as evidence that illuminated the processes of Creation.

CHAPTER 5

THE BIRTH OF GEOLOGY

Rocks including sands and sandstone, mud, clay shale and so forth, as well as plants and animals, are found in abundance everywhere. It was in the rocks that fossils were found, but until more was known about the arrangement and origin of rocks the study of fossils was under a severe handicap. The task of systematising plants and animals was comparatively easy because each specimen was self-contained and could be brought home for study. Not so with the rocks. Each specimen of rock was merely a broken fragment; the whole remained outside buried in the landscape and largely hidden by a covering of soil and vegetation.

The study of the rocks is nevertheless a very ancient one. It really began far back in the Old Stone Age when primitive man searched for suitable stones with which to make his implements. In the Bronze Age he carried it further; he explored his surroundings and burrowed in the ground for valuable and useful metals, for gold, copper and tin. Later the ancient writer of the book of Job describing the activities of the miner in his day uses such phrases as:—'He setteth an end to darkness'; 'Surely there is a vein for silver and a place for gold'; 'He overturneth the mountains' and 'his eye seeth every precious thing'; 'Wisdom cannot be valued with precious onyx and sapphire'; 'The price of wisdom is above rubies—the topaz of Ethiopia shall not equal it'.

Down through the centuries miners carried on their work and accumulated great stores of knowledge about minerals and precious stones and about their arrangement in the rocks. Eventually schools of mining were established. It was in such a school at Freiburg in Saxony, that late in the eighteenth century a great teacher arose who, for many years, dominated this newly emerging science of Geology. His name was Abraham Werner (1749-1817).

Werner was a great mineralogist and naturally looked at the rocks from the standpoint of their mineralogical make-up. His practical outdoor knowledge was, however, limited to Saxony where he found that granites and granite-like rocks underlay all other types. He therefore classed these as PRIMITIVE ROCKS. Granites consist of a number of minerals among which quartz and felspar are the most prominent. He also found calcareous rocks or limestones; sandstones which consist largely of grains of quartz; also clays, which look like consolidated mud. These he found overlying the Primitive rocks and classed them as FLOETZ, a term which implied that they were stratified rocks. Lying between these two sets of rocks he found grauwackes or hardened fine-grained sandstones, shales and slates, which he classed as TRANSITIONAL rocks because they were intermediate in position and character between the other two.

Though he had not explored beyond the bounds of Saxony he assumed that this arrangement was world-wide in extent. He taught that these rocks had been deposited on the floor of a universal ocean, first by chemical precipitation and later by mechanical sedimentation, in that order, Primitive, Transitional and Floetz. Students came to him from many lands. They imbibed his theories along with his mineralogy and were so intoxicated with his enthusiasm that when they returned home they were blind to any evidence that did not fit in with the Wernerian scheme.

Nevertheless, much new evidence contrary to Werner's teaching was being accumulated in another quarter, in Edinburgh.

Just ninety years after the death of Ray there appeared in that city a work entitled 'The Theory of the Earth' by James Hutton (1726-1797). This writer had studied medicine in Edinburgh, Paris and Leyden; but, on his return to Scotland, instead of practising as a medical doctor he turned aside and applied his scientific training to the study of Geology. He gave much of his time to elucidating the mode of origin of the Primitive rocks. He also uncovered those processes which had led up to the formation of the Floetz rocks, and in so doing opened the way to the understanding of the significance of fossils and of the ways in which they had been preserved. Hutton showed that these processes can be seen at work today along the sea-shore and everywhere on the face of the landscape. Usually they work so quietly and unobtrusively that they are unnoticed by the multitudes that pass by. He, on the other hand, saw the frost shattering and pulverising the rocks and making soil. He saw the rain-drops loosening the particles of soil and dissolving the limestone. He saw the runnels of water hastening with their tiny burdens to join the chattering brooks and brimming rivers. Transported thus, the mud and sand joined company with the boulders and stones that were rolled along in times of flood, and coming to rest on the floor of pools, of lakes and of the sea, buried the shells which animals had made of lime extracted from the water. Along the sea-shore he saw the waves during storms crashing against the cliffs, grinding and pulverising shells and boulders. On calm days he saw the surf sorting gravel from sand, and sand from mud, to be carried away by undercurrents from the beach and spread out on the floor of the sea, where they accumulated layer upon layer and buried the shells made by multitudes of creatures that lived and died there.

The deposits thus formed closely resembled the pudding-stone, sandstones and clays which he had seen being destroyed by frost and the waves. He realised that those rocks must also have been formed in precisely the same way. They too were old gravels, sands and muds that had been hardened into rocks. But again the rocks from which these old deposits were formed must in their turn have had a like origin. Thus Dame Nature took this pupil in her charge and guided his thoughts back and back into the long ages of the past so that in imagination he saw the same agencies and processes for ever working then as they do today. Then, as now, they worked silently, unceasingly, proceeding step by step, here a little there a little, until eventually great results accrued. Massive layers of rock were formed, uplifted and became land. On this, deep spacious valleys were excavated, high hills and lofty mountains were left standing. This is the doctrine known as uniformitarianism.

Hutton was not one who courted notoriety. He was content to contemplate Nature and to discuss his thoughts with his friends. It was only two years before he died that he published his book. Today it is one of the great classics of scientific literature; but at that time it created no appreciable stir, for the geological world was obsessed with the teaching of Werner. Moreover, scientist and theologian alike, found Hutton's style of writing obscure and his views out of accord with their own interpretation of the Mosaic stories. After his death, however, his enquiries were carried on by his friend John Playfair. This writer, by his attractive style, backed by many new illustrations and by experimental proofs devised and successfully carried through by James Hall, rescued Hutton's teaching from being forgotten. Gradually it gained ground in Edinburgh circles. Its chief opponent there was Robert Jameson, one of Werner's disciples, who in 1804 was appointed to the Chair of Natural History at the University: but in the end even he frankly confessed that "Wernerism is doomed and deserves to die." But the battle was not yet over, for the Diluvial Theory remained and was in the process of merging into the newly announced Catastrophic Theory.

At the other end of the kingdom, William Buckland (1784-1856) was rising into a position of great influence in the geological world. In boyhood, guided by his father, he explored the quarries near Axminster, his birthplace; and the rocks along the foreshore at Lyme Regis. Thus he became familiar with ammonites and many other kinds of fossils. In 1801 he gained a scholarship to Oxford where he studied theology and, eight years later, took Holy Orders. Meanwhile he persued his geological interests with undiminished enthusiasm. In his lodgings his breakfast table 'was loaded with beefsteak and belemnites, tea and terebratula, muffins and madrepores, toast and trilobites'. (Gordon, p. 8). In 1819 he was appointed Professor of Geology. He was a great teacher and investigator, hilariously energetic. Among many other valuable pieces of work he helped to nail the coffin of Wernerism by showing that some of the rocks in the Alps, classed as grauwackes, were full of the same fossils as those which abounded elsewhere in the latest Floetz rocks, and by suggesting that the best use for the latter term was as an adjective or an expletive. For more than a quarter of a century he was a virile centre of inspiration to his students and to fellow workers in the field of geology. This influence he continued to exert even though in 1845 he was appointed Dean of Westminster.

In 1824 Buckland published the second edition of his large work 'Reliquiae Diluvianae' which dealt very fully with the organic remains found in fissures, caves and surface deposits of Britain, Europe and North America. In these he discovered as sound evidence for the occurrence of a deluge not long ago as that provided by bedded rocks for the much more ancient revolutions on the face of this planet. Evidently, with the Huttonian teaching in mind, he quotes these as proof "that the surface of the earth owes its latest forms not to the gradual action of existing causes but to a sudden overwhelming and transient mass of water." This was, however, written before the discovery of the great work being done by glaciers and icefields and melt waters among the peaks of lofty mountain ranges and in the expanses of the polar regions.

In 1797, the year that Hutton died, Charles Lyell was born. He became a law student at Oxford University but, having an interest in natural history he attended Buckland's lectures and became infected with his enthusiasm for geology. While still a student he was deeply impressed by the sight of damage done by the sea to the cliffs of the Norfolk coast and by the additions made by the sea to the land at Romney Marsh. Several years later he spent a holiday on his father's estate in Scotland. There he saw workmen draining a small lake and excavating, for use in marling land, a limy deposit that had accumulated within living memory. This deposit was twenty feet deep. At its surface it was merely a pulverulent mass of lime extracted from the water and secreted by the little plant *Chara* (Stonewort). Below its surface the deposit was hardened and in its deeper layers had consolidated into a crystalline limestone. Here then was undoubted evidence that limestone rock was being formed by a process at work here and now. Thus Lyell rediscovered for himself the same principle that Hutton had taught. It is estimated that he spent no less than a quarter of his life travelling widely in this and far off lands, making fresh observations for himself, collecting the observations made by others and elucidating their meaning. The outcome of all this was his great work 'The Principles of Geology' which carried Huttonian teaching to its logical conclusion and laid the foundations upon which modern geology has been built. Thus the key to the solution of innumerable geological problems was found. The origin of the rocks and of the fossils they contain was no longer a mystery.

CHAPTER 6

A CLUE TO GEOLOGICAL TIME

FARMER Smith lived in the village of Churchill, Oxfordshire, and to him was born in the year 1769, a son, whom he called William. Like many another lad living in the country, William was thrown on his own resources for amusement. Some of this he found in his mother's dairy in the form of flattened bun-shaped stones, called 'pundstones', which she used as weights. These were pleasant to handle and easy to play with. Today in museums, where fossils are exhibited, 'pundstones' or 'quoitstones' may be seen; not under these names but labelled *Clypeus sinuata* and placed among the fossil sea-urchins. When he wandered about the garden or the ploughed fields he picked up from the soil other curiously shaped stones covered with smooth shells and familiarly known to country folk as 'pundibs'. They also may be seen in museums labelled *Terebratula* and placed with a less well-known group of shells called Brachiopods. Out of these playthings there grew a hobby. Just as a modern boy collects and examines stamps, William Smith collected fossils from clay-pits and quarries and, incidentally, developed his naturally keen powers of observation. His formal education he gained at the village school, but later, in his spare time, he taught himself geometry. Thus equipped he entered a land surveyors office at the age of eighteen. Eventually he set up independently as a land surveyor and civil engineer. This he did just at the time when canals were being developed as the main system for transporting heavy and bulky goods such as coal. His professional duties took him into coalmines and involved him in planning excavations for canals across the countryside. These provided him with ample opportunities for extending his knowledge of rocks underground and for adding to his collections of fossils. Many of the fossils were imbedded in the solid stone but sometimes he saw large numbers of them crowded together upon the surface of a rock layer (Plate XIV*a*). Gazing at these he realised that he was looking at an ancient sea-floor upon which these creatures had lived and died for a brief spell of time that elapsed between the formation of a lower and an upper layer of rock. Such observations led him to the conclusion that the series of layers had been formed in succession on the bed of the sea.

In his collections Smith arranged his fossils in groups according to the layers in which they had been found. Each group therefore represented the fauna that lived at the time when the corresponding layer of rock was being deposited as mud or sand or as an accumulation of shells and shell fragments. While comparing the successive faunas with one another he made the important discovery that, though some fossils ranged from one group of layers to another, others were confined to and were characteristic of one group only. Thus 'gryphites' characterised the Lias rocks; and 'trigonias', the 'under oolites'. This fact proved invaluable to him in his investigations. In a rich agricultural country like England the rocks are almost completely hidden from view under a covering of soil and vegetation, but many villages in those days had small quarries which supplied them with building stone and roofing slates, or small clay-pits adjoining brick and tile works. By comparing the fossils collected from those quarries and pits with his own systematically arranged collections he found out which exposures yielded the same fossils and were therefore in the same set of clay or rock layers. He assumed that the strip of country that lay between the exposures was underlain by the same set of layers. Marking the strip upon his map he proceeded to trace its boundaries more precisely by observing the shape of the ground and the character of the soil, for he realised that clay was usually associated with low-lying ground and sandstone or limestone with hills and sloping surfaces. Such maps, of course, show only the distribution of the rocks as they occur close to the surface. But in cliffs, quarries and cuttings the layers could be seen dipping under one another away from the surface. With the help of these he drew sections of the rocks as they would be seen in the sides of very deep trenches excavated across the landscape.

William Smith's first efforts in this kind of mapping were made near his own home in the country around the city of Bath. On this map he distinguished the outcrops of the various sets of rocks by painting them with different colours. This, his first geological map, he later presented to the Geological Society of London in whose rooms it may still be seen.

It is easy to see how valuable such a map would be to him in his work for it enabled him to tell at a glance the best line along which to make a new canal in order to secure the greatest extent of impervious foundation: where to find clay suitable for 'puddling' the floor of the canal as it passed across a zone of pervious rocks: and where to find stone for building bridges or for strengthening the towing paths. Today anyone who knows how to interpret a geological map can draw sections for any area in which he is interested and thus can solve many problems of water supply and mining.

Smith's professional work took him far afield to other parts of England and Wales and greatly extended his opportunities for studying fossils and the arrangement of the rock-layers, and for making geological maps. Though he made very careful notes and drawings and talked freely about his ideas and discoveries he experienced difficulty in writing for publication. Fortunately, two friends persuaded him to dictate to them his scheme for classifying the British rocks together with an account of the characteristic fossils. This scheme became the nucleus around which all modern classifications have crystallised. In 1815 he published a geological map for England, Wales and Southern Scotland. In recognition of his great contribution to the science of geology the Council of the Geological Society of London made him the first recipient of the Wollaston Medal (Feb. 1831), the highest honour the Society can bestow. The President, presenting the medal, described him as "The Father of English Geology."

It was soon realised that this kind of work was of great importance to the welfare of the country. Consequently, in 1835 the Geological Survey of Great Britain was established with a staff of officers to carry out detailed mapping and to collect every possible item of geological information revealed by excavations, borings and mines. Its work has been greatly augmented by other geologists, both private and professional, who have conducted invaluable researches into the geology of our land. It must not be supposed that this work of surveying is concerned only with economic problems. On the contrary, as will be seen later, backed by all this work in the field, the study of fossils has made most valuable contributions to human thought and knowledge.

So then when William Smith saw in the fossil-covered surface of a rock layer the floor of an ancient sea he also saw a picture of one incident in the history of the British area. Following the rocks in sequence from layer to layer, from group to group, from formation to formation, he, like his great contemporary Cuvier, discovered independently that the scenes which they recorded and the animals that peopled them were continually changing. By studying those changes he was able to hang his pictures in their correct order along the corridors of time. Most of his pictures related to that section of geological time now called the Mesozoic Era. A few indicated vaguely and in less detail scenes from the latter part of the foregoing or Palaeozoic Era. He lacked both time and opportunity for dealing with the far removed portions of the gallery as it passed back through the Transitional aeons and faded away into the Primitive Era of the Wernerian system. How that dimly lighted stretch of time became illuminated will be told later.

THE MAJOR DIVISIONS OF GEOLOGICAL TIME

Eras	Periods and Systems	Approximate date of the opening of each division in millions of years
CAINOZOIC	Quaternary	
	Recent	
	Pleistocene	1
	Tertiary	
	Pliocene	15
	Miocene	35
	Oligocene	50
	Eocene	70
MESOZOIC	Cretaceous	120
	Jurassic	150
	Triassic	190
PALAEOZOIC	Permian	220
	Carboniferous	280
	Devonian and Old Red Sandstone	320
	Silurian	350
	Ordovician	400
	Cambrian	500
PRECAMBRIAN		2200 +

CHAPTER 7

MUSEUMS AND EXPERTS

WILLIAM Smith was gifted naturally with an eye for fossils. By constant handling of his specimens he gained a remarkably detailed knowledge of their characteristic features and was thus able to recognise specimens from new localities either as being the same as those he had already found or as being different and even new forms. At first his thinking was necessarily in terms of his own specimens but he knew little about their names or their zoological relationships. Fortunately he lived near the city of Bath which during the eighteenth century was an important centre of culture. In the surrounding hills the rocks were relatively rich in fossils. It is not surprising therefore that some of the educated folk living there were natural successors of Lister, Ray and Woodward, and found pleasure in collecting shells and fossils. They were also familiar with the illustrated works of Lister and others and had gained an expert knowledge of the names and classification of their specimens. Fortunately for Smith and Geology, in the year 1799 he met the Revd. B. Richardson of Farley, and saw his large collection. Though Smith probably could not name many of the specimens as he inspected them he astonished his new friend by his close familiarity, not merely with the fossils but with the precise localities and the rocks where they were found. Thus began a friendship which proved invaluable to Smith as he extended his

---

PLATE III

FOSSILS FROM THE WENLOCK LIMESTONE

1. *Halysites*. 2. *Cyathocrinus*. 3. *Favosites*. 4. *Heliolites*. 5. *Acervularia*. 6. *Calymene*. 7. *Marsipocrinus*. 8. *Phacops* (*Dalmanites*). Most of these come from Dudley. Classification: Corals, 1, 3, 4, 5. Crinoids, 2, 7. Trilobites, 6, 8. (5, *H.M. Geol. Survey*. The rest *A. Ferguson*)

researches farther and farther afield to other rocks than those found in the vicinity of Bath.

This friendship was symbolical of the close and friendly cooperation which has continued to exist until the present day between the geologist who works in the field and the one who works indoors at the often tedious task of cleaning the fossil from the rock which adheres to it and obscures the details of its ornamentation; and of dissecting the fossil by sawing it into slices, by 'piggling' with needles or dissolving with weak acids. By such patient work minute details are discovered that throw light upon the growth of the fossil when alive and on its relationships to other species.

If the results of all this work are to be available to the maximum number of other students then accurate drawings as well as written descriptions must be published. Palaeontology owes a great debt to artists who have placed their gifts at its disposal. Among these special mention should be made of James Sowerby and his two sons who during the years 1822-1845 made artistic pictures of fossils submitted to them and produced a great work, 'The Mineral Conchology of Great Britain', in 6 volumes with 604 coloured plates. During and since their time various Societies have published numerous figures in their transactions and journals. One of these, The Palaeontographical Society, was established solely for the purpose of publishing as full descriptions and perfect figures as could be produced by specialists (Fig. 19, Plates XIV*b*, XIX). The long series of excellent monographs already produced is being added to every year and may be consulted in many public reference libraries together with some of the journals referred to.

No matter how careful the description or beautiful the drawing or

---

PLATE IV

SOME LATE PALAEOZOIC BRACHIOPODS

1. *Strophomena*. Coniston Limestone, Coniston. 2. *Longuilia*. Caradocian, Acton, Shropshire. 3. *Heterorthis*. Caradocian, Soudley, Shropshire. 4. *Chonetes*. Upper Ludlow. 5-7. *Productus*, (*Buxtonia*) Lower Carboniferous, Balladoole, Isle of Man. 5, Dorsal; 6, Ventral; 7, Posterior views. 8-10, *Spirifer*, Lower Carboniferous, Gameshill, Stewarton, Renfrewshire. 8. Dorsal; 9, Posterior; 10, Lateral views. 11, 12. *Atrypa*. Wenlock Limestone, Shropshire. 11, Dorsal; 12, Lateral views. 13. *Leptaena*. Wenlock Limestone, Shropshire. (*Photographs by A. Ferguson*)

photograph there is nothing to equal the specimens themselves. That is why the amateur is not content merely to build up a library but also acquires a collection. Though many collections thus formed have been lost or destroyed others have been preserved and have even become centres around which museums have grown. The oldest of these is the Ashmolean Museum at Oxford, founded by Elias Ashmole in 1679. Owing to the growth of its antiquarian and other collections the Natural History section was transferred to the New University Museum in 1860. In like manner the British Museum was established in 1753 for the preservation of the collections and library of Sir Hans Sloane, physician and naturalist. Its mere existence attracted other collections until in 1881 its natural history section was given a more spacious home at South Kensington. In 1837 the Geological Survey was given accommodation in Whitehall for its offices and for a Museum of Practical Geology. In 1850 these were removed to new buildings erected in Jermyn Street and again in 1934 to South Kensington. The collection given by Woodward to Cambridge University grew until a new home for it was also built and became a memorial to Professor Adam Sedgwick under the name of the Sedgwick Museum.

In addition to these large museums of national importance others have grown up in cities and small towns all over the country. Some of these have declined and perished, others have progressed and become important local and educational institutions. All these museums have provided centres to which sooner or later many of the best fossils found in Britain have gravitated by gift or purchase. No one who has developed an interest in the relics of the life of past ages is very far from one or other of these. The amateur may take his specimens there and learn much about them by comparing them with the collections in the show-cases. If difficulty arises he will usually find the curator or one of his assistants ready to help. He must not, however, take up much of their time for they are all very busy people.

After this long digression it is time to turn once more to the main course of our story. William Smith having blazed the trail for the geological exploration of Britain was rapidly followed by a growing army of professional geologists from the universities, official geologists from the Geological Survey, and many private individuals. These all found opportunity for mutual fellowship and discussion at meetings of the Geological Society of London where they often met the 'backroom boys' from museums and university laboratories who were ever ready to help with the identification of specimens and the elucidation of problems presented by fossils. A few of the earlier and best known of these consultants should be mentioned. W. Lonsdale, curator of the Geological Society's collections, though hampered by ill health, did such valuable work that his name was coupled by Buckland with that of William Smith as a great name in English Geology. Edward Forbes, who succeeded Lonsdale at the Geological Society, subsequently became naturalist to the Geological Survey and arranged the collections when these were transferred from Whitehall to Jermyn Street. Finally he became Professor of Natural History in the Edinburgh University but after a brief and brilliant career died at the early age of 39. He was succeeded at Jermyn Street by J. W. Salter who eventually moved to similar work at Cambridge, where he became closely associated with Professor Sedgwick.

Part Two

AN ERA OF BEGINNINGS
THE PALAEOZOIC

CHAPTER 8

MURCHISON IN THE
LAND OF THE SILURES

IN the first century of the Christian era the Romans fought their way westwards to the borders of South Wales. Here they came up against a great barrier, the Black Mountains, and encountered well-organised and fierce opposition from a warlike tribe, the Silures, under the leadership of Caractacus. As an attack on this front proved too difficult, the Roman Governor Frontinus changed his course, crossed the Bristol channel by boat and established a bridgehead at Caerleon near Newport. This gave him access to the valley of the Usk up which he advanced and, outflanking the Black Mountains, gained control of the Land of the Silures around the upper reaches of the Usk and Wye as far north as the river Severn.

Eighteen centuries later another soldier, Roderick Impey Murchison, invaded the same region but for a very different purpose. He set forth not to conquer existing inhabitants but to search for the remains of creatures that lived there long before the Black Mountains were carved out, before even their rocky foundations were laid down; creatures that lived at a time when that region was covered by a sea that stretched northwards over the whole of Wales, across the Lake District and the Southern Uplands of Scotland. Today it is estimated that this sea came into being 500 millions of years ago and lasted for nearly half the time which has since elapsed.

Murchison had served with the British Army in Spain throughout the Peninsular war. After the Battle of Waterloo he decided that there was no future for him in soldiering so he retired, got married and gave himself up to open-air sports on his estate. His wife, however, realising that his great gifts were being misdirected, inveigled him into turning his attention to this new science called Geology. In this he found an intellectual pursuit that rivalled sport in its outdoor demands and hazards and at the same time introduced him to an ever widening circle of scientific friends.

On William Smith's map it could be seen that Wales was occupied by three sets of rocks. In the south, Carboniferous rocks underlay and surrounded the coalfield. Along the northern flank of this the Old Red Sandstone rose up from beneath the Carboniferous and occupied a crescentic area of country. In the centre of the crescent lay the massive block of the Black Mountains that had baffled the Romans. The south-western horn of the crescent skirted the northern border of the coalfield as far west as Pembrokeshire. The other horn extended northwards into the fertile acres of Herefordshire. Between this crescent and the coast the map showed a uniform wash of dark grey colour representing rocks which in the Wernerian system were called 'Transitional' but which, as we now know consist of fine sandstone, shales and slates 12 times the thickness of the Jurassic rocks upon which Smith spent so much time. The latter are made up of alternating hard layers of resistant limestones and soft clays which at their outcrops have been carved into a succession of broad fertile vales and upstanding scarplands which to Smith's experienced eye revealed the general nature and arrangement of the rocks. But the scenery of central Wales gave little such help. It is a region of valleys, dour mountains and desolate moors.

Professor Buckland directed Murchison's attention to this great area awaiting exploration, recommending more especially the vicinity of Builth. Murchison accepted the challenge. Thus it came about that in the summer of 1831 he sallied forth from his London home accompanied by his wife and her two maids, in a carriage drawn by two grey nags. His passage westwards was leisurely, for interesting quarries and rocky exposures lay alongside his course and enticed him ever and anon to do a bit of hammering. He also sought out and visited any geologists who had been to Wales and absorbed from them such information as they could give.

Eventually he arrived at Swansea. From thence he struck across the coalfield and the narrow horn of the Old Red Sandstone crescent, and entered the Towy valley at Llandeilo. There he made contact with the "interminable grauwackes" of the Transition Series. The strategy he followed was to work from the known outcrop of the Old Red Sandstone into and across the outcrops of the unexplored rocks as they rose to the surface in the direction of Central Wales. He searched out the hidden recesses among the hills and mountains where little streams in times of turbulence had excavated deep gullies and exposed the rocks to view. Footslogging his way into these he worked his way up the Towy valley, which lay near to his known baseline, the inner margin of the Red Sandstone crescent.

Near Llandeilo the Transition Series as they emerged to the surface were found to consist of a varied assortment of rocks—of pebbly sand-stones and grits, of flags, black shales, volcanic ashes and limestones. Here he found many fossils and thus gained his first glimpse of the fauna of that ancient Palaeozoic Sea. Chief among these were the Trilobites, creatures that like the present-day insects had their bodies completely clothed in a thin armour of chitin. This was divided into a series of segments and was therefore flexible. The head was not so divided but was enclosed in a shield which carried on its upper surface a pair of eyes closely resembling those of an insect or crab in having numerous facets. In front was a pair of feelers or antennae. Subsequent work has shown that on its underside was a mouth surrounded by limbs that could function as jaws. On the under surface of the rest of the body each segment carried a pair of limbs made up of two branches, one of which was strong and jointed like an insect's leg and could be used for walking; the other resembled a feather and could be used for swimming. In some trilobites the tail segments were fused together into one piece. The middle segments of the body, however, were articulated so that the body as a whole could be bent freely and closed up like a wallet with the tailpiece fitting against the headshield.

Hidden away in these seemingly dry-as-dust details lie clues to the daily life of the trilobite. The presence of 'feelers' in front of the mouth and of legs on the underside of the body indicate that the animal normally wandered about on the muddy sea-floor searching for food. The situation of the eyes on the upper side of the head shows that the light came from above and that life was spent in depths sufficiently shallow for light to penetrate to the bottom. When the supply of food failed the creature could rise from the floor and swim with gently gliding motion in search of other feeding grounds. If on the way it met an enemy it gave a sharp flap forward with its tail-piece that sent it darting rapidly backwards. At the same time it closed up and sank out of sight to the mud below.

Not realising fully the structure of the region Murchison made

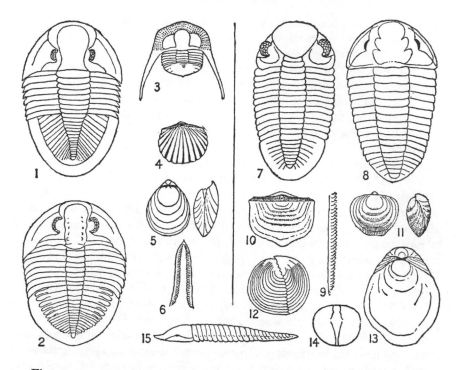

Fig. 3. THE EARLY AND LATE FAUNAS FOUND BY MURCHISON
Left. The Early Fauna. Trilobites; 1, *Asaphus*. 2, *Ogygia*. 3, *Trinucleus*. Brachio-
pods; 4, *Orthis*. 5, *Siphonotreta*, upper and side views. Graptolite: 6, *Didymograptus*.
Right. The Late Fauna. Trilobites; 7, *Phacops*. 8, *Calymene*. Graptolite; 9,
Monograptus. Brachiopods; 10, *Leptaena*. 11, *Atrypa*, upper and side views. 12.
Wilsonia. 13, *Pentamerus*. 14, Cross section of *Pentamerus*. 15, Side view of
Homalonotus a trilobite genus found in both faunas.

mistakes in the correlation of the strata. These have since been rectified
and the work done by him has been greatly extended. Nevertheless
he with indefatigable energy searched for and examined exposures of
fossiliferous levels in this thick series of apparently barren grauwackes,
and thus became the pioneer who first revealed the existence in these
very ancient rocks in Wales of a rich fauna characterised by distinctive
types of trilobites, brachiopods and other organisms.

Among the trilobites are *Asaphus* and *Ogygia*. Each has a large
tailpiece about equal in size to the headshield and separated from

this by only 8 freely articulating segments. *Trinucleus* is an attractive little form with a large headshield equal in size to the rest of the body. The margin of this shield is broad and decorated with markings which are useful in distinguishing different species from one another. From its outer angles two long posterior spines projected. *Homalonotus* is much less common. The front margin of the head is shaped like a shovel and its tailpiece is pointed. It was also nearly blind. These features together with the stream-lined form of the body were probably associated with a burrowing habit.

The Brachiopods were creatures with shells having two valves that covered the upper and under sides of the body respectively. Usually these were calcareous and were held together partly by a hinge at the hinder end and partly by muscles which passed through the body. From the latter a muscular stalk arose and emerging through an opening at the middle of the hinge-line, anchored the animal to one spot on the sea-floor. One of the most characteristic brachiopods is *Orthis*. Its hinge margin is straight and shorter then the greatest width of the shell. The surface of the latter is marked with ridges or ribs radiating from the umbo which lies close to the middle of the hinge line and marks the point from which the shell started to grow. Both valves are convex and differ in this respect from a form known to Murchison as *Leptaena* in which the shell is concavo-convex, a feature now known to characterise a number of genera. These all have a long straight hinge-line extending for the full width of the shell. *Siphonotreta* and *Monobolina* are primitive brachiopods in which the shell is horny and phosphatic.

Among other organisms must be mentioned the following. *Streptelasma* a small conical coral and two Molluscs, *Orthoceras* and *Bellerophon*. *Orthoceras* has a shell that is divided into chambers, as in the living Pearly Nautilus, but it is straight and not coiled. *Bellerophon* belongs to the small snail like Gastropods but unlike most of these it could swim freely. Finally reference should be made to the Graptolites. (c.p. Fig. 5 and Plate II: *1, 2*). These are preserved as pencil-like markings upon the surfaces of black shales, and were originally known as Grapholites. They have distinctive shapes not unlike those of some present-day sea-mosses or Hydroids. Some floated in the water or hung down from floating seaweeds, others were attached to the sea-floor.

In the course of his explorations Murchison found, close to the

margin of the Old Red Sandstone, a narrow outcrop of rocks overlying the series just described and therefore later in age than these.
Followed northwards in the direction of Radnor and South Shropshire
it broadened considerably and brought him into the vicinity of Builth
where, to his joy, the scenery reflected the underground structure
more clearly and became like that of Smith's Jurassic belt with its
succession of scarplands and vales. This upper series consisted of alternating limestones and mudstones based upon thick sandstones and grits.

In this upper series were found a later fossil fauna having the same
general characteristics as that in the lower series. For this reason he
included both in one great system which he called the Silurian, after
that early tribe of British warriors that lived on and fought across their
outcrops. Nevertheless changes in the nature of the rocks combined
with some distinctive differences in the fossil faunas led him to divide
the system into two parts, the Lower and Upper Silurian with earlier
and later faunas respectively.

The presence of trilobites in the Upper Silurian was a link with
the Lower but they were less abundant and the important genera
Asaphus and *Trinucleus* were absent. Other genera such as *Phacops* and
Calymene rose into prominence. The former, as its name suggests, had
well-developed faceted eyes. The glabella or central part of the
headshield was smooth and swollen. This feature together with the
lateral and forward position of the large eyes may reflect a habit of
diurnal migration up and down in the water as the light faded or
strengthened. In *Calymene* the glabella is narrow in front and of normal
size. Its sides are divided into lobules by deep grooves.

Among the Brachiopods *Orthis* was absent. Others, such as *Leptaena*,
are closely related to older forms and also serve as a link between the
two series. *Strophomena* is semi-circular in outline, like *Leptaena* but its
concavity is ventral. New genera included the large *Pentamerus*, which
has a short curved hinge-line, and its inner cavity as implied by the
name is divided by thin partitions. *Rhynchonella*, a genus which still
lives in existing seas, was represented by the species *R. wilsoni* and
has a similar ornamentation to that already described for *Orthis*, its
hinge-line is, however, very short and curved.

Towards Central Wales these rocks become finer-grained. In them
the fauna which is of deeper water type is characterised by graptolites
belonging to the genus *Monograptus*.

Two limestones, well exposed near Wenlock and Aymestry, are

so rich in fossils that they had already attracted the attention of local naturalists who, with characteristic generosity, placed their knowledge and collections at Murchison's disposal. Reference should be made to the Revd. T. T. Lewis of Aymestry, whose skill as a field geologist rivalled that of Murchison himself. The personality of the latter not only elicited the enthusiasm and co-operation of grown-up workers, but inspired boys and girls to place their sharp eyes and active limbs at his service.

Though Murchison had a quick eye for finding fossils he made no pretensions to a profound and detailed knowledge of them. He therefore enlisted the services of such experts as W. Lonsdale who willingly identified and described his specimens and thus enabled him to classify the strata more precisely.

CHAPTER 9

SEDGWICK AND THE
EARLIEST BRITISH FOSSILS

THE credit for unearthing the earliest fossil-bearing rocks in Britain must be accorded to Adam Sedgwick. Though he became a great geologist his initial interest was in theology. After entering Trinity College, Cambridge, as a scholar he became a Fellow in 1810, and eight years later was admitted to Priest's Orders in the Anglican Church. About the same time he was made Woodwardian Professor of Geology. His qualifications for this important position were naively described by him in the remark "Hitherto I have never turned a stone, now I shall leave no stone unturned."

In 1807 the Geological Society of London was founded and became an important centre for mutual help among geologists who met to discuss work that was being done and new discoveries that had been made. Here Sedgwick met Murchison and the two struck up a friendship that led to many excursions, geologising together, in Britain and abroad. Sedgwick was a native of Dent, near the borders of Yorkshire and Westmoreland, and he was naturally drawn to investigate the Transition Series of rocks in the neighbouring Lake District. Here, as we now know, the rocks had lost their original simplicity of arrangement and had been torn and shattered by faults, pierced by volcanic vents and interleaved with lavas or intruded by large volumes of hot magma which had solidified into masses of granite. Working out the intricate pattern thus imposed upon the rocks of this region was a type of task in which Sedgwick delighted and for which his gifts proved to be peculiarly well suited.

With the experience gained in the Lake District he joined Murchison in the exploration of Wales but gave his attention to the north which, like the Lake District but unlike Murchison's domain further south, was a region of great structural complexity. Here he found the base of the Transition Series resting upon the Primitive Rocks of Werner's classification. While therefore Murchison worked on the whole from above downwards in the series, Sedgwick worked from the base upwards. The former made extensive use of fossils as guides to the correlation and succession of rock formation, the latter relied upon detailed mapping of the structure and nature of the rocks themselves. For him, therefore, a fault, a calcareous sandstone, an igneous rock, a lava, a volcanic neck was much more fascinating than a brachiopod or a trilobite. Nevertheless such fossils as were found were not neglected but passed on to a young palaeontologist, J. W. Salter, who sometimes accompanied him in the field and, following up the clues, discovered many others of which he published accounts in 1845-46. Most of these proved to be closely similar to those already found by Murchison. It then became evident that the sets of rocks discovered by Murchison and Sedgwick and named Silurian and Cambrian by them respectively were not, as they at first thought, quite distinct, but were in fact overlapping systems. What the overlapping portion should be called was a problem that remained unresolved in their life-time.

Two levels recognised by Sedgwick should be mentioned. First were the Bala Beds at the top of the 'Cambrian' which yielded a similar suite of fossils to those found by Murchison at Caradoc in Shropshire and subsequently recognised as defining the top of his Lower Silurian. The second he called the Tremadoc Beds after the town near which they lay and which were eventually recognised as the top of his Lower Cambrian. The fossils found in these were described by Salter in 1853.

It is not surprising that, as the outcome of these discoveries, others joined in the hunt for rocks of the same age elsewhere. Their presence in Pembrokeshire was proved by W. Hicks and in Shropshire by C. Callaway, both of them medical doctors. They were also found near Nuneaton. The search thus begun was carried further afield, even as far as the extreme north of Scotland, by officers of the Geological Survey, by members of various universities and by many amateurs.

Of especial interest was the finding by Professor C. Lapworth (Birmingham) of the trilobite *Olenellus* in a thin limestone at the base of the sandstones quarried near Comley in Shropshire. This trilobite type did not originate in Britain but belonged to a stock which evolved in North America during early Cambrian times. For most of this period Britain was dry land, but eventually became submerged just in time to be invaded by the latest members of this olenellidian stock. With them came many other organisms which together make up the assemblage of fossils known as the Olenellidian fauna. Much of our detailed knowledge of this fauna we owe to E. S. Cobbold, a civil engineer who went to live at Church Stretton.

During the early years of this century Cobbold searched the rocks of that district assiduously, broke up promising lumps of stone and, with infinite patience, extracted and cleaned every fossil fragment he could find. In this way he conjured from the darkness of 500 millions of years ago a picture of this, the earliest fauna known to have inhabited Britain (Plate I*b*). In it were such trilobites as *Callavia*, originally known as *Olenellus*, and *Micmacca* which had elongated eyes and triangular bodies with every segment as far as the tip of the tail freely articulating. *Microdiscus*, one of the smallest of known trilobites, differed strikingly from the rest in having a large tailpiece as well as headshield. These were hinged together by only 3 free segments. There were also primitive brachiopods such as *Obolella* and *Paterina* with horny shells slightly phosphatised. The two valves enclosing the body tended to be oval or rounded in outline and more or less convex like a watch-glass. The fleshy stalk emerged at a point between their margins. Swimming about in the water were molluscs, allied to snails but with long tubular conical shells, known as *Hyolithus* and *Hyolithellus*. They probably had wing-shaped extensions of the 'foot' with which they were able to flit about in the water like butterflies or the modern pteropods. No doubt there would be myriads of other organisms such as protozoa, jellyfishes, worms and larvae of various molluscs that lived and died but left no memorial of their existence.

The exploration of the higher Cambrian rocks resulted in the discovery of two later faunas characterised respectively by the presence of the trilobites *Paradoxides* and *Olenus*. These and the other genera that occurred resembled the earlier Cambrian forms and differed from the "silurian" trilobites in the multiplicity of free segments and the absence of a large tailpiece. One exception was the very small and ubiquitous *Agnostus* which resembled *Microdiscus* but had only two free segments.

The Tremadoc beds have yielded the remains of faunas with points of resemblance on the one hand to the Cambrian forms and on the other to those which occurred in Murchison's 'Lower Silurian.' They are therefore of peculiar interest because of their intermediate or transitional character.

None of these faunas was native to Britain but invaded this area after evolving elsewhere. Their remains consequently serve as valuable links between these ancient British rocks and those of distant parts of the globe. Thus the technique of using fossils invented by William Smith and applied by Murchison and Sedgwick and their followers to the study of the Welsh rocks opened a way to the unravelling of a very ancient but important phase in the geological history of the world.

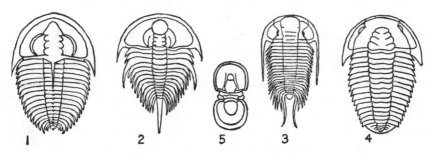

Fig. 4. CAMBRIAN TRILOBITES
1, *Callavia*. 2, *Olenellus*. 3, *Paradoxides* 4, *Olenus*. 5, *Agnostus*.

The trilobites form only one division of that major group of animals known as the Arthropoda. Though they no longer exist their place in the economy of the seas is taken today by the Crustacea which include the lobsters, shrimps and crabs. This group of Arthropods is represented among cambrian fossils by the small *Hymenocaris* which closely resembled *Nebalia*, a little creature that swarms in the open waters of existing seas.

The most extensive area of Cambrian rocks in Britain occurs in the North-west Highlands of Scotland, and extends from the Isle of Skye in the south to the extreme north coast. At the base is a sandy series of beds some of the layers of which are riddled by vertical pipes which were originally worm burrows. Though no actual fossilised remains of worms are found these burrows show that they lived in profusion in early Cambrian waters. Nor were they insignificant

creatures for they were large enough to make 'pipes' one or even
two inches in diameter; large enough in fact to provide a substantial
meal for a vertebrate fish which, however, did not yet exist. The precise
age of these beds has been fixed by the discovery in them of fragments
of *Olenellus*.

Next above these beds come impure limestones containing calcareous tubes similar to those secreted by such worms as the living
Serpula. These rocks in turn are succeeded by a great thickness of
limestones which have yielded a fauna strikingly different from that
found in South Britain but closely resembling that found in certain
of the Cambrian and immediately succeeding rocks as far away as
North America. Only a few trilobites were present and the fauna
consisted mainly of molluscs. Among these the cephalopods were
dominant and included the earliest known ancestors of the Pearly
Nautilus which lives now in the Pacific ocean. It has a shell that is
coiled into a tight logarithmic spiral and is divided internally into
many chambers. In the upper levels of these rocks the most prominent
nautiloid is *Orthoceras* whose shell is similarly chambered but has the
form of a long straight cone. In *Piloceras* the shell is shorter and internally
exhibits features characteristic of a still earlier stage in the evolution of
the cephalopods. These primeval relatives of the nautilus could swim
as well as crawl. With them there lived an interesting assortment of
snail-like creatures or gastropods that crawled about on the sea-floor:
and of bivalve forms, pelecypods or lamellibranchs, that ploughed
their way through the mud. Other creatures included sponges and
a fascinating type of animal, *Archaeocyathus*, combining features found
in corals and sponges, which though it was then abundant here and
elsewhere in the world soon became quite extinct.

From this brief survey of the animal life in Cambrian seas one

---

PLATE V

a. SECTION OF RHYNIE CHERT

In the left centre is an oblique section along the stem of the plant *Rhynia
gwynne-vaughani*. In the right centre is a horizontal section through a minute
air-breathing arachnid, *Palaeocharinus*. (*W. Sutcliffe*)

b. SECTION OF CARBONIFEROUS LIMESTONE

This shows that the matrix of this rock consists largely of minute shells and
shelly fragments of *Foraminifera*. (*W. Sutcliffe*)

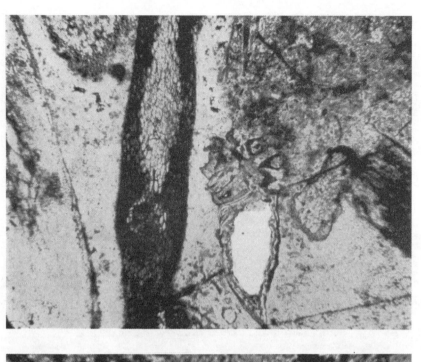

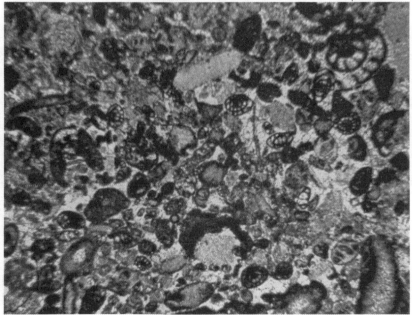

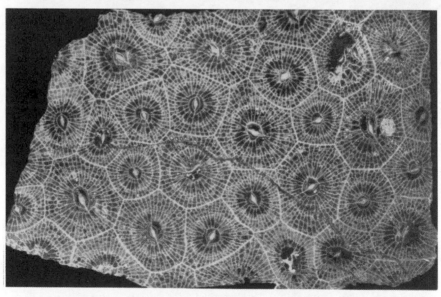

striking fact emerges. It is that as long ago as the early part of the Palaeozoic Era every major group of the animal kingdom, with the exception of the vertebrates, had already come into being. Not only so but a number of the main subdivisions of those groups were already differentiated. The series of evolutionary changes which culminated in these complex faunas must have required for their accomplishment vast periods of time: now estimated to be at least three or four times as long as that which has since elapsed.

Fossil evidence for these changes is very scanty and has been found in the latest Precambrian rocks of other lands. This is probably largely due to the fact that the ability to secrete shells and other structures capable of being fossilised came late in evolution. Moreover those remains that were buried must often have been destroyed by the same agencies that completely changed the character of vast thicknesses of the Precambrian rocks. The many discoveries that have been made in this small area called Britain, in the brief space of time that has passed since William Smith unlocked the outer doors and Murchison and Sedgwick sallied forth, encourages the hope that even greater advances will be made when other as yet unexplored regions are opened out. Such dreams must not, however, entice us from exploring. our own land in still greater detail and investigating its fossils yet more carefully. The half has still not been told.

PLATE VI

a. CORALS IN CARBONIFEROUS LIMESTONE

Rain water washing over the face of the limestone has dissolved the rock slightly more quickly than the fossils which consequently stand out in relief. Clisiophyllid corals are exposed on the upper layer; and a large fasciculate colony of Lithostrotion is seen in the left on the lower layer. Monsal Dale, Derbyshire. (*F. M. Taylor*)

b. SECTION OF A COMPACT CORAL COLONY

Section of *Lithostrotion arachnoideum* showing the closely packed corallites separated from one another only by a thin wall. In the centre of each is a solid rod and the space around this is divided by radiating septa.

(*F. M. Taylor*)

FOS—E

CHAPTER 10

LAPWORTH FACES A DILEMMA

A T THE base of the transition series Sedgwick found conglomerates and great masses of grits about 5000 feet thick. These passed upwards through light coloured shales into a series of fine-grained and well-bedded sandstones and flagstones succeeded by dark grey and black shales like those which engaged so much of Murchison's attention. Throughout the whole of this great thickness of rocks Sedgwick found no marked break or unconformity in the sequence. He therefore regarded them as one system and called it the Cambrian. When the fossils found in the domains of these two explorers were compared it was discovered that the two sets of rocks, which had been engaging their attention separately, overlapped one another; that Murchison's Lower Silurian corresponded with Sedgwick's Upper Cambrian. Here then was a dilemma; what should this overlapping portion be called, Lower Silurian or Upper Cambrian? The two friends never came to any agreement and the dilemma remained unresolved for many years. In 1838 Murchison published a detailed record of his work in 'Siluria', a book which has become for all time a classic in geological literature. He himself became Director of the Geological Survey of Great Britain and naturally his terminology for these rocks was adopted officially for all the literature and maps published by that body.

Murchison had been a soldier; Sedgwick was a clergyman; but Lapworth, who resolved the dilemma, was a schoolmaster. Charles Lapworth was born in Berkshire just eleven years after Murchison set out to explore the land of the Silures. At the age of 22 he gained a First Class Government Certificate as a teacher and started off on his career in a school at Galashiels, a town situated in the Southern Uplands of Scotland; another extensive area of unexplored 'Transition Rocks'. Accompanied by his friend James Wilson, he spent his spare time and holidays in examining the rocks around Galashiels and discovered that, contrary to existing opinion, they did contain fossils. These were mainly graptolites similar to those found in Murchison's Silurian. The relative abundance, so close at hand, of the remains of these obscure little creatures presented him with an excellent opportunity for studying them carefully and adding greatly to the knowledge already acquired by Marr, Nicholson and other workers. He maintained his interest in them throughout life and, enlisting the skilled co-operation of two young Cambridge enthusiasts, Miss Gertrude Elles and Miss Wood (Dame Ethel Shakespeare), ultimately produced a monumental work of four volumes exquisitely illustrated and published by the Palaeontographical Society. With the help of this work we are able to make a rapid survey of the history of the graptolites and thus to grasp more clearly the path along which Lapworth groped his way and, in the end, unravelled both the evolution of the graptolites and the complicated structure of the Southern Uplands.

A graptolite fragment looks like a piece of a fine fretsaw, each tooth of which marks the opening of a tube-like chamber or *theca* made of a horny substance. This was originally the home of a minute creature possibly not unlike a hydroid polyp. At its base it produced a bud that grew into another 'polyp' lying alongside its parent which in turn secreted a theca for itself. In like manner a third and many succeeding polyps and their chambers were produced side by side. The long straight row of little thecal dwellings thus formed is known as a *stipe*.

The earliest graptolites had many stipes radiating from a central structure which seems to have functioned as a float. From this the rows of polyps hung heads downwards and fed upon the minute plants and animals that infested the warm surface waters. When the colony died its horny framework sunk as a whole or in pieces to the sea floor and was there buried under slowly accumulating mud.

With the onward sweep of the ages the graptolites passed through a 'programme-like' series of changes. Starting with a large and indefinite number of branches or stipes, these were rapidly reduced in number to 64, 32, 16, 8 and then 4. This four-stiped or *Tetragraptus* phase remained stable for a while and was in turn succeeded by a two-stiped or *Didymograptus* phase which lasted for a much longer time. In the different species belonging to these phases the stipes assumed varying attitudes. In some they hung down like the prongs

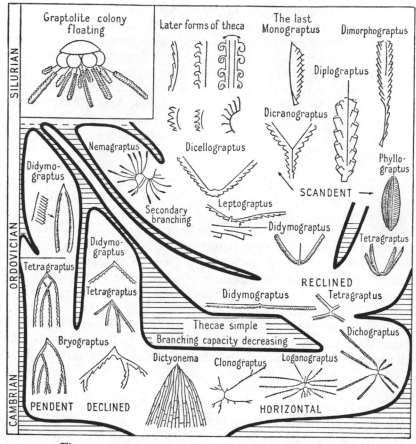

Fig. 5. THE GENERAL EVOLUTIONARY HISTORY
OF GRAPTOLITES

of a tuning fork (pendent). In others they diverged (declined), or
became horizontal (extensiform). At a later stage they turned upwards
(reclined) and at last came to lie back to back (scandent) along a thin
tubular structure that hung down from the 'float'. In this last, the
Diplograptus phase, the polyps faced upwards instead of downwards.
Eventually on one side of this diplograptid type of colony the thecae
began to disappear from the proximal end of the stipe, as in *Dimorpho-*

graptus and then the process extended to the distal end later. On its completion it ushered in the *Monograptus* phase. This arose several times independently in separately evolving series of diplograptids.

These phasal or more precisely gradal terms were first used as generic names and are still used as such. Within each genus various species are recognised. They are based upon such characters as the angle between the axis of the theca and that of the stipe; or upon the form of the theca or the shape of its aperture.

For Lapworth this study of the graptolites was essentially a side issue: nevertheless these organisms provided him with the means by which he set these ancient rocks talking and revealing their story. He rapidly developed an eye for detecting the minute specific differences shown by these fossils in the contiguous layers of rock. Indeed the rate of change in the graptolites as compared with that of deposition of sediment was apparently so rapid that specimens preserved on the upper and under surfaces of the same thin slab often belonged to quite distinct species. He kept detailed records of every exposure examined and noted the precise level from which each fossil or fragment was extracted. At home he studied and identified the species and thus built up a reliable record of the sequence of their occurrence in the rocks and therefore of their evolution in time.

Before Lapworth began his work in the Southern Uplands it had always been assumed that these were made up of rocks of enormous thickness. All his careful recording, however, proved to be the prelude to a wonderful discovery which dawned upon his mental horizon as he worked up and down those deep gullies in which the rocky exposures are kept perennially fresh by the continual washing and excavating action of the sparkling mountain streams. In Dobbs Linn, near Moffat, he found as he worked along the stream that the fossils occurred in the usual order for some distance and then were repeated in the reverse order. From this fact he quickly realised that some of the layers of rock had been turned upside down. Thus, for example, if the next ten pages of this book are folded over backwards it will be found that in one half of the fold the pages will follow one another in the normal sequence from 55 to 65; but in the other half the order will be reversed. With some such image in his mind Lapworth concluded that the only explanation for this topsy-turvy arrangement of the successive zones of graptolites was that the rocks had been intensely folded.

This fertilising idea led him to explore a greatly extended area. With the help of large-scale maps, often made by himself, he recorded carefully the precise spots where the graptolite zones cropped out to the surface. In this way he detected fold after fold and proved that the rocks of these uplands were originally spread out as vast but relatively thin sheets of deposits. Great pressures in the earth's crust then ensued, resistlessly folding and crimping these sheets into a state like that of a pleated skirt or a concertina and squeezing the folds against one another, packed them into a mass of rock of prodigious thickness. Thus with the aid of fossils he unravelled the complicated structure of the Southern Uplands.

Fossils other than graptolites were rare in these black shales. But at the western end of the uplands, near the coast in the vicinity of Girvan and Ballantrae, these slates and fine-grained shales became interleaved with and then replaced by calcareous sandy and even gravelly deposits which indicated the former proximity of the western coastline of the Palaeozoic sea. Lapworth extended his investigations into this region in the hopes of discovering the relationships of his graptolite sequence to that of other fossil types; more particularly the brachiopods and trilobites. Remains of these were in places so abundant that they had previously attracted the attention of Mrs. Robert Gray, a local resident who had built up a valuable and instructive collection. When Lapworth appeared upon the scene she gave him free access to her collection, with the result that he rapidly acquired a comprehensive knowledge of the fossil faunas in these rocks. In the field he discovered that the graptolitic shales occurred interbedded with layers containing trilobites and brachiopods and was thus able to dovetail the three types of fossil sequences into one another.

The shelly fauna from this northwestern side of the Palaeozoic sea resembled that discovered by Murchison and other workers along its southeastern shores. Thus Lapworth's work completed the general picture of the physical conditions and of the faunas of that ancient sea. It showed that over most of the area the water was deep and open and in it the generations of graptolites drifted freely so that at any given time the fauna was practically the same everywhere. But in the shallower waters towards its coastal margins trilobites, brachiopods, corals and stone lilies found congenial homes. Along this narrow belt the animals migrated round the sea either as floating larvae or as freely swimming and crawling adults and so established a general similarity of faunas everywhere along the coastal margins. As, however, the successive generations evolved, the faunas in both types of habitat also changed and their remains consequently mark out for us the successive periods of time and stages in evolution.

Turning his attention to the unresolved dilemma (v. p. 47) Lapworth pointed out that in the rocks which Sedgwick called the Lower Cambrian graptolites were absent except for the presence, near the top in the light-coloured Tremadoc Beds of very primitive forms. These included *Dictyonema*, a genus with numerous stipes linked together by thin cross connections which converted the whole into a delicate network (dictyon—a net). On the other hand the graptolites found in the Upper Silurian of Murchison belonged to the *Monograptus* type. He therefore agreed that these two sets of rocks belonged to two independent systems for which the names Cambrian and Silurian should be retained. But he emphasised the fact that the Upper Cambrian of Sedgwick and the Lower Silurian of Murchison were both characterised by the same graptolitic sequence ranging from many stiped forms through the *Tetragraptus* and *Didymograptus* to *Diplograptus* grades. He therefore concluded that these rocks contained sufficiently distinctive faunas to be treated as another and separate system. As their outcrops occupied the original home-land of the Ordovices, another Celtic tribe, he suggested for them the new named Ordovician. This threefold division of the Older Palaeozoic rocks is now universally adopted, a state of affairs made possible by the worldwide distribution of these successive graptolitic phases.

In 1881, shortly after he put forth his solution for this longstanding dilemma, he was appointed Professor of Geology at Mason's College, Birmingham, and became for many years the instigator of a vigorous exploration of the rocks in the Midlands and the Welsh Border country. That, however, is another story.

This close interweaving of the study of the graptolites with that of the rocks has provided material which illustrates the processes of evolution and the problems of classification and nomenclature which confront the palaeontologist. The broad outlines of their story portrayed above shows the progressive change from forms with many stipes to those with only one and supplies an excellent illustration of the fact that evolution sometimes proceeds by reduction in numbers of repeated structural features.

Within the final stage, the passage from the *Diplograptus* grade to that of *Monograptus* another principle emerges. The disappearance of the little living chambers from one side of the *Diplograptus* colony did not take place all at once but gradually, beginning in the early life or youth of the colony. Consequently, for a brief period, graptolites existed which in early life were monograptid and in late life diplograptid. These were labelled *Dimorphograptus*. In this sequence there is a reversal of the more familiar principle so often referred to as that of 'Recapitulation of adult stages' or *Palingenesis*, in which the indications of forthcoming evolutionary changes often appear for the first time only in late life. This tendency for conditions seen in 'youth' sometimes to anticipate the later course of evolution occurs not uncommonly in other fossil sequences and is an example of another equally important principle, that of *Proterogenesis*.

It should be noted that the set of terms *Tetragraptus* to *Monograptus* is fundamentally descriptive only of grades passed through several times independently during the history of separately evolving series, so called 'lineages' or lines of descent. Nevertheless they are in common use as generic names. These genera are therefore not based upon genetic affinity but upon outstanding similarities of form. They are in fact morphological or form genera marking grades of evolution. This type of nomenclature is usually adopted when new ground is being broken in the study of geological and palaeontological problems. Not until the solution of these is approaching completion do the underlying genetic relationships generally become fully apparent and a 'natural' as opposed to an 'artificial' classificatory system becomes possible. Meanwhile such artificial terminology pinpoints many facts the knowledge of which is essential to the clarification of evolutionary problems.

Much less important for stratigraphical purposes are the dendroid graptolites which are found throughout the palaeozoic rocks up to and including the Carboniferous. These form irregularly branched colonies which are attached to the sea-floor like tiny sea-weeds. In recent years interest has been renewed in these by the discovery that they have a structural resemblance to the framework enclosing the body of *Cephalodiscus*. This curious little creature is found today living in southern seas from Borneo to the Antarctic at depths ranging from low-tide mark down to 600 fathoms or more. It was shown long ago that *Cephalodiscus* belongs to a lowly group of animals that lie close to the root from which all vertebrates, including man, evolved. Fossil records suggest that the vertebrates first came into being during early palaeozoic times. If this resemblance should prove to have real significance the superabundance of graptolites at that time may be no mere coincidence but a fact of more than passing interest.

'ONE CROWDED HOUR . . .'

'ONE crowded hour of glorious life—', those words of the poet aptly describe the experience of any young geologist who, wandering among the beauties of Shropshire comes upon a good exposure or quarry in the Wenlock Limestone. Here in the brief space of one hour he may gather up a bigger load of fossils than even his youthful zeal will dare to take home.

If he has some slight knowledge of marine zoology he will, as he selects his specimens, catch fleeting glimpses of the submarine life in the ancient Silurian Sea. But the need for careful collecting will postpone the flights of his imagination until his precious finds are spread out before him in his den. There as he scrubs and cleans them he will begin to distinguish different kinds and to arrange them into groups. He may make drawings of some and thus begin to see details that would otherwise escape his notice.

With the help of reference books, of expert friends and of visits to museums he will discover their names and, what is more important, learn how to classify them. Classify! How dull! Nevertheless classification is like an aerial photograph of the realm of living things. It shows at a glance the precise place of a specimen in the Society of Fossils; it helps the student to detect quickly the salient features which distinguish them one from another; it collates those that are related and those which are strangers. By the time that he has learnt all this he has begun to become an expert on the few fossils he already possesses and will be able in his turn to help some other beginner in this fascinating study.

Thus out of his 'crowded hour' there has grown a fuller picture of marine animal life in late Silurian times. Many of the larger specimens are shaped like petrified cushions, often with a honeycomb pattern shown upon their surfaces (Plate III). On some cushions the pattern is large-

scaled with the cells or meshes nearly one inch in diameter. Each
cell encloses a deep saucer-like hollow with its floor crossed by a
number of thin walls or septa radiating from the centre. A look at
the underside of the cushion will often show that each cell is the upper
end of one individual coral or corallite and that the cushion as a whole
is made up of a number of these closely packed together. It is in fact
a compound coral or colony, such as that of *Acervularia,* which thus
shows a pattern not unlike a large bunch of daisy flowers. During life
the surface was crowned with sea-anemone-like polyps which stretched
themselves out towards the light and formed a lovely diadem. This
coral, with many others akin to it, beautified the reefs on the Silurian
sea-floor. Similar corals occurred singly: one of the largest of these
was *Omphyma.* From the lower conical portion of this, root-like struts
grew down into the mud and anchored it in an upright position. The
hollow or theca at the top was spacious and was occupied by a polyp
two or more inches in diameter.

A second type of cushion is *Favosites,* popularly known as 'honeycomb coral' for it is covered with numerous small cells comparable in
size with those on the bee's honeycomb. At the bottom of the theca
there is a flat floor but no septa. Allied to it is the 'chain coral',
Halysites, so called because the individual corallites, instead of lying
closely packed together, are arranged in rows so that their thecae, as
seen on the surface of the cushion, look like the links of a chain.
Another type, *Heliolites,* has the same shape as *Favosites* but its surface
is pitted with round cells of two sizes. The larger have short septa
around their margins and are separated by wide spaces filled with
much smaller cells.

Another and more massive cushion, *Stromatopora,* has its surface
punctured by numerous small holes, like pores, each of which was
occupied in life by a hydroid polyp. These pores are the openings of
calcareous tubes. When such a colony is cut across it is seen to be
made up of a feltwork of such tubes arranged in thin layers. It belongs
to the Hydrocorallinae, a lower or more primitive type than the
ordinary coral, but equally important as a rock-builder in middle
Palaeozoic seas.

Yet another type of cushion is represented by *Monticulipora.* In
this the honeycomb pattern is much finer, for the individual cells are
no more than a millimetre in diameter. This, however, is not a coral
for the little creatures which made it were not coral polyps but more

highly organised animals known as Polyzoa. To these belong the sea-mats which litter present-day beaches after a storm. People who make a hobby of studying pond life under the microscope are familiar with a freshwater example known as *Plumatella,* an exquisitely beautiful little creature which has a tiara of tentacles, used for collecting food, arranged in the shape of a horseshoe. In the sea myriads of similar animals live together in populous colonies. In the Wenlock limestone sea they built their minute single-roomed dwellings of lime and crowded them together in massive or in stout branching coral-like forms which also played an important part in reef-formation.

Among the specimens spread out on the collector's table are many Brachiopods. Examination of the few species which still live in existing seas shows that these animals were more closely allied to the Polyzoa than to any other fossil-producing creatures. The individuals are, however, much larger than in the Polyzoa and live singly. The shell margin which carried the hinge varied greatly in length. In *Leptaena* this extends the full width of the shell which has the front margins bent sharply upwards (Fig. 3). In *Rhynchotreta* and *Wilsonia* the length of the hinge is reduced to a minimum. In the former the shell has a triangular outline with the umbo drawn out into a sharp beak. In both genera the surface of the shell is ornamented with fine ribs radiating from the umbo. In *Spirifer* and *Atrypa* the hinge line is longer (Plate IV). The name of the former is based upon the presence inside the shell of two narrow ribbons of lime associated with a plume-like gill bearing organ which also sifts out food from the water. These are coiled into delicate conical spirals having their apices pointed towards the ends of the hingeline. In *Atrypa* the spires point towards the upper valve.

In some places such as the Wren's Nest, near Dudley and Benthall edge, near Ironbridge in the Severn Gorge, the beds of the Wenlock limestone are tilted up at steep angles and large surfaces of it are exposed. During the ages that have elapsed since men first occupied Britain, rain has washed their sloping surfaces, slowly dissolving the limestone and etching out in low relief the multitudes of fossils buried in the rock. Thus nature prepared marvellous displays of fossils which quickly caught the eyes of the early collectors, who in a few years skimmed off the cream of these wonderful natural exhibitions of the sea-floor as it appeared in Silurian times. Fortunately not all of their collections have been lost for many have found their way by gift and purchase into the museums that, as already seen, began to spring up in many places. Today it is everyone's privilege to visit these museums and see much more complete displays of fossils from the Wenlock limestone than any private individual could now possibly collect in a lifetime.

Among the most striking fossils to be seen in the showcases are the Stone-lilies or Crinoids, for these beautiful creatures, so rare in our seas today, attained their heyday in the Silurian waters. Crinoids, along with starfishes and sea-urchins, belong to that great division of the animal kingdom known as the Echinodermata. Could anything be less like an animal than a fossil stone-lily, with its tall slender calcareous stem swollen at the top into a bulb crowned with delicately divided petals? Nay, rather it looks like a lily carved in stone. That they were animals has been proved by the discovery of almost identical organisms living today on the floor of clear sunlit tropical seas. There they can be seen with their petal-like arms outspread. Along the upper surface of each arm runs a narrow groove furnished with innumerable vibratile hairs which, by their rhythmic movements set up strong currents of water sweeping towards the mouth and bringing to it minute animals and plants to serve for food. Nourished in this way the 'lily' grows and by secreting lime builds up its stony skeleton. This process takes place most actively at the base of the bulb where round discs are formed continually and, being placed one upon another build up the tall stem. Under unfavourable conditions the animal snaps its stalk and by wafting its arms swims away in search of other feeding grounds. Having found these it becomes attached once more and begins a sedentary life anew.

Yet another interesting feature about these limestone exposures is frequently overlooked, especially where the stone is thinly bedded. Between the beds there are often films or laminae of soft shale. When a slab of stone is wedged off by frost it slides down to the ground and leaves the film exposed. This is then washed off by the rain and accumulates on ledges, in pockets or along runnels. Some of it should be gathered and taken home to be panned in a dish of water. On examining the coarse sediment left behind a rich collection of minute fossils will be found. Many a pleasant hour may speed away as these are being sorted out, mounted and examined. In this way a micro-museum may be created made up of remarkably clean and perfect

specimens of minute shells of the single-celled animals called Foraminifera, and of early stages in the development of higher animals
such as Brachiopods, Corals, and Polyzoan colonies. In it will be
found an introduction to palaeontological embryology and the
Foraminifera that will open out many fascinating lines of study and
research.

CHAPTER 2

A NEW VISTA IN TIME

T HE coming of steam power with its insistent demand for coal and yet more coal soon led geologists to concentrate their attention upon the coal-bearing or Carboniferous rocks. The drab coloured soils naturally produced from these presented a striking contrast to the warm red soils of the country on either side which were derived from two sets of red rocks that bounded the Carboniferous below and above, and became known as the Old Red and the New Red Sandstones respectively. As already seen the former were in turn underlain by the Older Palaeozoic rocks. As the Old Red Sandstone had an estimated thickness in some places of 10,000 feet it rivalled the Carboniferous in geological importance and was accordingly promoted by British geologists to the status of a 'system'. Continental geologists, however, found no comparable rocks in their regions and refused to regard it as anything more than a local type. As will be seen later they proved to be mistaken.

In 1826 Murchison and Sedgwick went off to Scotland to examine the 'Old Red' there. Hitherto this was thought to be unfossiliferous, but they had the good fortune to discover fossil fishes, a thrilling experience, for these proved to be the oldest vertebrate remains hitherto found in Britain. They were submitted to Agassiz, a Swiss palaeontologist at Neuchatel, who had made a special study of fish-like remains, and he identified them as belonging to the genera *Cephalaspis, Dipterus* and *Holoptychius*. An account of this discovery was published in the Transactions of the Geological Society for the year 1827.

This catch of fishes, however, was only preliminary to a much larger draught subsequently caught by others. Foremost among these fishermen was Hugh Miller, a native of Cromarty, who came from a seafaring stock. He was born in 1802, ten years later than his fellow-countryman Murchison. As a boy he attended a local grammar school but though he imbibed there a love for literature he gained the major part of his education while roving round the countryside, drinking in the beauties of nature and hunting among the cliffs and along the beaches for glistening crystals and for curious and prettily coloured stones. At the age of fifteen he elected to earn a living by working in his uncle's quarries. One of these was situated in a line of cliffs south of Cromarty and overlooking Moray Firth. Here it was that in his eighteenth year, when wandering along the beach, he found a place where the sea had washed many limestone nodules out of the Lias clays. A sharp tap with his hammer split one of these open and revealed an ammonite whose graceful coils were enamelled with a pearly lustre. Splitting other nodules he found many interesting fossils, including fishes. The sight of these fired his enthusiasm and canalised his geological activities, thus adding fossil-hunting to his zeal for writing poetry.

Ten years later, in 1839, he discovered similar nodules from the Old Red Sandstone. The first one he cracked open revealed a fossil which he described as "the effigy of a creature fashioned apparently out of jet with a body covered with plates, two powerful arms articulated at the shoulders with a head as completely lost in the trunk as that of the ray or the sunfish, and a long tail." Other nodules yielded equally fantastic fishes which, as far as he knew, had never been found before. Henceforth he spent much of his spare time collecting and investigating these fascinating fishes.

Ill-health, brought on by breathing quarry dust, forced him to change his occupation. His great natural ability and success in private study are proved by the fact that after serving as an accountant in

---

PLATE VII

MARINE CARBONIFEROUS FOSSILS

1. *Euomphalus*, Carboniferous Limestone. 2. *Lonsdaleia*, Carboniferous Limestone, Derbyshire. 3. *Reticuloceras*, Millstone Grit, Ireland. Note the finely striated ornamentation. 4. *Gastrioceras*, Lower Coal Measures, Lancashire. 5. *Anthracoceras*, Coal Measure, Nottinghamshire. Compare the ornamentation pattern with that in 3. 6. 'Zaphrentis' sp. Carboniferous Limestone, Ireland. 7-9. *Aulophyllum*, sp. Carboniferous Limestone. 7. Complete coral. 8. Cross section. 9. Longitudinal section. 10. *Goniatites*, Carboniferous Limestone, Derbyshire. Internal cast showing suture lines. (1, 3-5, 6, *F. Hodson*. 7-9, *A. Ferguson*. 2, 10, *W. Sutcliffe*)

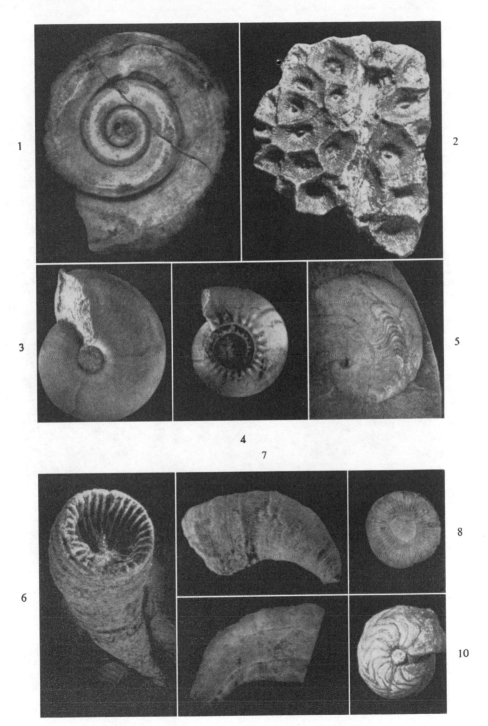

a bank he became editor of a local newspaper, and in 1840 was invited by the leaders of the Presbyterian Church in Edinburgh to take up the editorship of 'The Witness'. For this he wrote a series of articles describing his discoveries, which attracted the attention of geologists at the British Association then meeting in Glasgow.

These articles were subsequently published in book form. A copy of this found its way to the little town of Thurso on the north shore of Caithness, into the library of the local baker Richard Dick, another born naturalist who knew Caithness as he did the palm of his hand. His herbarium included examples of every species of plant growing in the county. To him it seemed nothing to walk 20 to 30 miles to see a rare flower blooming afresh in its secret haunts.

After reading Miller's 'Old Red Sandstone' he turned his attention to hunting for fossil fishes. Rising early each morning he made and baked his batch for the day then, leaving the bread to be sold, he set out on his fossil fishing foray. With unexampled energy and endurance he walked sometimes fifty miles in the day to distant exposures and returned heavily laden in time for some sleep and another early baking before repeating the programme the next day. With equal generosity he placed his specimens at Miller's disposal. B. N. Peach, a member of the Geological Survey Staff, wrote of him that "Dick was Hugh Miller's greatest benefactor." Miller confirmed this by saying "He robbed himself to do me service." Publicity of any kind he eschewed, nevertheless he became well known, at least by

---

PLATE VIII

a. 'THE FOSSIL GROVE' VICTORIA PARK, GLASGOW

Actual site and remains of a Lower Carboniferous Coal Measure forest showing stony casts of the stumps of *Lepidodendron* trees. Note the bifurcating root bearing branches radiating over the ground.

b. NON-MARINE CARBONIFEROUS FOSSILS

1. *Prestwichianella*, an arachnid from the Middle Coal Measures, Barnsley, Yorks. 2. Worm borings in the Giffnock Sandstone, Glasgow. 3. *Tealliocaris*, a crustacea from the Calciferous Sandstone, Gullane East Lothian. 4. *Gyracanthus*, a fish spine, 5½ inches long, from the Upper Coal Measures, Denbighshire. 5. *Carbonicola*, a lamellibranch, Coal Measures, Notts. 6. *Naiadites*, a lamellibranch, Coal Measures. (1-3, *A. Ferguson.* 4-6, *H.M. Geol. Survey*)

name. Meanwhile new bakeries were set up in the town and Dick's business declined so that in the end he died in a state of dire poverty.

Between them these two men enriched the annals of palaeontology, and the showcases of museums with fossil fishes whose story will be told presently, for the time being they need only be referred to under such epitaphs as *Pterichthys*, *Coccosteus*, *Diplopterus*, *Asterolepis*, *Dipterus*, *Osteolepis*, *Glyptolepis* and the like.

Now that the value of the Old Red Sandstone as a fossil fishing ground had been proved workers elsewhere were on the alert. The same and allied genera and species were now found in other parts of Scotland and in the Welsh border country. The outcome of all this activity was a remarkably complete picture of the fish fauna that lived in the freshwaters of the Old Red Sandstone continent.

Such then is the romantic story of the discovery of fossil records in these apparently barren rocks. These fossils have not been merely stored away in drawers or put on exhibition, in museums, but have supplied material for detailed study and description by a succession of workers. From all this there is gradually emerging a full picture of nature in one of the most inspiring of her creative moods, when she was laying down in bold outlines the structural bases of all later vertebrate evolution.

Leaving that picture for a while we must adjourn to the other end of the kingdom, to Devon and Cornwall. Here there existed a smaller area of unexplored Transitional rocks, to which Murchison and Sedgwick turned their attention in 1835. These rocks underlay the dark shales of the Culm, which Smith had placed in the Carboniferous system. In South Devon many fossils were found in the limestones which crop out between Plymouth and Torquay. Collections of these were submitted to Lonsdale who reported that while they had much in common with the Silurian fauna they also bore some resemblance to the fossils from the Carboniferous Limestone. He therefore suggested that these rocks were intermediate in age between the Silurian and the Carboniferous. As this view was supported by their work in the field Murchison and Sedgwick in 1839, gave the name Devonian to this new set of marine rocks. Since the Old Red Sandstone occupied a similar position they regarded it as a *facies*, a different type of development of rocks of the same age as indeed the terrestrial equivalent of the Marine Devonian. This view has been substantiated in more recent years by the discovery within the Devonian sequence of red and purple beds bearing a resemblance to some parts of the Old Red Sandstone. This similarity has been further emphasised by the presence in the lower levels of the fossil remains of *Pteraspis*, *Coccosteus*, *Cephalaspis*, and Acanthodian fishes and, in the upper levels, of *Bothriolepis* and *Holoptychius*. These discoveries clinch the correlation of this marine facies of Cornwall and Devon with the terrestrial facies found elsewhere in Britain. In this way there has been established the existence of a new rock system, that of the Devonian and Old Red Sandstone, or more briefly the Devonian. Thus with the aid of fossils yet another long vista of geological time has been opened out to human contemplation.

CHAPTER 13

FAREWELL TO THE
EARLY PALAEOZOIC SEA

THE actual transition from Silurian to Devonian has not been seen in Devon and Cornwall but in the Welsh borderland detailed work in the area round Downton, near Ludlow, has proved the presence of rocks whose transitional character is indicated by the fact that, though at first they were classed as the uppermost Silurian, they have been transferred to the lowest Old Red Sandstone. Corresponding rocks have also been found and explored in Lanarkshire and Forfarshire.

These rocks, with the fossils they have yielded, furnish glimpses of the final phase in the story of the Palaeozoic sea. As the Silurian waters withdrew westwards off the British area its margins became fringed with brackish estuarine waters in which only a few marine creatures survived and, after carrying on a precarious existence for a while, degenerated and disappeared. Some bivalve molluscs, the Pelecypods (Lamellibranchs) such as *Modiolopsis* flourished temporarily but together with the Brachiopods *Lingula* and *Orbiculoidea* and with the Gastropods *Holopella* and *Platyschisma* became dwarfed and finally extinguished. Some Arthropods survived and became adapted to the new conditions. These included Ostracods, minute crustacea enclosed in a bivalvular covering; and also large Arachnids bearing the names *Eurypterus*, *Pterygotus* and *Hughmilleria*. These so called 'sea-scorpions' had long scorpion-like bodies, broad in front and tapering backwards towards a fin-like tailpiece. Attached to the head were four pairs of legs. Of these the first pair were elongated and armed with pincer-like claws; the last were stout and flattened to form paddles. Guided by well-developed eyes they were able to pursue and prey upon smaller creatures. They were, however, merely diminutive representatives of a race which reached its climax in the Silurian seas in which they grew to as much as five or six feet in length and played a part as tyrants of the deep. Towards the end of the period they seem to have met their match in the newly evolving vertebrates. Before leaving these strange arachnids reference must be made to *Palaeophonus* which, apart from the fact that it lived in the sea and must have breathed by means of gills, was a true scorpion; which it resembled much more closely than it did the sea-scorpions.

At the base of the Downtonian is a widely distributed but insignificant deposit which caught the eyes even of the early geologists. It is known as the Ludlow Bone Bed and contains a medley of fish scales and spines as well as fragments of sea scorpions. It is indeed symbolic of the struggle which the imagination pictures as having taken place in late Silurian waters; a struggle for mastery between the ancient race of arachnids whose history as shown by the rocks in America dated back into Precambrian times and the newly appearing vertebrates of which this bone bed gives the British student his first glimpse.

The scales found in the bone bed are like minute collar-studs in shape, and have a bony base with an enamel top. They belonged to a small fish called *Thelodus*, of which more complete remains have been found in the Midland Valley of Scotland and also in the Welsh Border country. It is only four inches long and has a tadpole-shaped body completely covered with these scales. In Scotland it is associated

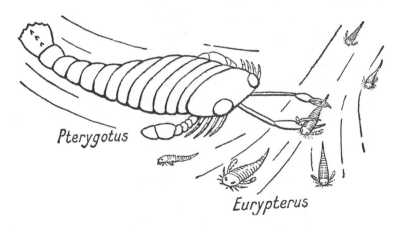

Fig. 6. ARACHNIDS IN THEIR PRIME

with another similarly shaped fish, *Lanarkia*, and a number of others such as *Birkenia* and *Lasanius* which were about the same size but were more normal in shape and were coated with thin bony plates. All these fishes lacked paired fins and their mouths, having no jaws, could only have taken food up by suction. These Agnatha or jawless fishes represent a most important early stage in the evolution of the vertebrates.

It is difficult to see what, if any, advantage these little fishes had over the much larger eurypterids. But perhaps the real rivals of these are indicated in the bone beds by spines belonging to Acanthodian fishes, shark-like forms of which more complete remains are known from the Old Red Sandstone and Carboniferous rocks. These were swift swimmers having paired fins and also jaws armed with scales modified into sharp teeth. They must have been agile creatures that could not merely evade *Pterygotus* and its relatives but could even disarm them by snapping at their pincer-like claws or outflank them by devouring their young. Because they had jaws as well as paired fins these fishes are called Gnathostomes or jaw mouthed creatures. As yet, however, these forerunners of all the higher vertebrates formed but an insignificant section of the marine population.

The withdrawal of the Silurian sea did not seriously affect the Cornwall-Devon area for there marine conditions persisted throughout much of Old Red Sandstone times and the fauna, while retaining some resemblance to that of the Silurian, underwent changes which led up to that of the Carboniferous. On the reefs which studded the floor of the Devonian sea large septate, as well as honeycomb corals and hydrocorallines like *Stromatopora* occupied a prominent place. Single corals were also present and included one attractive little form which, because it is shaped like an eastern sandal has been given the euphonious name *Calceola sandalina*. Cephalopod mollusca were still represented by the straight chambered *Orthoceras*; but now an entirely new type appeared in the genus *Bactrites*. At first sight this may be mistaken for *Orthoceras* but closer inspection shows that the edges of the septa instead of being straight were gently folded, a feature which became increasingly marked in its descendants. In the allied *Tornoceras* the shell was coiled and its septal margins or sutures anticipated the carboniferous *Goniatites* in their more advanced degree of folding. Among the Brachiopods the Silurian genera *Wilsonia*, *Atrypa* and *Spirifer* were still present along with *Stringocephalus*, a large new lorm in which the hinge-line was very short and the internal ribbon of lime formed a long and simple loop closely following the internal outline of the shell. The trilobites, while still resembling those of the Silurian, showed a decline in numbers and variety. This was the beginning of the steady movement towards their extinction that took place subsequently during the Carboniferous and Permian periods.

CHAPTER 14

EVOLUTION AT
THE CROSS ROADS

THE earth's crust is never at a standstill. Usually its movements are more gentle than the rocking of a cradle, but from time to time they increase in intensity and minor or even major mountain ranges slowly emerge. Movements of the latter type took place in the British area during Devonian and Old Red Sandstone times and, as already noted, the sea with its estuarine margins withdrew everywhere except in the south. At the same time belts of highlands developed over much of Wales, the Lake District and Scotland. Though the climate was dry, rain fell upon these high grounds and the rivers that developed carried the rock debris away and spread it out over the lowlands. For the most part this was muddy or sandy but at times it was coarse and gravelly. These riverine waters on their way to the sea passed through and replenished large freshwater lakes; thus providing homes for a rich aquatic life and a stage for some dramatic phases in organic evolution.

The withdrawal of the sea had for its counterpart the extension of lands which already existed elsewhere in Silurian times. These seem to have been already occupied by a very lowly type of vegetation which naturally invaded the newly emerging landscapes of the Devonian. Though plant fossils are rare in the Old Red Sandstone they have been found at a number of places scattered about Britain from Caithness to Cornwall and more especially at Rhynie in Aberdeenshire and at Kiltorcan in Kilkenny, Eire.

In Scotland during Middle Devonian times volcanoes and hotsprings were rife. The waters of the latter, like those of Yellowstone Park and New Zealand today, contained silica in solution. At Rhynie, Aberdeenshire, this water found its way into a bog and, permeating the newly forming peat, mummified the plants and enclosed them

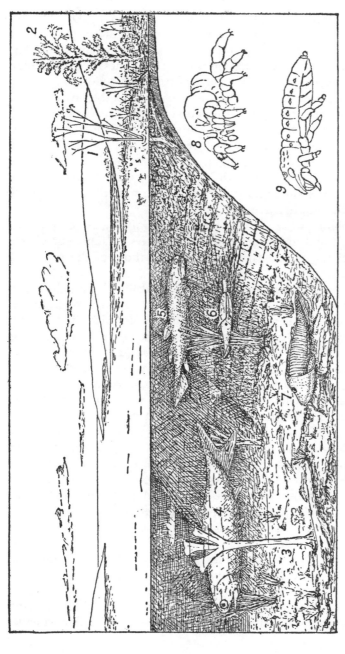

Fig. 7. LIFE IN EARLY OLD RED SANDSTONE TIMES

Plants: Vascular. 1, *Psilophyton*, without leaves. 2, *Asteroxylon*, covered with leaves. Non-vascular. 3, *Nematothallus*, here shown submerged in water, but it also grew in swamps to a great size exposed to the air.

Animals: Vertebrates. Fishes with jaws and paired fins: 4, *Cheirolepis*, fins supported only by fin rays. 5, *Osteolepis*, fins supported by a fleshy lobe fringed with fin rays. Fishes without jaws and paired fins: 6, *Pteraspis*. 7. *Cephalaspis*. Invertebrates. The earliest airbreathing arachnids. 8, *Protacarus*. 9, *Palaeocharinus*. (greatly magnified).

in a shroud of chert. A mass of this was discovered by Dr. Mackie in 1913. Not only did it contain complete plant bodies but the minute structure even of the tissues and cells was exquisitely preserved (Plate V*b*). Microscopic examination showed that these were vascular plants whose stems had a central strand of tissue for conducting water and nutritious fluids to and fro within the plant body; an essential function in the life of a true land plant. This body consisted of a creeping underground stem or rhizome from which upright shoots with few branches arose. In *Rhynia* these shoots were 18 inches high and carried at their tips spore-cases or sporangia. *Hornea* was smaller and had a tuberous rhizome. *Asteroxylon* was the largest for its shoots were half an inch thick but, unlike the other two, which were smooth and naked, it was covered with minute leaves.

All these plants were closely related to *Psilophyton*, carbonised remains of which had long been known from the sandstone elsewhere. In it the tips of the branches were coiled like those of the fronds of young fern leaves.

Among the fossils found in the Old Red Sandstone by Hugh Miller was a fragment of wood named *Palaeopitys*, which had the microscopic structure of a primitive gymnosperm comparable with that of the pine or other conifer. Other specimens have since been found, among them a common fossil wood named *Thursophyton* (Thurso, Caithness) which was probably related to *Asteroxylon*. The presence of tree forms, thus indicated, is confirmed by more complete remains from the Upper Devonian of Kiltorcan. Among these were *Protolepidodendron* and *Cyclostigma*. The former was about 20 feet high and its tall stem broke up at the top into a cluster of bifurcating branches covered with small pointed leaves. At the tip of some of its twigs the leaves were crowded together as in a pine-cone and bore sporangia with both small and large spores. In these respects it closely resembles the living clubmoss, *Lycopodium* but was much bigger. With these plants were found the leaves of a typically fernlike plant, *Archaeopteris*.

From all these remains it is evident that by Upper Devonian times parts of the landscape had become clothed with a miniature woodland flora and an undergrowth of smaller plants. These merged into the richer and much more luxuriant vegetation of the Lower Carboniferous forests. In view of this abundant evidence that in Old Red Sandstone times plants had already overcome the difficulties of living on land, any remains of terrestrial animals are of peculiar interest.

Fig. 8. LIFE IN LATE OLD RED SANDSTONE TIMES

Plants, Lycopods: 1, *Protolepidodendron*. 2, *Cyclostigma*. Ferns: 3, *Archaeopteris*. Inset below shows detail of the leaf, sterile leaflet (left) fertile leaflet (right). Primitive vascular plants: 4, *Psilophyton*. 5, *Zosterophyllum*.

Fishes, with jaws and paired fins; 6, *Holoptychius*, length 2½ feet, fins with long fleshy axis fringed with fin rays. Without jaws and paired fins; 7, *Bothriolepis*, length 1 foot, allied to *Pterichthys*, cp. Fig. 10: 2.

Reference should therefore be made here to two minute air-breathing animals found in the Rhynie chert. One was an arachnid, a mite called *Protacarus* (Fig. 7: 8), the other, a primitive wingless insect, *Rhyniella*, related to the present-day springtails, of the Order *Collembola*. Further evidence that other types of arthropod had also solved the same problem is provided by the discovery, in the Lower Old Red Sandstone in Forfar, of *Archidesmus* and *Kampecaris*, relatives of the Millepedes, of which the common garden pest *Julus* is an example.

All these carbonised and silicified remains show that there was ample food in the form of vegetable debris and small animals to supply the needs of the many fishes that lived in the fresh waters of the Old

Red Sandstone continent. It is time now to look more closely at these interesting fishes for they represent an early phase in the evolution of that wonderful diversity of vertebrates which are alive today; and they were in that fascinating stage when jaws and paired limbs, two structures essential to vertebrate success, were being evolved.

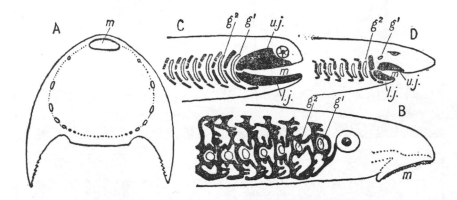

Fig. 9. THE EVOLUTION OF JAWS IN PRIMITIVE FISHES

A. *Kieraspis*, a primitive cephalaspid, underside of the head showing the many gill openings. B-D. Diagrams of the headskeleton (black). B. *Petromyzon* the living lamprey. C. *Acanthodes* (cp, *Diplacanthus*, Fig. 10: 3) an ancient shark. D. *Scyllium* (dogfish) a small modern shark. *g* 1, 2. First and second gill openings. *l.j*, *u.j*, lower and upper jaws. *m*, mouth.

The most primitive known member of those ancient races was *Palaeospondylus* (Fig. 10: *1*) from the Caithness Flagstones near Thurso. It was less than two inches long and was of very primitive structure. For a backbone it had an elastic rod, the notochord, which extended the whole length of the body and was similar to that found in the early stages in the growth of all vertebrates. It was enclosed in a series of thin rings, the vertebrae, and supported a framework of rays forming the foundation of a continuous fin that extended along the back and round the tip of the tail onto the under surface. At its front end was a simple cartilaginous skull which housed a small and primitive brain. Paired fins were absent and the mouth was without jaws. In these respects it resembled the other lowly fishes found in the Downtonian and in the Old Red Sandstone proper (Fig. 7).

The best known of the latter fishes is *Cephalaspis* which though it was the largest member of this fauna was only 7 inches long. Its head was flattened from above downwards, crescentic in outline and completely covered in bony armour. The trunk and tail were more normal in shape but they too were covered with a cuirass of bony plates. Its mouth was without jaws and was suctorial. Instead of the usual 4 or 5 gill-openings found in most fishes it had ten (cp. Fig. 9a). In this respect it resembled the living lamprey which, anatomically, is one of the most primitive among living vertebrates. The broad depressed form of *Cephalaspis* with its eyes on the top of the head suggests that it lived on the bottom and fed by sucking up vegetable debris and soft bodied organisms, such as worms, from the lake floor. *Pteraspis* was a free-swimming fish of more normal shape (Fig. 7: 6). Its tail was covered with scales but the front of the body was covered with large bony plates above and below. Above and in front of the mouth was a long snout-like projection also enclosed in bone. Here again both limbs and jaws were absent.

All the fishes so far mentioned were without jaws and are classed as Agnatha (—having no jaws). Some with jaws classed as Gnathostomata were also present for swarming in the same waters were small shark-like fishes differing from those just described in having paired fins and strong jaws armed with teeth. The body was clothed with a fine texture of enamel clad bony scales. This flexible covering accorded well with the long lithe body and the presence of a tail fin, a combination of features which betokened swift agile movements. The head was blunt and rounded in front with large eyes situated far forwards. The front margins of both paired and median fins were strengthened by stout spines, a fact which is reflected in the name *Acanthodes* for the best-known genus (cp. Fig. 10:3). These were the most durable parts of the body and, with the small scales, are often the only parts which are preserved in the fossil state. Their presence in the Ludlow bone bed and also in the rocks below proves that similar fish existed also in the Silurian seas. Much careful work has been done on more perfect specimens of *Acanthodes* found in later rocks and has brought to light the fact that the jaws of these fishes were only loosely suspended from the skull; an arrangement that was much more primitive than that found in modern sharks or indeed in any other known fishes. They have therefore been placed by D. M. S. Watson, to whom most of the credit for this work is due, in a separate and more lowly

1. *Palaeospondylus gunni*, length about 1 inch. (After Traquair).

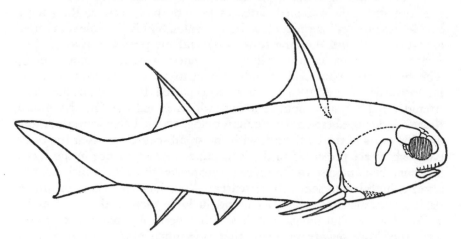

2. *Pterichthys milleri*, length 8 inches. (After Watson).

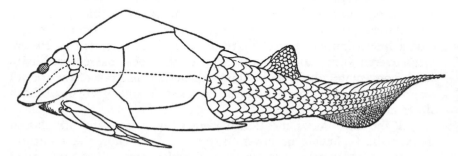

3. *Diplacanthus striatus*, length 3½ inches. (After Watson).

Fig. 10. MIDDLE OLD RED SANDSTONE FISHES
By permission of H.M. Stationery Office

classificatory group having the curious name Aphetohyoidea (apheto – let loose). Another primitive feature was the presence of more than two paired fins arranged in series along each flank. This condition is apparently a relic of an early stage in the evolution of fishes in which a pair of continuous finfolds ran along the whole length of both sides of the body.

Along with these spine-bearing aphetohyoids have been placed some of the heavily armoured types such as *Pterichthys*, the first fish found by Hugh Miller (Fig. 10: 2). Another is *Coccosteus* so called because of the berrylike markings upon its armour. This latter fish grew to a length of 14 inches and was the largest of those which swarmed in the Lower Old Red Sandstone rivers and lakes.

The fishes that remain to be considered all exhibit a more advanced grade of organisation for the jaws were stronger and more firmly articulated to the rest of the headskeleton. They also had well developed paired fins. Among these *Osteolepis*, as will be seen, was closely related to the stock which gave rise ultimately to the terrestrial vertebrates. A mosaic of platelike bones shielded the head and enamel clad or ganoid scales covered the rest of the body (Fig. 7: 5). The latter were rhomboidal in shape and consisted of a bony base coated with hard shiny enamel. The paired fins had long skeletal supports covered with flesh forming a lobe which carried along its margins a broad fringe of fin-rays. This is a characteristic of that important division of fishes known as Crossopterygii (fringe-finned). They were swiftly swimming predaceous creatures which had a protective covering of thick scales together with jaws armed with sharp teeth. Thus equipped they were successful rivals to those Eurypterids that still survived. *Dipterus* was larger, slightly more than one foot long, with fins similarly constructed to those of *Osteolepis*. In it, however, the teeth were situated on the roof of the mouth and on the inner side of the lower jaws and were adapted for crushing soft aquatic vegetation with any small molluscs or other creatures entangled in it. In these and other respects it resembled the Mudfish, *Ceratodus*, which lives today in the rivers of Central Australia. During dry seasons these shrink and break up into putrid pools and patches of sloppy mud. Under such circumstances the gills become ineffective and the fish then resorts to breathing air by means of a peculiarly contructed lung. Because these fishes are also endowed with this additional means of breathing they are classed as Dipnoi or double-breathers. Whether *Dipterus* had lungs is not known but its many structural resemblances to Ceratodus leave no doubt about its close affinity to this fish.

Cheirolepis belongs to a quite different category, for it represents a very early phase in the evolution of the multitudinous types of bony fishes which dominate all the waters of the world today (Fig. 7: *4*). Unlike the lobe-finned Dipnoi and the ganoids described above, its paired fins were entirely supported by fin-rays, a fact which led to the establishment of the division Actinopterygii (ray-finned) for this and similar fish. Its large mouth armed with an array of sharp teeth, and its large tail-fin proclaim it to have been a powerfully swimming rapacious fish.

Lower and Middle Old Red Sandstone times were brought to a close by the onset of considerable earth movements and severe denudation of the landscape. These were followed by a resumption of the earlier conditions, and a return of some of the fishes just described. Jawless types were fewer in number and were distantly related to *Pteraspis*. Aphetohyoids were represented by *Bothriolepis* (Fig. 8: *7*), an ally of *Pterichthys* in which the bony armour had almost disappeared; and by *Cosmacanthus* a relative of *Acanthodes*. *Holoptychius* (Fig. 8: *6*), a characteristic Upper Old Red Sandstone fish, was a giant relative of *Osteolepis* three feet long. *Phaneropleuron* was one of the Dipnoi.

The base of these newly deposited rocks rested with marked unconformity upon the middle and lower series. On the other hand their uppermost layers gradually merged without break into the Lower Carboniferous rocks. This passage marks the end of a vital period in the history of life on the earth; a period during which plants broke loose from the restrictions of an aquatic existence and, coming out onto the land, began to cloth the continents with beauty and verdure. Their presence here was a necessary prerequisite to the conquest of land by animals; a conquest first achieved on a large scale by such arthropods as insects and arachnids. Meanwhile the vertebrates emerged out of an obscure invertebrate ancestry and, after attaining lordship in the waters, finally outstripped the arthropods as air-breathing conquerors of land and sky.

CHAPTER 15

BRITAIN IN CARBONIFEROUS TIMES

CONTEMPORANEOUSLY with the early development of modern Geology there was a greatly increased demand for coal on behalf of industry. This led naturally to a concentration of attention on the rocks of the coalfields and of the adjoining areas, not only by individual geologists, but also by the newly established Geological Survey which, without neglecting the rest of Britain, has produced a unique series of maps and memoirs that continue to provide invaluable help to the industrial exploitation of coal and of other useful products of the coalfields.

Even today many a collier, as he returns home from work in the mine may lift up his eyes and see in the distance the hills where, in holiday times, he goes in search of refreshment for body and spirit by wandering over the spacious grit moorlands or by exploring the rugged dales and gentle scenery of the limestone uplands. Thus within his own experience he links together three sets of rocks —limestone, grit and coal measures —which to the geologist are known collectively as the Carboniferous rocks; the limestone, as the Lower Carboniferous; the grits and measures, as the Upper Carboniferous.

The 'Mountain Limestone', as William Smith called it, is more widely distributed than the Wenlock Limestone and is so massive that it forms such prominent landscape features as the Uplands of Derbyshire and of the Mendips, with their attractive dales and gorges. From the earliest days of fossil study this rock has proved a fruitful hunting ground for collectors and has provided abundant material for such experts in research as Phillips, Davidson, Nicholson and many others. The fossil fauna thus made known bears a general resemblance to that of the Wenlock Limestone in the presence of corals, stone-lilies and other animals that flourish best in the clear waters of comparatively shallow but warm sunlit seas. Such, at first, was the Carboniferous sea which came into being by the spreading northwards of the Devonian

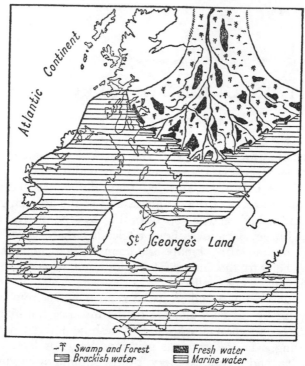

~T Swamp and Forest   ▓ Fresh water
▤ Brackish water   ▤ Marine water

Fig. 11. IDEALISED MAP OF THE BRITISH AREA
IN CARBONIFEROUS TIMES
Shows the general distribution of conditions of life

sea and the consequent submersion of much of the Old Red Sandstone
landscape.

Except for a small island, St. George's Land, which stretched
across the Midlands into Wales, this clear blue sea extended northwards as far as Yorkshire. Beyond that the nature of the Lower
Carboniferous rocks and fossils point to great changes in the subaqueous scene. The clear views became dimmed by the continual
drizzle of sand or clouded with mud which as it settled built up deposits
now represented by great thicknesses of shale. These sediments were
brought by rivers from a great northern continent which had persisted
through Old Red Sandstone times. The climate yonder had, however,
changed greatly. Rain, possibly also frost, pulverised the rock surfaces

everywhere and produced waste that was washed into the rivers and transported down to the sea. Here the sediment, silting the waters up to the surface, contributed to the formation of coastal swamps and a delta of low-lying sand banks or fenlike flats and freshwater 'Broads' where swampy vegetation grew, perished and piled up debris destined to become coal.

This phase was brought to a close by renewed subsidence accompanied by further deposition of mud. Sometimes the subsidence was so rapid and extended so far over the whole area that marine waters came stealing back again across the North of England into Central Scotland bringing with them corals and other clear-water creatures. These conditions sometimes persisted for so long a time that limestone deposits of considerable thickness were formed. Muddy conditions returned intermittently and thus the limestone became interbedded between shales. Such then were the conditions that prevailed over part of Britain during Lower Carboniferous times but they were brought to an end by minor earth movements accompanied by local uplift and denudation.

The swampy deltaic conditions, hitherto prevalent in the north, now crept southwards over England and parts of Wales, thus ushering in Upper Carboniferous times, during which enough mud accumulated to produce clays and shales some thousands of feet thick. At intervals in the early part of this period great quantities of sand and grit were brought along and formed extensive sandbanks which ultimately became those rugged and massive rocks known as Millstone Grits.

During most of the period, however, mud was the dominant deposit. At times when subsidence was very slow the rate of deposition more than balanced the sinking. Then mudflats and 'Broads' emerged and, becoming covered with vegetation, gave habitation and food to, the earliest of the air-breathing fourfooted animals. It was then that vegetable debris ten, twenty and even forty feet deep accumulated. Out of this raw material nature manufactured seams of coal, the presence of which inspired the name Coal Measures for this massive accumulation of clays and shales.

At wide spaced intervals, however, the rate of subsidence surpassed that of deposition to such an extent that salty water returned over much of the area, bringing with it an impoverished marine fauna, the remains of which were buried in dirty calcareous deposits that hardened into thin layers of rock now known as Marine Bands.

From this rapid summary it is evident that, though living conditions were predominantly marine during the Lower Carboniferous and freshwater during the Upper Carboniferous, the change over from one to the other was not complete and permanent but oscillatory, swinging from one extreme to the other. There was, however, an important stage in each oscillation that must not be overlooked. As it swung across the area it brought also a zone of brackish water that lay between the regions occupied by marine water on the one hand and by freshwater on the other.

This great Carboniferous system is therefore immensely interesting for in its rocks are hidden the records of four main types of living conditions—marine, brackish, freshwater, and also terrestrial. These will now be considered more fully in the following chapters.

1. *Cordaites,*
   with inflorescences
2. Tree Fern
3. *Neuropteris,*
   a seed bearing fern
4. *Lepidodendron,*
   with sporangial cones
5. *Sigillaria*
6. A Fern
7. *Calamites*
8. *Eogyrinus,* a large
   amphibian about
   15 feet long
9. *Meganeura,* a giant
   "dragonfly"

AN ENGLISH LANDSCAPE IN
COAL MEASURE TIMES
see frontispiece

CHAPTER 16

LIFE IN MARINE WATERS

WHEN the polished surfaces or thin slices of pieces of Carboniferous Limestone are powerfully magnified they reveal a rich variety of Foraminifera, minute organisms that abounded near the surface in the Carboniferous sea (Plate V*b*). These shells, together with fine calcareous mud produced the hard rocky matrix which encloses the remains of innumerable larger creatures. This usually makes it difficult to extract the fossils. But nature has been kind to the amateur and has done much of the work for him already. She has dissected many fossils out on the surface of the limestone wherever she has been able to wash it for centuries by downpouring rain or etch it with acidified water that has seeped down through the soil. By searching such surfaces he will be able to collect many good specimens (Plate VI*a*). Portions of the stems of stone-lilies are quite common. Associated with them and lying about loosely are a number of the ring-like sections of stems, popularly known as 'fairy beads' or, in Northumberland, St. Cuthbert's beads. Bodies of crinoids with arms attached, and the corresponding portions of the closely allied blastoids are things of beauty but unfortunately are rare. Sometimes thick layers of rock are made up largely of brachiopods whose shells are much more compact and therefore do not produce such tough matted masses. A judicious use of hammer and chisel will frequently be rewarded with specimens of whole shells. The most characteristic of these is *Productus*, a concavo-convex shell having a long straight hinge-line (Plate IV: 5-7). Its many species vary much in size and include *P. giganteus* the largest of known brachiopods. *Spirifer* and many other genera occur. Gastropods are less frequently found but the flat coiled *Euomphalus* (Plate VII: *1*) and the low turreted *Pleurotomaria* should be mentioned. Among the cephalopods *Orthoceras* is still prominent and is accompanied by *Goniatites* which has a shell as closely coiled as that of the modern *Nautilus*. In it, however, the septal margins are strongly folded with the crests of the folds sharp and angular, a feature reflected in the name (gonia—angle). Trilobites were at the time drawing to the close of their career and their remains are comparatively rare. Polyzoa also are less prominent than in the Wenlock limestone; nevertheless good specimens of *Fenestella* with its beautiful muslin pattern will bring a gleam of pleasure to the collector's eye.

For the study of the Carboniferous Limestone and its fossils the Avon Gorge, near Bristol, has been of unique interest. This striking feature in the landscape, 200 feet deep and a mile and a half long, winds its way through Clifton Down, a valuable amenity to the city. In its vicinity, during the opening years of this century, lay a well-known army coaching school that had upon its staff a science master, Arthur Vaughan by name. Under the inspiring influence of Edward Wilson, Curator of the Bristol City Museum, he made a hobby of collecting and studying the fossils found in the limestone cliffs that overlook the gorge. As the outcome of his work a remarkable and fertilising stimulus was given to research upon the Lower Carboniferous rocks and their fossils not only in this country but throughout the world.

At the northern end of the gorge the layers of Old Red Sandstone are seen disappearing under the limestone. Those of the latter dip south-eastwards and in turn are seen to disappear at the other end of the gorge under the Millstone grits. This gorge therefore furnishes a unique exposure of the limestone which gives a more complete view of the whole sequence of its strata than is to be found elsewhere in Britain or even in Europe. Hitherto the collecting of fossils from the limestone had been sporadic and little notice had been taken of their precise positions in the succession of rock layers. Vaughan, however, gave to this work the same meticulous care in collecting and recording that enabled Lapworth to wrest such striking results from the rocks of the Southern Uplands of Scotland. In some respects Vaughan's task was more difficult. Lapworth's graptolites were simple creatures in which the main structural features were visible externally; but Vaughan's fossils included a rich variety of more complicated types which, as already seen, had been inherited from the Devonian sea; types whose distinctive features were not externally visible and could be discovered only by cutting the specimens into thin slices or by the much more tedious process of dissecting. Nevertheless Vaughan succeeded in accumulating a large body of accurate knowledge of the fossils preserved in the successive layers of limestone, more especially of the corals and the brachiopods.

The assemblages of fossils found in successive layers may be compared with the group photographs of a games club or team hung upon the walls of the headquarters. For the first few years the groups are closely similar, though a few old faces go and new ones appear. A time comes, however, when with rare exceptions, the personnel has completely changed. So likewise the assemblage of fossils remains but little changed throughout several adjoining layers of rock which may then be spoken of collectively as a zone and the community of fossils as the zonal assemblage. From each such assemblage Vaughan selected one important type to serve as the 'captain' or *index* for the whole, and its name was given to the zone. He recognised five major zones in the limestone of the gorge and named them as follows from the oldest to the youngest:—*Cleistopora* Zone (K), *Zaphrentis* Zone (Z), *Caninia* Zone (C), *Seminula* Zone (S) and the *Dibunophyllum* Zone (D). These were in turn subdivided, but these divisions will suffice for the present purpose. It may be noted in passing that in this scheme time is indicated not by rocks but by faunas.

The features of these index fossils may be briefly stated as follows and further details can be culled from the figure.

Cleistopora is a compound coral that grows as an incrustation upon some solid object, a stone or a shell.

Zaphrentis is a simple conical coral in which the septa are arranged symmetrically about a plane.

Caninia has, in youth, a similar structure to that of *Zaphrentis* but in later life it becomes cylindrical and its septa are almost radial in arrangement.

Seminula is a brachiopod but is usually accompanied by a compound coral *Lithostrotion* in which the individual corallites may be cylindrical or compressed into prisms (Plate VI*b*). Its septa are few and radially arranged. They do not extend as far as the centre where there is a solid rod or columella.

Dibunophyllum has numerous long septa radially arranged. Their outer ends are enclosed in a zone of vesicles. Their inner ends are similarly enclosed and these two features together form a pattern similar to that of a spider's web.

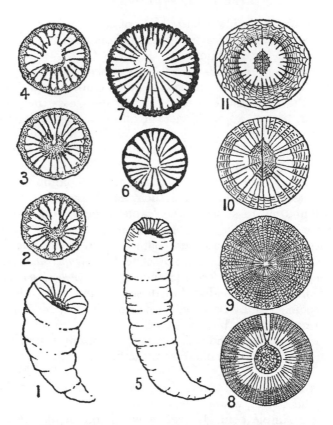

Fig. 12. STRUCTURE AND DEVELOPMENT
OF SOME CARBONIFEROUS CORALS

1. *Zaphrentis*. 2-4, sections. 2, *Z. delanouei*. 3, *Z. delanouei* var *constricta*. 4, *Z. delanouei* var *disjuncta*. 5, *Caninia cornucopia* with sections 6, of early and 7, of late stages in development. (All after Carruthers). 8-11 sections of more advanced corals. 8, *Aulophyllum*. 9, *Palaeosmilia*. 10, *Dibunophyllum*. 11, *Lonsdaleia*.

By 'zoning' the Carboniferous Limestone Vaughan opened the way to many researches and discoveries, some of which threw a flood of light upon the changes undergone by the physical geography of Britain during the millions of years represented by the rocks alongside the Avon Gorge. Thus for example the same or a similar sequence of zones was found by other workers wherever the limestone occurred but they discovered that the zones were not coextensive everywhere and that the positions of their original margins could be traced. Thus for example, in the gorge the lowest beds of the *Cleistopora* zone were transitional in character between the Old Red Sandstone and the Carboniferous Limestone and the fauna was not normal. Though corals were absent marine organisms characteristic of marginal waters were present; brachiopods, gastropods, lamellibranchs, calcareous worm-tubes and algae. This fact indicated that the old landscape at that spot had just become submerged. Further north, as the vicinity of St. George's Land was approached, the zones overlapped one another against the rising slopes and the upper layers of limestone came to rest directly upon the precarboniferous rocks. Meanwhile, as early as *Zaphrentis* times, the sea flowed round the western end of the island and entered a northern estuary which extended later to Westmoreland. Thence the sea continued to spread and in *Caninia* times entered the Midland Valley area of Scotland. By *Dibunophyllum* times it had widened and completely submerged Derbyshire where it remained long enough for limy deposits, nearly 2000 feet thick, to accumulate.

By establishing this valuable time-scale for events which happened in the Lower Carboniferous period Vaughan cleared the way for numerous researches into the evolution of corals and brachiopods. One illustration must suffice. Though *Zaphrentis* gives its name to one of the lowest zones it must not be assumed that it was confined to that zone. Thus the first appearance of *Caninia* marks the opening of the next zone but not the disappearance of all species of *Zaphrentis* which, as a matter of fact, occur also in the higher zones. Careful work by R. G. Carruthers within the next decade on specimens of *Zaphrentis* collected from the Carboniferous Limestone of Scotland showed that this genus underwent a continuous series of changes (Fig. 12: *1-4*) so that the later members differed sufficiently from the earlier to justify the use of different names for the more distinctive phases. Even in the ordinary affairs of daily life, though time is continuous from noon to midnight, it is found to be a great convenience to give names, such as one o'clock, five o'clock to moments which occur at regular intervals between these two extremes. To such recognisable steps in the evolution of organisms W. Waagen gave the name *mutation* in 1868. During the present century biologists unwittingly used the same term in a quite different sense for sudden structural and individual changes of genetic origin. In this more appropriate sense the term rapidly passed into almost universal use. Recognising this fact F. A. Bather, a distinguished palaeontologist and thinker proposed that the mutation of Waagen should be replaced by the term *transient*, which indeed is much more in accordance with his meaning and has become generally acceptable.

Work of a similar kind has been done by foreign as well as British workers upon many types of coral. Much still remains to be done but it already seems evident that these also underwent comparable evolutionary changes with the passage of time and that some of them such as *Caninia* and *Palaeosmilia* (formerly *Cyathophyllum*) and *Dibunophyllum* have all descended from a zaphrentid ancestry within the limits of Lower Carboniferous times (Fig. 12: *8-11*).

This last statement is of peculiar interest for some of the Silurian corals closely resemble these Carboniferous genera. Thus *Streptelasma* is very similar to *Zaphrentis* and is, indeed, regarded as the forerunner of this. *Omphyma* resembles *Caninia*. *Cyathophyllum* is almost identical with *Palaeosmilia*. Indeed, until recent work showed that it had evolved from a zaphrentid ancestor during carboniferous times, it was called *Cyathophyllum*. The curious spider-web pattern seen in the centre of *Dibunophyllum* was present also in some Silurian corals. Most of these early modifications died out in Devonian times, but, as just seen, they reappeared later. The *Streptelasma–Zaphrentis* series, which itself changed only slightly, may be thought of as the radicle stock for, during the very long period of its existence, it seems to have given rise at intervals to comparatively short lived evolving series, such as those just indicated, following closely similar trends of change. Such repetition is described by some as 'iterative' evolution. Why offshoots, widely separated in time, should have evolved along these closely similar lines is still an unsolved problem. Since they came from the same radicle stock they must have been endowed with a similar genetic outfit and may therefore have responded to comparable environments in similar ways. Thus as our knowledge of the evolutionary changes increases our terminology sloughs off its artificial aspect and begins to approach the natural.

With all this in mind and with the eyes of the imagination wide open we may revisit the Avon Gorge, pausing for a while at some viewpoint where our vision can travel along the gorge. Doing so we find ourselves on the floor of that ancient sea gazing across a broad submarine seascape made up of coral reefs, forests of stone-lilies, of mud-covered plains inhabited by polyzoa, brachiopods, lamellibranchs and worms; with occasional trilobites, orthocerates, goniatites and fishes either resting on the floor or swimming in the clear waters above, surrounded by myriads of minute crustaces and swarms of foraminifera.

But while we are standing still in space our thoughts move swiftly through time. Though the general constitution of the scene remains practically constant all its elements—corals, stone-lilies, brachiopods and the rest—change slowly but continuously. These changes are not confined merely to stages in individual growth from birth through youth to maturity and death, for in the successive generations there are also changes due to the fact that some individuals reach stages in development beyond those attained by their parents. This is repeated perpetually until the later populations as a whole differ from the earlier. We are in fact witnessing the phenomenon that is called evolution.

But as already seen these clear-water conditions that prevailed in the south were replaced in the north, from time to time, by muddy conditions. While these latter persisted some elements in the fauna, corals and stone-lilies, disappeared. Those that remained were the brachiopods—*Lingula, Chonetes* and *Productus;* the polyzoa—*Fenestella;* the pelecypods—*Posidonia;* and the cephalopods—*Goniatites, Orthoceras,* and *Pleuronautilus.*

During Upper Carboniferous times non-marine waters were predominant; but at wide intervals and for brief spells of time marine waters came flowing back bringing with them marine faunas. These included several goniatitic genera:—*Reticuloceras, Gastrioceras, Anthracoceras*—and the pelecypod *Pterinopecten* which had a delicately ornamented shell. The goniatites found in successive marine levels or marine bands were occasionally preserved in the solid state but more usually they were crushed flat (Plate VII: *3, 5*). Nevertheless their surface ornamentation was frequently preserved and, as shown by W. S. Bisat, exhibits a series of changes which is useful for the recognition of different bands. Consequently in recent years they have proved of value in the search for oil as well as coal.

Like water, oil is widely disseminated in the sedimentary rocks but unlike water its origin was closely associated with that of the rocks themselves. The sediments from which these were formed sometimes contained up to as much as 20% of organic mud or finely divided debris derived from minute organisms and from the disintegration and pulverisation of dead animals and especially of seaweeds. With the passing of the ages chemical processes have changed much of this into mineral oil. As with water a large portion of it was held firmly in the pores of the finely textured rocks such as clay and shale. Nevertheless some of the oil seeped out slowly under pressure and found its way into the more porous coarse texture rocks such as sandstone and grits. In areas where interbedded shales and sandstones have been folded the oil, being lighter than water, works its way past this up the sloping flanks of the upfolds and, accumulating in the crests, forms pools and reservoirs.

During the years following the First World War a systematic search for oil in Britain was organised and one of the most successful finds was made in Nottinghamshire, north of Newark in the neighbourhood of Eakring (Plate XI). Here the first boring, after passing through Triassic and Permian rocks penetrated through the Coal Measures and eventually struck a sequence of sandy and gritty rocks containing pools of oil. In the shales between these rocks marine bands containing goniatites were found belonging to the Millstone Grit series. Guided by the goniatites the borers worked with clearer view and greater confidence as they put down other borings for the purpose of extracting the oil from these pools. Since the discovery of the Eakring oilfield the search has continued southwards as far as Leicestershire, and northwards into Yorkshire and Lancashire, with goniatites serving as guides to the identification of the productive beds in other places. Seven oilfields have been established in the Millstone Grit of the Midlands area, two or three thousand feet beneath the surface.

CHAPTER 17

LIFE IN NON-MARINE WATERS

—

A LARGE proportion of the area now covered by the Upper Carboniferous rocks and parts of the Lower was originally occupied by freshwater which, along its seaward limits, merged into a broad brackish water zone. This shifted to and fro with every influx and recession of the sea. Since the sea was the original home of living things there was throughout geological time always a tendency for some marine organisms to seek new habits by migrating towards the estuaries and rivers. The decrease in salinity, however, acted so adversely that relatively few succeeded in completing the passage through this zone and becoming established in the freshwaters. Consequently the freshwater faunas have always been greatly impoverished as compared with the marine. Thus for example, in the freshwaters of today, there are no echinoderms and brachiopods and only isolated representatives of the sponges, coelenterates, worms and polyzoa. Among the mollusca there are no cephalopods and only a few kinds of gastropods and pelecypods. On the whole, the brackish-water faunas more closely resemble those of the fresh than of the saline. This was equally true also for Carboniferous times. It will therefore be more convenient to deal with these two faunal types together under the heading Non-marine.

Unlike the contemporary marine faunas the non-marine were relatively rich in vertebrates, especially fishes. For this reason careful searching among the shales on almost any colliery tip-heap will reward even the novice with a good collection of fish fragments, of scales, bones, vertebrae, teeth and even complete jaws and more rarely an imperfect head or trunk. At some levels in the coal measures heavy nodules of ironstone abound. In the early part of the nineteenth century these were gathered up from the workings, where coal or clay for bricks and pottery had been extracted, and were smelted for iron. These nodules often contain good fossils but they are difficult to split open for they splinter badly when hit with a hammer. Nevertheless many which contain fossils split easily after they have been exposed to rain and frost and have yielded a rich harvest of well preserved fishes and other organisms.

In contrast with the marine faunas of Mid-Palaeozoic times those that are non-marine include a wide range of fishes. Bearing in mind that the Old Red Sandstone continent with its rivers persisted into the Carboniferous period it may be assumed that the fishes in the latter were descendants of those which were brought to light by Sedgwick and Murchison, by Miller and Dick. During the long stretch of time that separated the Old Red Sandstone period from the Upper Carboniferous great changes took place in the forms of life. Armoured fishes with and without jaws were no more. On the other hand fishes with jaws and two pairs of fins and a covering of scales became supreme. The lowly Aphetohyoids were represented by *Acanthodes, Gyracanthus* and *Sphenacanthus* in which the fins were all strengthened with stout spines (acanth- =a spine). The existence of a number of cartilaginous and unarmoured shark- and skate-like fishes is inferred from the frequent occurrence of fossil teeth and spines. Some of the teeth resemble those of present-day sharks in being small and sharply pointed. In *Diplodus,* as the name implies, the jaws were arrayed with numerous double-pointed teeth which enabled the fish to seize and hold its prey easily. Other types such as *Pleuroplax* had teeth with flattened and sometimes curved surfaces so that as they lay side by side on the jaws they converted these into efficient organs for crushing weeds and small shells. Some of these fishes must have been of great size for occasional spines are found ten or fifteen inches long (Plate VIII*b*: *4*).

Close allies of the Old Red Sandstone type *Osteolepis* formed a more important element in this fish fauna, which included the genera *Megalichthys, Rhizodopsis* and *Strepsodus.* Of especial interest is *Coelacanthus,* a fish which had an air-bladder enclosed in bone. This type also lived during the Mesozoic era. After that, according to known fossil records it apparently became extinct. Nevertheless it must have taken refuge in unknown seas for in recent years a living relative —*Latimeria*—has been caught alive in the seas off the east coast of South Africa, and is a good example of a 'living fossil.'

Uronemus represented the Dipnoi which, though they continued to flourish during the Carboniferous had almost run their course. But even today they still linger on and survive in the genus *Ceratodus* and several allied genera in the rivers of the southern hemisphere.

The actinopterygian fishes with fins supported solely by fin-rays, which were represented in the Old Red Sandstone by *Cheirolepis,* now started off on an evolutionary career that has resulted today in their complete predominance over all other kinds of fishes. Some of the carboniferous genera, *Elonichthys* and *Rhadinichthys,* were of normal shape and were evidently swift swimmers. Others like *Mesolepis* and *Platysomus* resembled the modern John Dory in having deep laterally flattened bodies. In them the mouth was small and provided with teeth that were suited for consuming vegetation and thin-shelled mollusca.

The invertebrates are represented almost entirely by lamellibranchs and arthropods. The former are abundant in the shales and will receive special attention in a later chapter. The latter are less common but include a greater range of types, many of which have been found in the ironstone nodules. Among collectors Dr. Lewis Moysey, a medical doctor in Nottingham during the early years of this century, should be mentioned. He concentrated much of his spare time and attention on the coal measures of Derbyshire; and could often be seen returning from a distant foray carrying on his bicycle a small sack full of nodules. These he had collected judiciously, for experience had taught him how to tell at a glance which were the most likely to contain fossils. Hitherto it had been the practice to break open such nodules by heating them in a fire and then dropping them into cold water. This method, however, was accompanied by some danger for frequently a nodule in the fire exploded violently and the fossil was destroyed. Dr. Moysey adopted nature's technique. He first soaked the nodules in water and then deposited them in the ice-chamber of a local fishmonger; for in those days domestic refrigerators were unknown. A few days later he brought his sack home and tumbled its contents into a bucket of boiling water. As a result many nodules split naturally along the plane of weakness induced by the presence of a fossil; thus the remains of delicate organisms were obtained and a rich contribution to our knowledge of the natural history of Upper Carboniferous times was made.

While discussing earlier the migration of marine organisms into freshwater no reference was made to the arthropods, some of which not merely survived but thrived and evolved into new types unknown in saline waters. The reason for this is obscure but it may be that the impervious covering that completely enclosed all parts of the body limited the osmotic exchanges between the fluids of the body and of the surrounding waters to a gaseous exchange of oxygen and carbon dioxide. The fact that so many of the non-marine arthropods found in the Coal Measures were already perfectly adapted to the new conditions is an indication that their migration had been successfully accomplished at a much earlier date.

Among the crustacea the minute forms known popularly as 'water fleas' are represented by the beautifully decorated *Leaia* and by the more simple *Estheria*. In both of these the body was enclosed in a shield or carapace which strikingly resembled the bivalved shell of a lamellibranch. Among the larger crustacea the primitive *Palaeocaris* (*Preanaspides*) is of special interest. In it all but one of the thoracic segments are freely movable upon one another, a condition which gives it an extraordinarily close resemblance to *Anaspides*, a rare crustacean still living in the freshwaters of Tasmania. Here then is an arthropod which, like *Latimeria*, is a primitive survival from the long distant past—yet another 'living fossil'. *Anthrapalaemon*, which was about the size of a prawn, represents an early stage in the evolution of larger crustacea akin to the lobster. Closely allied to it was *Tealliocaris*. (Plate VIII*b*: *3*).

Among arachnids *Eurypterus* survived but had decreased still further in size. Its allies *Belinurus* and *Prestwichia* belong to an ancient stock of small creatures remains of which have been found in the Cambrian and Silurian rocks of other parts of the world (Plate VIII*b*: *1*). That stock survives today in the much larger *Limulus* (King Crab) yet another and quite abundant living fossil which lives in the

---

PLATE IX
a. SECTION OF A 'COAL BALL'
A 'coal ball' is essentially a lump of calcified coal measure peat in which the microscopic structure of the plants is remarkably well preserved. The round object near the centre is a section of the stalk of a fern, *Botryopteris cylindrica*. From the Bullion Mine Coal, Todmorden, Lancashire. (*W. Sutcliffe*)

b. SEEDS FROM A CARBONIFEROUS 'FERN'
Sandstone casts of the inside of the coat which covered the seed. This coat bore three longitudinal ridges which left the grooves seen on the inside surfaces of the external casts. *Trigonocarpus parkinsoni* Peel Hall Quarry, Bolton, Lancashire. (*H. M. Geol. Survey*)

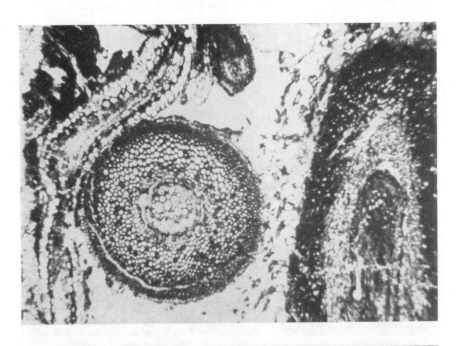

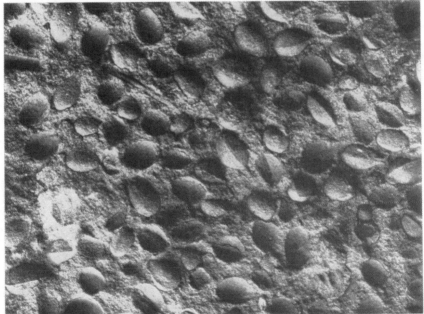

1   2   3

4   5   6

warm seas that wash upon the shores of North America. The very close resemblance of its newly hatched larva to the fossil *Prestwichia* leaves no doubt about the close affinity of these two creatures that are widely separated from one another in time, by more than 200 millions of years.

Rare impressions of insects wings in the nodules are a reminder that other arthropods remain to be considered. They, however, had not merely migrated from marine to freshwater but had taken a great step forward by becoming air-breathers. Because these had found their way on to the land and even into the sky they must be considered later. In conclusion it should be noted that in addition to fossil fishes these nodules frequently yield complete remains of eggs, eg *Palaeoxyris*, resembling those of that strange cartilaginous fish *Chimaera*, the 'King of the Herrings' which still lives along the margins of the North Pacific Ocean.

PLATE X

a. CONDITIONS OF LIFE IN THE TRIASSIC LANDSCAPE

The background of this picture is based on Central England. On the right is the Mercian Highland (1) with its flanks dissected by valleys partly filled with deltaic fans (2). From the rims of these water seeped out and gave rise to oases (3) and to streams which flowed across the lowlands which were covered with sand dunes (4) or with gravel and facetted pebbles (4). They then discharged their water into an inland lake (5).

Plants:
(6) *Voltzia*, a coniferous tree.
(7) Cycadeoids, and
(8) Equisetites, horse tails.
Animals:
Invertebrates, (9) Scorpion.
(10) Dragon fly.
Vertebrates, (11) *Cynognathus*, a mammal-like reptile.
(12) *Rhynchosaurus*.
(13) *Scleromochlus*, a minute jumping dinosaur only 9.4 inches long.

b. PLANTS FROM THE COAL MEASURES (C.M.)

1. *Lepidodendron.* L.C.M. Stalybridge. 2. *Sigillaria.* C.M. Barnsley. 3. *Alethopteris.* C.M. Ashton u. Lyne. 4. *Mariopteris.* Seed fern, C.M. South Wales. 5. *Neuropteris.* Seed fern, C.M. South Wales. 6. *Calamites.* Giant horsetail. C.M. North Staffs. (*Photographs by H.M. Geol. Survey*)

FOS.—H

CHAPTER 18

LIFE ON LAND

THE emergence of living things from their ancestral home in the sea and their ascent up on to the land was one of the most sensational events in the long history of life on this world. The fossil records of this event are tantalisingly scanty, especially in the British Rocks. That the main movement took place during the late Silurian and Devonian times seems certain but here, unfortunately, climatic and physical conditions were favourable only in limited localities. With the opening of Carboniferous times living conditions improved greatly and vegetation became established on an extended and even luxuriant scale, first in the Midland Valley of Scotland and the North of England, and later over South Britain. The opening stages of that great event had, however, been already passed through and the processes of adaptation had attained a scale comparable with that seen in the virgin forests of the present day. Giant trees spread their canopy over lower strata of smaller trees, bushes and carpet verdure. But there the similarity ceases. Nothing like flowering plants, elms, fruit-trees, rose-bushes, daffodils had as yet appeared.

Fossil remains of this vegetation abound in the shales thrown out on colliery tip-heaps, where in the course of an afternoon a novice may fill his knapsack with a varied assortment of fragmentary plant fossils. The earliest of these are yielded by the cement stone of the Lower Carboniferous of Scotland. Visitors to South Kensington will be familiar with the fossil tree-trunk erected in the grounds of the Natural History Museum. That came from the cement-stone beds at Craigleith, near Edinburgh.

As compared with the very compact body of a fossil coral or a mollusc that of a plant is a straggling assemblage of roots, trunk, branches, twigs, and leaves which, when the plant dies are sundered from one another and lie scattered about in fragments. It is in this state that the remains are usually preserved as fossils and thus confront the student with the problem of discovering which belongs to which. Occasionally, however, specimens show two or more parts united; a seed to a leaf, a leaf to a twig, a stem to a root. By assembling all the information yielded by such finds more or less complete pictures of whole plants have been reconstructed. Until this has been done disjointed fragments must be labelled with different names.

Usually the fragments are carbonised or turned into coal, a process which often culminated in the complete destruction of their tissues. Sometimes, however, the process has not gone very far and the minute structure of the plant may be studied in thin slices under the microscope. In association with some seams of coal, especially in Lancashire, round boulders occur known as 'coal balls'. These were formed at the time when the peat, out of which the coal has been produced, was accumulating. Here and there very hard, so called petrifying water entered the peat and impregnated it with lime which crystallised as calcite. In this way the most delicate tissues were preserved. By the microscopic study of thin slices cut out of the coal balls a wealth of information has been gained about the minute structure of many Carboniferous plants (Plate IXa). The knowledge thus gained from these different sources, as the result of the patient labours of R. Kidston, A. C. Seward, E. A. N. Arber and many others, has produced a picture of this remarkable primeval vegetation of which only a brief description must now be attempted.

As compared with that of the present day the Carboniferous flora had a topsy-turvy constitution in which spore-bearing plants, now so insignificant, dominated the scene and included the largest and the stateliest trees in the forests. On the other hand true seed-bearing plants were unknown. But nature was even then conducting some fascinating experiments in the formation of seeds.

Those two words, *seeds* and *spores*, must now be briefly explained if the problem of the adaptation of plants to terrestrial conditions is to be understood. They represent the opposite extremes, the lowliest and the highest, of plant development. Fortunately, spore-bearers such as ferns and clubmosses exist today side by side with seed-bearers and so the life story of both types can be studied in detail stage by stage. An ordinary spore resembles the more familiar pollen grain in size and shape. When the spores are released from the spore cases or sporangia, which lie in the brown spots on the back of a fern leaf, some fall on to damp ground and germinate. They do not, however, give rise directly to a new fern plant but to a 'prothallus', a small disc-like plant body which carries on its under side the sex organs that contain, on the one hand, egg cells; and on the other, sperm cells. When the latter are set free they can reach the egg to fertilise it only by swimming through water to their destination. This necessity is the shackle which binds the spore bearing plant to damp or wet situations and prevents them from living in truly terrestrial habitats.

In the Lesser Clubmoss, *Selaginella* the spores are of two sizes. The larger, called the macrospore, produces a prothallus with sex organs and egg-cells, but these are retained within the spore covering. In seed-bearing plants the macrospore, with its spore case, becomes enveloped in protective coverings and the whole complex thus formed remains attached to the parent plant as an incipient seed. The small microspore develops into the equivalent of a prothallus with sperm-cells. At certain seasons of the year it is carried, like pollen, by the wind or is borne by an insect to the organ which contains the im-mature seed and there fertilises the egg cell without the intervention of water. The fertilised egg-cell then developes into an embryo. The seed thus matured breaks loose from the parent plant and falling to the ground, begins to germinate and the embryo, sending out a root and shoot, becomes a new plant.

Selaginella is the present-day relative of *Lepidodendron* and *Sigillaria*, the largest trees that grew in the Carboniferous forests (Plate VIIIa). Their stout trunks rose to a height of as much as 100 feet and carried at the top a thick cluster of bifurcating branches clothed with a fur-like covering of small lance shaped leaves (Frontispiece). Dangling from the tips of many twigs were long cones packed, not with seeds, as in pines, but with large and small spores as in *Selaginella*. The trunk itself was coated with bark. In the fossil *Lepidodendron* the surface of this is decorated with diamond-shaped scale-like markings (lepido=scale) arranged spirally round the trunk (Plate Xb). In *Sigillaria* the corres-ponding markings are arranged in vertical rows separated by grooves. Where the trunk passed into the ground it divided into bifurcating branches that carried numerous small roots which, when they broke off, left scars or 'stigmata' on the surface. Fragments of such scarred underground branches were found long before their relationship to these trees was known, and were called *Stigmaria*.

Calamites, a tree of smaller stature, was a relative of the horse-tail which now grows so abundantly in marshes or on waste ground.

Its stem was hollow and fossil casts of the cavity are common. It may be recognised by the fluted markings of the surface which give the fossil a striking resemblance to the stem of the horse-tail (*Equisetum*).

There are no living representatives of *Sphenophyllum*, an attractive fossil which, as its name implies, has wedge-shaped leaves. These were attached to the stem in a circlet of six or some other multiple of three. As the stem is slender and long this fossil closely resembles superficially such climbing plants as the cleavers are goose grass (*Galium aparine*) of our hedgerows.

The commonest fossils found on colliery tip-heaps are plant fragments which even beginners recognise as 'fern leaves'. These exhibit an almost endless variety in the pattern of their fronds and in the shape of their leaflets. For the purposes of description and reference many names have been created for them, some of which will be referred to in the next chapter. There is no doubt that some of these were true ferns for they carried sporecases filled with spores. Others belong to a much higher category, the Pteridosperms, for they bear seeds (Plate IX*b*). This fact marks a great step forward in the process of adaptation of plants to life on the land.

Less attractive, though not less significant, are the impressions upon slabs of shale or on broken surfaces of nodules of strap-shaped leaves with numerous parallel veins. When complete these were several feet long and belonged to *Cordaites* (Frontispiece). This small tree exhibited features that link it with the Gymnosperms, more particularly with the Monkey Puzzle tree *Araucaria* of the Chilean forests and with the Kauri Pine, *Agathis*, of Australia. In *Cordaites* the reproductive apparatus was more advanced for the small leaves which carried the seeds were clustered together on separate twigs in the form of catkins or cones.

The coming into being of semiaquatic and even of true land plants provided a new source of food and a new environment which opened the way to the evolution of semiaquatic, fully terrestrial and even flying animals. For many millions of years during Precambrian and early Palaeozoic times plants had remained mainly at low algal levels. The animals, on the contrary, evolved from low to higher grades along many different lines of development so that by the time plants began to gain a foothold in the freshwaters, on the marshy borders and on the drier rising ground beyond, all the major divisions of the animal kingdom had already come into being. Of these only two types, the arthropods and the vertebrates, streamed along the trail blazed for them by the plants and became conspicuously successful upon dry land. Of all the other types only a few sections of the Protozoa, the worms and the snails gained a place in these new living quarters.

In the initial stages of adaptation to life on the land the arthropods had several advantages over the vertebrates. Their bodies were already shielded from the drying action of air by a completely impervious covering. They also had legs already strong enough to carry the weight of their bodies when these were no longer supported by submersion in water. On the other hand the necessity for shedding their rigid impervious covering periodically and the type of their breathing apparatus put definite limits to their growth in size.

The fossil evidence for the earliest phases in the evolution of land animals is even less abundant than that for the plants. This is not surprising for even in the scenery of today it is the vegetation that at once strikes the eye while the presence of the animals is revealed only by occasional glimpses. The evidence already noted from the Old Red Sandstone, with the Rhynie chert, indicates that the arthropods were in the vanguard. Earlier still the Upper Silurian *Palaeophonus* seems to have been just on the eve of effecting a landing, for though it still lived in the sea it was structurally an almost perfect scorpion. True air-breathing scorpions have not yet been found in the British Carboniferous rocks though they do occur in the coal measures of Illinois, U.S.A. Nevertheless their close relatives, the Whip Scorpions, are represented by *Geralinurus* in the English coal measures. Here also have been found such primitive spiders as *Protolycosa* and the typical millepedes *Euphorberia* and *Xylobius*.

By Coal Measure times insects had also become well established, for even in Britain about 80 fossil species have been collected and described. In general appearance half of these resembled such familiar living forms as cockroaches and grasshoppers, dragonflies and mayflies. Nearly one-third were allied to the cockroaches and like them had two pairs of wings which, when out of use, folded backwards over the body. The front pair were much stouter and served as a protection to the much more delicate hind pair as the creature pushed its way through vegetable debris in search of food. In several species the hind limbs were elongated and thus anticipated the structure upon which the leaping habits of the grasshopper are founded. The largest insects were the forerunners of the dragonflies which they closely resembled in their long slender bodies and two pairs of delicate membranous wings. These could not be folded back but, when the insect was at rest, they lay stretched out at right angles to the body. In some examples the wings in this position had a span of two feet from tip to tip so that the creature was a veritable giant among insects. Moreover they were in no danger of being devoured for as yet there were no flying vertebrates ready to hunt them on the wing.

Half of the insect species that have been found fossil belong to a group, the Palaeodictyoptera, which were more primitive than any of those already mentioned and are regarded as the ancestral stock from which the multitudinous kinds of insect alive today evolved. Among themselves they exhibit differences that foreshadow these later types.

Many of these fossils have been found in ironstone nodules from the seat earths or Carboniferous soils and consist merely of impressions of wings. Examples from foreign coalfields show that during evolution a gliding phase preceded the development of the ability to fly. In this the insect had short flat parachute-like extensions projecting from the sides of a number of the body segments so that when it jumped or tumbled from the bush, up which it had climbed, it fell only slowly or glided gently to the ground.

Evidence from the Devonian rocks of Canada show that air-breathing vertebrates had already come into existence. The evolution of legs soon followed but it was not until the end of Carboniferous times that adequate devices were developed for countering the excessive loss of moisture from the body during prolonged exposure to air. Meanwhile all these animals were amphibious and, like the ferns among plants, were in a transitional phase between purely aquatic and truly terrestrial dwellers. The air-breathing apparatus, consisting of lungs in close association with an efficient blood-circulation, solved the respiratory problem for those with large as well as small bodies.

Among British fossil amphibia *Eogyrinus* from the Middle Coal Measures of Staffordshire and Northumberland was no less than fifteen feet long (Frontispiece). It still resembled the ancestral fishes in its almost cylindrical body and long laterally compressed tail. When moving across the watery swamps from one river or pool to another it must have slithered over the ground with serpentine movements while the presence of a bony shield on its belly saved this from injury. Its legs

were too weak to lift the body for any length of time above the ground
but by pushing their flat expanded ends or feet into the mud the
creature was able to make its way up and down the slippery slopes. As
in fishes and other Carboniferous amphibia its head was completely
roofed over with a mosaic of prettily sculptured bony plates. This
feature gave rise to the name Stegocephalia for the larger amphibia.
The older name Labyrinthodontia is still frequently used and refers
to the complex pattern into which the enamel that covers the teeth is
folded.

Skulls and parts of skulls of other species have been found. They
show that the head was usually triangular in outline. The mouth was
large, extending almost to the back of the head, and was furnished
with numerous small but sharp teeth that enabled the creature to
catch the worms, grubs and possibly small fishes upon which it must
have fed. Its eyes and nostrils were situated on the top of the head,
as is usual in animals which lie largely submerged in water. A young
frog just passing out of the tadpole stage and beginning to walk about
bears a general resemblance to many Coal Measure amphibia in its
short stout body and stumpy tail, with its legs sticking out sideways
almost at right angles. Normally the animal rested with its body on
the ground but when occasion arose it could lift this slightly and move
away with a waddling gait. In addition to the large amphibia were
many small ones more like newts in shape. Various special adaptations
had, however, already arisen. In some the body was much elongated
like that of a snake and, as in this, the limbs had degenerated and
disappeared.

Because of the predominance, during the Carboniferous period of
these hybrid vertebrates, half water, half land animals, it is often
called 'The Age of Amphibia'.

CHAPTER 19

FOSSILS AND THE RESOURCES
OF COAL AND OIL

THE discovery of new sources of power does not necessarily throw older ones completely out of use. Even though coal has been the dominant source for more than a century water-falls still drive turbines; windmills pump water; and horses draw lorries. On the other hand, despite the discovery of petroleum and the development of atomic energy, coal will long be needed on an extensive scale, not merely for power but for the multitude of valuable products that it yields. It is therefore most important for geologists to go on collecting and examining every scrap of evidence that is likely to throw light upon the extent and availability of future supplies that must still be hidden deep below the ground. Direct evidence can be obtained only by means of the boring tool and by examining the cores and chips that it brings to the surface. But a much greater volume of evidence is gained during the costly and less frequent sinking of colliery shafts and the subsequent working of the mine for coal.

In the interpretation of both these kinds of evidence the examination of the fossils plays a prominent part. The geologist therefore qualifies himself for the task by studying fossils carefully collected from precisely known levels in the measures wherever these are exposed at the outcrop in quarries, cuttings and cliffs. As already seen three categories of fossils are found, marine, non-marine and terrestrial.

Though, during Millstone Grit and Coal Measure times, much of Britain was covered by non-marine waters or by forested swamps the sea returned from time to time and flooding extensive areas brought with it marine faunas. Sometimes these were rich and included goniatites, nautiloids, bivalves, brachiopods and fishes. The deposits laid down from these waters varied in thickness up to as much as thirty feet and were as widely spread as the waters themselves. These sheets of marine rocks may be of vast extent and, when they contain large assemblages of fossils, are of especial value. Thus, for example, one such marine band, found in a Nottinghamshire colliery near Mansfield, yielded upwards of 70 species of fossils; its equivalent, as proved by these, has been found in borings, shafts and quarries in other coalfields from South Wales to Scotland. It has therefore furnished a valuable datum level, not only for correlating the seams which are situated above and below it in the Nottinghamshire coalfield but also for linking with one another corresponding levels in widely separated coalfields.

Marine bands, both rich and poor in organic remains, have been found at a number of other levels in the Coal Measures. Usually the beds above each band occur in a regular repetitional sequence of shales and mudstones; often containing numerous bivalve shells and capped by a type of clay known as 'seat earth' because, it is penetrated by stigmaria bearing many rootlets; thus proving this layer to have been the soil upon which the trees grew. Sometimes this earth is overlain by a coal seam. That regularly recurring sequence calls up a vivid picture of the scene as it changed from marine to brackish and fresh water and then to forested swamps and mudflats.

In the non-marine deposits fossil shells are at times so abundant as to form beds known to coal workers as 'mussel bands'. That name reflects the close resemblance these shells bear to the common freshwater mussel of our canals and rivers. They are, however, smaller and more varied than these shells, and are known by a number of different generic names such as *Carbonicola*, *Anthraconaia* and *Naiadites* (Plate VIII*b*: *5-6*).

Dr. Wheelton Hind, a medical practitioner in the Potteries district of Staffordshire, became interested in the problem of zoning the Coal Measures and soon realised the possible value of these 'mussels'. For this purpose they had two advantages, they were abundant and they were to be found at many different levels in the measures. These advantages were, however, offset to some extent by the fact that, unlike such organisms as graptolites and corals, their shells were very simple affairs which, like a professor's gown, threw very little light upon the structure of the creature they enclosed. Each shell consisted of two more or less oval valves joined together along the top margin by a simple hinge and a semicylindrical springy ligament. The shell was built up by the addition of successive delicate laminae to its inner surface. Each of these extended beyond the margin of its predecessor except along the hinge line and their other edges showed upon the outer surface as lines of growth excentrically arranged about the 'umbo'.

Hind collected many of these fossils, carefully recording not only the place but the precise level where they were found. The main difficulty that presented itself was their great variability. Thus for example the general outline ranged from elongate-oval to almost circular, from rhomboidal to acutely egg-shaped, and so on. The position of the umbo also varied from the front to the centre. He tackled the problem by following the usual practice of selecting well-preserved specimens that exhibited distinctive features. To each of these 'types' he gave a generic and specific name, accompanied by a detailed description and excellent illustrations. These he published along with similar accounts of types selected by other workers. By producing these standards of reference he laid a sound foundation upon which future workers could build. Notwithstanding this valuable work the problem of zoning the Coal Measures effectively remained unsolved. Collectors still tended to search for good specimens of the types and to pass the multitudes of other specimens which, because they varied so much from the type, defied identification.

About that time a boy at High Pavement School, Nottingham, A. E. Trueman by name, was led by his interest in natural history to make a study of the shells of the common banded snail (*Capaea nemoralis*) which abounded alongside the country lanes near his home; for he became intrigued by the great variability in their colour decoration. Later as a university student he continued his enquiry and eventually produced a remarkable little paper on 'Variation' which was based, not on selected typical examples but upon 25,000 specimens! As a post-graduate research student he became familiar with the methods of measurement and their application to the study of fossils. He next applied these to the study of those common and highly variable shells *Ostrea* and *Gryphaea* yielded by the lower Liassic rocks of South Wales. Later, in his position as Professor of Geology at Swansea, he took a deep interest in the geology of the coalfield and turned his attention to the problem of zoning the Coal Measures. With this background of experience and training he realised that the key to the problem lay, not so much with the types as with the study of large numbers of variable specimens which could be collected from specific sites. With his trained gifts he could visualise each collection as a whole. He could see them each as a community of individuals

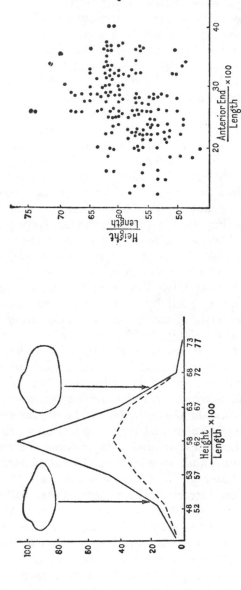

Graph showing variation within two contemporaneous communities. Number of individuals plotted against variation expressed in terms of the ratio of height to length of shell.

A scatter diagram showing distribution of variation within one community expressed in terms of height against length of the anterior end of the shell. (After A. E. Trueman.)

Fig. 13. VARIATION IN CARBONIFEROUS NON-MARINE LAMELLIBRANCHS

which during life interbred freely with one another and had a characteristic unity of its own. To help the less experienced worker to catch the same vision he resorted to graphic representation of such salient features in shape as length and height of the shell and distance of the umbo from the front in comparison with the total length (Fig. 13). Expressing the height as a percentage of length he plotted this figure against the number of individuals. The resulting graph showed a range of variation from as low as 46% to as much as 74%, and the curve rose to a peak, or *mode*, at about 60%. The regularity of the curve showed that the specimens belonged to a community that was homogeneous and not a mixture of different species. Doing the same for another collection, taken from a corresponding horizon at a site situated some miles away, he found that it also showed the same range with a mode in the same position. This other community was evidently in the same evolutionary phase as the first and consequently provided independent evidence that the strata from which these fossils were collected were formed at the same time and that the layers of rock were in a closely similar if not identical position in the sequence of coal measures. All specimens showed some degree of resemblance to the type species *Carbonicola communis* and therefore constituted a community of *Carbonicola aff communis* closely related to the type.

This method of studying non-marine lamellibranchs in communities was extended to collections from many different levels in all the British coalfields. By its means a system of 7 zones has been recognised which is applicable, not only to the coalfields of Britain, but also abroad (p. 113). Its value may be illustrated by the accompanying diagram produced by one of Trueman's co-workers from measurement made upon numerous specimens of *Carbonicola* collected from several of the zones in the Notts-Derbyshire coalfield. The outlines of three typical specimens, such as Hind might have described, are shown. In each zone the specimens showed a continuous range of variation of height in relation to length. It should be noted that these ranges overlap considerably and therefore some shells identical in shape occur in two and possibly three zones. This makes it clear why it was so difficult to zone the measures by means of type specimens only, for even such a type may trespass across the boundaries of several zones. It will be seen that the total range of variation shifts slightly from zone to zone, a fact which is expressed more precisely by a shifting of the mode from 65% across 55% to 47%.

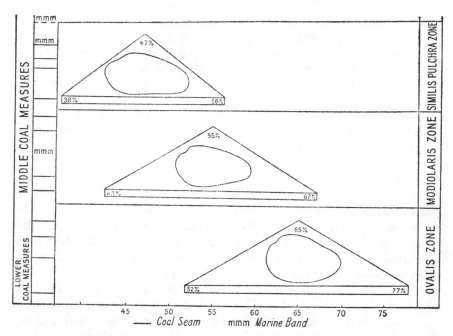

Fig. 14. EVOLUTION IN CARBONIFEROUS
NON-MARINE LAMELLIBRANCHS

These three graphs are similar in construction to that shewn in Fig. 13 (left), but they represent communities of fossils collected from successive zones in the coal measures. Note the progressive shifting of the mode and of the range of variation with the passage of time. (After S. G. Clift.) N.B. The lower mmm is now taken as the dividing line between Lower and Middle Coal Measures.

Evolutionary changes such as these became established simultaneously over extensive areas and therefore the fossil remains which record them in addition to providing a delicate indication of the passage of time, can be used for zoning the measures by means of the communities of fossils they contain.

Another type of graph, the scatter diagram, was also used in these studies and throws much light upon the structure of these communities (Fig. 13b). In this the height and thickness expressed as percentages of the length are plotted against one another. In the diagram each dot represents one specimen. Assuming that the central dot represents a type species it is evident that the great majority differ from this in varying degrees. It is this fact that creates such difficulty in the identification

COAL MEASURE ZONES AND MARINE BANDS

1	2	3	Non-marine	Marine	Land plants
UPPER COAL MEASURES	STEPHANIAN	RADSTOCKIAN	Anthraconaia prolifera	4	Pecopteris lamurensis
UPPER COAL MEASURES	MORGANIAN	STAFFORDIAN	Anthraconauta tenuis		Neuropteris scheuchzeri (*Etruria Marls*)
UPPER COAL MEASURES	MORGANIAN	STAFFORDIAN	Anthraconauta phillipsii	ANTHRACOCERAS	Neuropteris rarinervis (*Floral break*)
				— (*Top Marine Band*) —	— (*Floral break*) —
MIDDLE COAL MEASURES	AMMANIAN	YORKIAN	Anthracosia similis } Upper		Neuropteris tenuifolia
MIDDLE COAL MEASURES	AMMANIAN	YORKIAN	Anthraconaia pulchra } Lower	— (*Mansfield. M.B.*) —	
MIDDLE COAL MEASURES	AMMANIAN	YORKIAN			Neuropteris gigantea — (*Top Hard Seam*)
MIDDLE COAL MEASURES	AMMANIAN	YORKIAN	Anthraconaia modiolaris	— (*Clay Cross Marine Band*)	Alethopteris lonchitica (*1st Piper Seam*)
LOWER COAL MEASURES	AMMANIAN	LANARKIAN	Carbonicola communis	GASTRIOCERAS	— (*Kilburn Seam*) Neuropteris schlehani
LOWER COAL MEASURES	AMMANIAN	LANARKIAN	Anthracomya lenisulcata		
				— (*Pot Clay Marine Band*) —	
MILLSTONE GRITS	NAMURIAN			RETICULOCERAS	

1. The old stratigraphical divisions. 2. The continental divisions.
3. The British divisions. 4. Goniatite genera.

of so many specimens. The convention that has been adopted is to call those specimens that lie close to the type by the same specific name as that of the type, e.g. *Carbonicola communis;* those which are not far removed are then called *C. aff communis;* and those which lie near the outskirts *C. cf communis.*

Apart from their practical uses in the investigation of and zoning of the Coal Measures such studies throw valuable light on many evolutionary problems.

With the failure of early attempts to use the mussels for zonal purposes attention was concentrated upon the possible value of plant fragments. In addition to being abundant these vary greatly and are widely distributed. As with the 'mussels' initial success depended upon the expert's ability to visualise the characteristics of the assemblages collected from different horizons. The simplicity of a 'mussel' assemblage made it possible to portray its essential features to the less expert collector by graphs. The complexity of a plant assemblage, however, baffles any attempt to produce a comparable graphic representation; for it includes examples of every grade of plant structure from spore-bearers such as ferns, calamites, and lyco-pods, through seed ferns or Pteridosperms to the gymnospermous *Cordaites;* from stems of herbaceous simplicity to those strengthened by highly developed woody tissue. Plants belonging to all thse grades were present throughout the coal measure sequence of rocks. As leaves were the most abundant fragments they naturally attracted the major share of attention. Some, such as those of *Lepidodendron* and *Cordaites,* were simple in outline and exhibited but little tendency to change. Fern leaves on the contrary showed an almost endless variety in the outlines of leaflets and in their arrangement on the leaf (Plate X*b*: *3-5*). In Britain it was R. Kidston, a Scottish palaeontologist, who first realised the value of these fragments as 'test of age'. On the basis of a careful study of collections made from successive levels he recognised a

---

PLATE XI

BRITISH OILFIELDS

Left. Plungar, Leicestershire. General view of the drilling outfit at No. 3 Well with derrickman on the platform.

Right. Eakring, Nottinghamshire. Pump working amidst the stooks each of which consists of twelve sheaves of corn stacked together. Duke's Wood Well 65. (*Photographs by British Petroleum Co. Ltd.*)

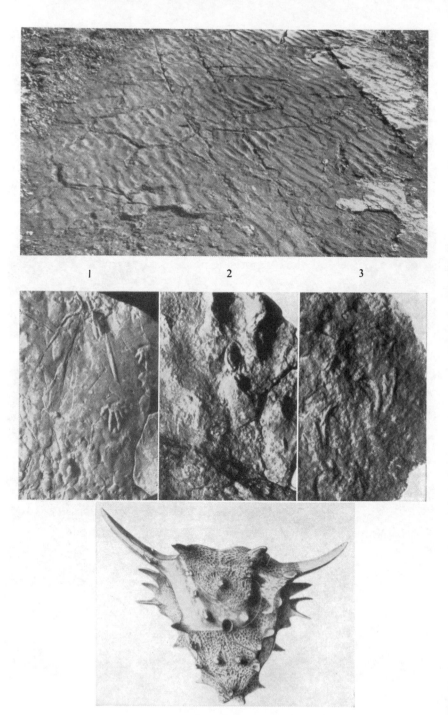

1   2   3

4

number of zones with which he associated the names of representative species which the less expert worker could soon learn to recognise.

The general relationships of the marine bands and of the non-marine lamellibranch and plant zones to one another are summarised in the accompanying table (page 113).

Among the interesting facts that emerged from all these studies was the presence of a break in the succession of both plants and animals at the level of the top marine band. Before this was deposited conditions for coal formation were very favourable. Afterwards living conditions began to deteriorate and the climate became increasingly dry and even arid. This change was associated with earth movements which eventually produced the Pennines in the north, several upland blocks known to geologists as the Mercian and Malvern Highlands in the south, and the Armorican mountain system, which extended from Brittany across the channel and athwart the Cornwall Devon peninsula to South Wales. These features all played an important part in controlling both physical and living conditions during the subsequent Permo-Triassic period.

PLATE XII

a. RIPPLE MARKED SANDSTONE

This surface is criss-crossed by reptilian tracks. Lower Keuper, Mapperley Park, Nottingham. (*W. Sutcliffe*)

b. PERMO-TRIASSIC FOSSILS

1-3. Casts of impressions made originally on a muddy surface. 1. Prints made by both right and left feet, and by the dragging tail of an unknown lizard-like reptile; Permian, Warwickshire. 2. Cheirotheroid prints of both fore and hind feet made probably by a dinosaurian reptile. Lower Keuper, Mapperley Park, Nottingham. 3. Rhynchosauroid prints of fore and hind feet. Lower Keuper, Ramsdale, Notts. 4. *Elginia*, dorsal view of skull, Triassic sandstone, Elgin. (1, *R. D. Vernon.* 2, 3, *W. Sutcliffe.* 4, *H.M. Geol. Survey*)

FOS—I

CHAPTER 20

THE END OF AN ERA

FOR the south countryman on holiday in the Midlands one of the attractive features about the landscape is the warm red colour of the soils and rocks. This recalls to the geologically minded the red lateritic soils of tropical regions where long hot dry seasons are followed by heavy annual rains. Further examination of these Midland rocks brings to light much evidence that similar semi-arid and even desert conditions became established in Britain as the Palaeozoic Era moved to its close. Meanwhile elsewhere in the world normal living conditions still prevailed and, as the abundance of fossil remains attest, the full flow of organic evolution continued. Here in Britain, however, such remains are scanty and the evolutionary story is obscured behind this veil of almost barren red rocks.

This remarkable change-over, from the moist climate and verdure-clad landscapes of coal measure times, took place first in the north where the upper measures of the *Phillipsi* and higher zones are predominantly red and yield relatively few fossil remains. But across the South of England and Wales the forests and swamps persisted for a while longer. When at last these also disappeared the long Permo-Triassic period had set in.

Rocks formed during this period are present on a grander scale on the continent where the older portions cover much of the province of Perm in northern Russia. There they were first examined by Murchison between the years 1840 and 1845 and were classed by him as the Permian System. The younger portions are well developed in Germany where they have a threefold division and are accordingly named the Triassic System. In Britain the boundary between these two systems is ill-defined.

During the earlier or Permian period, slowly acting earth-movements, which had started in Coal Measure times, continued and the British area became folded and fractured, upheaved here and depressed yonder. Thus the configuration of the countryside became a medley of highlands separated by inland basins. The uplands situated in South Wales, in the Malvern area and Mercia, in the Pennines and Scotland became stony deserts where rapid and extreme ranges of temperature shattered and pulverised the rocks. The waste thus formed was swept away by torrents in the rainy seasons. The coarser debris was dumped in the form of screes and deltaic fans along the lower slopes; the finer sand and dust were carried out on to the lowlands where they were drifted about as sand-dunes by winds or carried by rivers in times of flood beyond the bounds of Britain. Consequently the fossil records for this period of time are scanty (Plate Xa).

The deep accumulations of coarse debris in the deltaic fans absorbed much water and became underground reservoirs from which the water oozed out in springs along the margins. There the moisture stabilised the loose sand that lay nearby and turned it into fertile soil. Trickles of water united into streams and even rivers which poured into pools and lakes or lost themselves in the sandy wastes beyond. In the South Midlands, including parts of Warwickshire and Staffordshire, lay a block of country that went on sinking continuously from Coal Measure into Permian times. Into this ever-deepening depression waste from the adjoining Mercian Highlands was swept and, under the conditions just described, oases were established. It must have been in some such circumstances as these that those plants grew whose fragmentary remains have been found in the brick-fields near Kenilworth. These fossils show that vegetation akin to that of the Coal Measures still survived and was represented by the seed-ferns *Alethopteris* and *Sphenopteris* and by *Asterophyllites* which was the foliage of one of the Calamites. On the other hand *Lepidodendron* and its allies were apparently now absent and their place as the dominant trees was taken by Gymnosperm plants which form seeds but do not hide them in closed cases. These included the older type, *Cordaites* and the allied *Dadoxylon* now preserved as fossilised wood. In addition there were new types as for example *Walchia*, *Ullmannia* and *Voltzia*.

Two fragments of animal skeletons have been found. One belonged to *Dasyceps* a small amphibian probably representing the stock from which the newts and then later the frogs descended. The other was part of the jaw of *Oxyodon*, one of the earliest mammal-like reptiles; so called because, in the structure of their skulls and the differentiation of the front teeth into nibbling incisors and piercing canines, they were departing from the reptiles and starting off on lines of development that ultimately merged into the mammals.

The carnivorous character of the teeth of *Oxyodon* is a tantalising reminder that there must have been other animals living in these oases of which no remains have hitherto been found. This last remark is still more true for the fossil footprints that have been discovered in several places. No less than eleven types of such prints have been found at Hamstead, near Birmingham.

During Permian times a great inland sea, in some respects comparable with the Caspian, stretched from Russia across Central Europe. In the latter half of the period its western end invaded northern England as far as and eventually beyond the Pennine belt. As this advanced it buried the sand-dunes and stony screes under its deposits.

The earliest of those deposits, known as the Marl slates, have yielded well preserved remains of such palaeozoic fish types as *Palaeoniscus* and *Platysomus*. The remains of a small land reptile, *Adelosaurus* have also been found. Its presence in these marine deposits suggests that it may have been poaching for fish, a not unlikely proceeding for an animal belonging to the stock from which descended those large aquatic reptiles the plesiosaurs that hunted in the Jurassic seas.

The later deposits became the Magnesian Limestone which crops out along the strip of country that runs from Nottingham to Durham. Here it attains a thickness of 600 feet and forms prominent cliffs along the coast. Some of the layers are richly fossiliferous and yield a fauna with marked palaeozoic affinities. Corals are rare, their place as rock-builders being taken by the more abundant polyzoa, crinoids, brachiopods and molluscs which are also represented. This richness of fauna is, however, not maintained continuously but undergoes progressive decline. The crinoids, polyzoa and larger brachiopods disappear first. The remaining brachiopods and molluscs persist longer but then they in turn die out. This sequence of faunal changes reflects a deterioration in living conditions brought about by excessive evaporation, leading to increasing salinity. All this was only one aspect of the general dryness of the climate that prevailed in Britain; and culminated in the precipitation of those massive deposits of salt and calcium sulphate in the form of anhydrite upon which the chemical industries of Middlesbrough depend.

Along their southern and western margins these Upper Permian rocks merge into marls, shales and sandstones. Near Appleby in

Westmoreland, in the Penrith sandstone, fossil remains of *Alethopteris,* *Sphenopteris* and *Ulmannia* have been found. In the Permian Sandstone near Mansfield fossil footprints and tracks also occur.

The presence of similar impressions at other places as far apart as Exeter, Dumfries and Cummingstone near Elgin, shows how widely distributed were the elusive creatures which made them. Some inkling of what they looked like comes from the sandstones of Cutties Hillock not far distant from Cummingstone. In the middle of the nineteenth century curious cavities were found in this stone. As it was suspected that they originally contained bones, which had in the course of time been dissolved away by percolating water, they were submitted for examination to the palaeontologist of the Geological Survey, E. T. Newton. By pressing guttapercha into the cavities and fitting the squeezes together, he made solid reconstructions of the cavities, and thus proved that they originally contained the skulls of three types of reptiles closely related to some of those whose skeletons had been found in the uppermost Permian beds of South Africa and Russia. One of them showed close affinity with the well-known genus *Pareia-saurus*. Though a true reptile this creature was sufficiently primitive to have retained resemblances to its *Labyrinthodont* ancestor in the complete bony roof to the skull and its massive body supported by strong squat legs. *Pareiasaurus* itself was nearly nine feet long. The British genus *Elginia* was only about one-third that size but its head was armed with a pair of sharp horns and many spiny tubercles (Plate XII*b*: *4*). The other two types *Gordonia* and *Geikia* were shown, by comparison with South African forms, to belong to the family *Dicynodontidae*. This was a family of vegetable-feeders some of which, like the living Hippopotamus, must have led an amphibious life. From a study of the more completely known skeletons from South Africa it seems not unlikely that the Mansfield footprints were either those of *Gordonia* or of a close ally. One of the wildest dreams of some palaeontologists is that some day they may find the skeletal remains of those creatures that made all those different footprints that are so widely distributed in the British Red Rocks.

Part Three

AN ERA OF
TRANSITIONS
THE MESOZOIC

CHAPTER 21

THE DAWN OF A NEW ERA

A s youth passes gradually into manhood so the Palaeozoic Era merged imperceptibly into the Mesozoic Era, so called because its plant and animal fashions lay betwixt and between those of the ancient and the recent modes. They were in fact transitional from those of early to those of late geological times. In his written record the geologist draws a boundary line between the Palaeozoic and the Mesozoic eras but there is no corresponding break in nature's own story. When he goes out into the field the British geologist finds no sharp line that divides the Permian from the Triassic rocks for the climatic and geological processes remained practically unchanged. He therefore frequently refers to the two sets of rocks as though they belonged to the same system, the Permo-Triassic (New Red Sandstone).

Nevertheless a broad general change came slowly over the landscapes of Britain as a whole. During the Permian period erosion was dominant and much of the waste was carried away and dumped outside the region. Towards the end of that period, however, the balance of change began to tip the other way and Britain became a reception area for the waste brought down by rivers that flowed not only from its own native highlands but also from the Armorican system, whose lofty heights stretched athwart the path of the rain-bearing southwesterly winds as they approached our area.

In the early part of the Triassic period the waste was predominantly sandy and formed the rock now known as the Bunter Sandstone. As this accumulated it completely buried much of the hilly scenery adjoining the highlands, filled up the depressions that lay between them, and attained its maximum thickness of 2,000 feet over the Cheshire region. The finer sand was carried along by the wind or was drifted to and fro in sand-dunes and thus distributed far and wide. In some areas much of the sand was coarse and included pebbles and even boulders. These consisted of such very hard rock as quartzite and must have been borne from far off, for they are often very smooth and beautifully rounded. Even up to the opening of this century they were in common use for surfacing paths and roads. The larger ones came under the hammer of the roadmender whose heaps provided budding geologists with the only fossils they ever found in the Bunter Sandstone—worm-borings, *Orthis* and other brachiopods, and also simple corals—all providing evidence that these stones had been derived from the Silurian and Ordovician rocks of South Wales and Brittany. Coming from the other geographical extreme were pebbles of purple grit and sandstone that could be matched with the Torridonian rocks of the North-west Highlands of Scotland. Occasionally, in the sandstone, there occur lenticles of grey clay. These have yielded the remains of *Estheria* a small crustacean which is found alive today, in arid regions, swarming in the pools formed during the rainy season.

The rocks which overlie the Bunter usher in the Upper Triassic or Keuper Beds. Over extensive areas these are evenly bedded, for they were at first laid down in freshwater lakes. In the country around the lakes arid sandy wastes with occasional oases persisted. Relics from these have been found near Bromsgrove in Worcestershire and near Leicester. They include plants allied to *Equisetum* and pieces of coniferous wood. At the former place the plants were standing in the position in which they originally grew. Along with them were found many fragments of *Mesophonus*, a scorpion, the presence of which throws an interesting ray of light upon the climatic conditions of the time.

In their lower levels the Keuper deposits exhibit a rhythmic repetition of thick beds of medium-grained sandstone alternating with zones made up of thin bands of sandstone and red marl. In later phases the sandy element diminished and the marl increased until the top 600 feet consisted almost exclusively of red marl; with only rare and widely-spaced belts of skerry, a very fine-grained sandstone. In an exposure of the Lower Keuper Sandstones it is easy to strip away these layers one by one and thus lay bare a succession of surfaces, not merely of layers of rock, but of the ground as it appeared in early Keuper times. The following picture of conditions which existed then is based on a detailed study of the features seen in such a dissected exposure.

In Britain at that time there existed extensive sheets of water which contracted and expanded with the passing seasons. As the dry season advanced they shrank slowly, leaving gently sloping shores of sand, silt and mud. Here and there pools were left in which many fishes were trapped. In due time these pools evaporated and even disappeared. The fish, in a last effort for survival buried themselves in the moist subsurface. Meanwhile various four-footed beasts traversed the beach in search of water or food and left behind them the impressions of their feet on the soft silts (Plate XIIa). In the day time these were soon dried and baked hard by the hot sunshine which thus petrified the footprints and also the suncracks and the dints made by passing showers of rain; that foreshadowed the end of the dry season.

With the onset of the rainy seasons the lakes were refilled and restored to their original boundaries. Sometimes the pools were renewed in time for the fish to rise from their temporary tombs and begin life anew. Sometimes it was too late and the self-buried refugees became those shoals of fossil fishes the finding of which, at rare intervals, thrills the heart of the genuine student of fossils (Plate XIIIa). The flooded rivers brought loads of sediment which as it settled on the floor of the lake, filled up and then buried those prints, cracks, dints and other hollows the sight of which made the construction of this story possible.

Fossil footprints are much more common and widespread than the bony remains of the animals that made them (Plate XIIb). Though they are merely impressions on the petrified mud they do yield a modicum of information about these creatures. Take for example those prints which are referred to collectively as Cheirotheroid footprints. As this term implies they bear an appreciable resemblance to the human hand. They have been found in many places, especially in the sandstone quarries of Storeton in Cheshire. Each print of both fore and hind foot shows the impression of five digits. Four of these lie side by side but the fifth sticks out sideways at right angles to the others. There is a strong temptation for the amateur to call this last the thumb, but comparison with the feet of lizards and other living reptiles shows that it is the fifth or little digit. The impression of the palm or sole, to which these were attached, is also shown and indicates that the animal was almost plantigrade; that is to say walked with the foot planted flat upon the ground.

The prints are usually present in twos, a small one in front and a large one behind. Evidently the animal resembled a kangaroo in having small front and large hind legs. Sometimes the prints of both sides followed one another in series in an almost straight line, with the little digit projecting alternately left and right. In these respects the track resembles that made by a dog running along with wet feet upon a dry pavement and shows that the legs of the reptile projected, not sideways but downwards from the body. They therefore lifted this well above the ground so that it cleared any obstacles that lay upon the surface over which it was running, a feature quite new in evolution. Frequently the impressions of the front feet were weak or even absent. This may be taken to indicate that the animal could raise itself up into a bipedal attitude and walk or run on its hind legs. The length of stride was about 3 feet and suggests that the animal was 4 to 5 feet high.

Other prints, described as Rhynchosauroid, are also frequently found. In these the forefeet are slightly smaller than the hind and all the toes of both feet were long and clawed. This creature ran with all four feet upon the ground but the prints of the opposite sides were some distance apart, like those of frogs and lizards, in which the elbows and knees stick out sideways from the body and thus impose a waddling gait. Fragmentary remains of the makers of these prints have been found in different parts of Britain, but from Shropshire came a skeleton sufficiently complete to give an accurate picture of the whole animal. It has been called *Rhynchosaurus*, because it has two beak-like teeth that project downwards from the front of the mouth. It is recognised as a member of the same primitive type which still survives in the New Zealand lizard, the *Sphenodon*. When this interesting 'living fossil' was first discovered it was common everywhere throughout that country; but the introduction of other animals into the islands threatened it with extinction. Because of its great scientific interest the government placed *Sphenodon* under protection and gave it sanctuary in a small island offshore from the mainland.

Hyperodapedon belongs to the same type. Up to the present only its skull has been found, but that indicates a much larger animal, between 7 and 8 feet long. As in *Sphenodon* the front of the upper jaw was armed with two large and powerful hooked teeth that could be used for grubbing food up from the banks or floor of the rivers, in or near which it lived.

In the search for the skeletal remains of land animals the sandstone quarries of Lossiemouth near Elgin have proved more fruitful. It was here that in 1851 Patrick Duff found considerable fragments of *Teler-peton,* a relative of but much less clumsy than *Pareiasaurus.* It was indeed one of the last representatives of a stock that, having passed its heyday, was speeding its way to extinction.

Other finds have been made from time to time which, taken alto-gether, have made a most valuable contribution to our knowledge of the fourfooted animals of the Triassic period. One feature of interest about them is that they foreshadow some of those great races of reptiles that dominated the less austere landscapes of the Jurassic and Cretaceous periods. They include *Ornithosuchus* and *Erpetosuchus* which had a body like that of a stout lizard but unlike this reptile the strong development of the hind limbs show that they were bipedal runners. The little *Scleromochlus,* less than one foot long, exhibits the same feature in a more highly developed state and along with other structural details convinces some students that it was indeed an ancestral dinosaur (Plate X*a*). If that view be the correct one then the smallness of this creature illustrates the common principle that large results may accrue from small beginnings. *Thecodontosaurus,* from the Keuper conglomerate near Bristol, was also a true but very small dinosaur.

Of *Stagonolepis* only fragments were found at Lossiemouth but more complete skeletons of near relatives from other regions of the world show that it anticipated the crocodiles in habits and habitat. Like these they had a long snout associated with a great mouth and a fearsome array of teeth. The nostrils, however, were not on the tip of the snout as in the crocodile, but were far back on the top of the head close to or even between the eyes; so that while the animal lay submerged near the water's edge, it could breathe freely and keep an outlook for animals coming down to the river in an evening to slake their thirst.

The discovery in the Midlands of fragmentary remains of such large amphibia as *Mastodonsaurus* and *Capitosaurus* brings out the curious fact that, notwithstanding the extreme dryness of the climate, some labyrinthodonts still survived.

From all this it will be seen that the careful search, made in these apparently barren rocks, throws some useful gleams of light upon the changes that were taking place in land animals outside Britain during the transition from Palaeozoic to Mesozoic times. It has revealed part of the story of the decline of the amphibia from their position of pre-eminence in Carboniferous times and also some of the initial phases in the rise of reptiles and of their early adaptations to the strange and varied modes of life in those very unfavourable Triassic surroundings.

Finally a moment may now be spared for a look at those shoals of fishes that sought refuge from drought in the floor of drying-up beach pools (Plate XIII*a*). There they were, in their hundreds, lying side by side or piled one upon another. These fishes varied in length up to a foot or eighteen inches but were few in number of species. Almost lost amid this multitude was little *Woodthorpea*, which possessed features reminiscent of the Carboniferous *Palaeoniscus*, but was well on its way to becoming a typical Mesozoic fish. Among the many anatomical features which illustrate this remark is the structure of the tail. In *Palaeoniscus* the elongated and tapering tail end of the body is tilted upwards only moderately and the fin lies along its underside. During the evolution of the Mesozoic fishes the end of the tail was gradually shortened and became tilted upwards more steeply. This movement carried the fin into a vertical position so that it spread out fan fashion from the end of the body and could be used more effectively either as a rudder or a propeller. In *Woodthorpea* and *Semionotus* the tail exhibited an intermediate stage in this evolutionary sequence. *Dipteronotus*, complete specimens of which have also been found, closely resembled *Semionotus* but had a much deeper body. Teeth of *Ceratodus* have also been found. They indicate that the seasonal regime of the rivers was similar to that of some of the present rivers of Central Australia.

CHAPTER 22

EVENTS OUTSIDE BRITAIN

IN the Precambrian and early Palaeozoic seas animals, being freely moving organisms, flourished abundantly and evolved in many and varied directions. Our study of British Coal Measures has shown that out of the multitude of marine animals that had evolved in the earliest times very few gained a foothold on the land and only two types, the arthropods and the vertebrates, found terrestrial conditions sufficiently favourable to open out for them many new paths of progress. Plants on the other hand were sedentary organisms tied to relatively uniform conditions on the sea-floor where moisture, food and oxygen lay ready to hand in the all-enveloping water. On land they found greatly different conditions. Though still sedentary they had, under the stimulus of stronger sunshine and variable temperature and moisture, to satisfy their needs by foraging down into the soil and rocks beneath and up into the air above. It is not surprising that, released from the bonds of uniform conditions they were free to progress by leaps and bounds in several directions.

Conditions on the land were, however, not uniformly favourable. On the contrary in regions where and periods when climates were arid both animals and plants led a precarious existence. Unfortunately for British students such conditions predominated here during the 70 millions of years which separated the passing of the Coal Measure forests and the return of the sea at the opening of Jurassic times. The scanty remains of plants and animals found in the British Red Rocks give only fleeting glimpses of the remarkable changes that were taking place in the organic world in other regions, where conditions were more favourable. Apart from a few fossils these rocks are like a red curtain that is dropped and hides the players for an interval in the middle of a play. For the better understanding of the mesozoic part of our story it will be useful if, with the help of visits to museums, we peep behind this curtain and glance at some of the changes which took place among animals in other parts of the world during the interval. The consideration of the plants may be left to a later chapter.

Among fourfooted creatures the Amphibia, both large and small, declined from their dominant position and became only an insignificant item in the land fauna. On the other hand the Reptilia gradually sloughed off their resemblances to their clumsy amphibian ancestors. Their eggs became fewer and larger and enclosed in a shell. The moisture of the body was conserved by the development of an impervious cuticular covering. With these adjustments to being surrounded by air instead of water they became adapted to the very varied habitats which the land with its abundant and open vegetation cover, offered. They waddled. They ran on all fours. They raced or hopped along upon powerfully developed hind legs. Some climbed the trees and then, launching themselves into the air, learned to glide and even to fly. Others explored the rivers and seas and became partly aquatic, like crocodiles and turtles; or wholly aquatic, like the extinct ichthyosaurs or fish-lizards. Most fascinating of all were those reptiles that so closely approached the mammals in the structure of their skulls and limbs as to leave little doubt that they were evolving in that direction though often along parallel lines that never quite arrived. Such was the lively phase in evolution already attained by land vertebrates when the red curtain was raised and the Jurassic scene was exposed to view.

Among aquatic animals some types of fishes had completely disappeared and were represented only by 'relicts'. These included isolated survivals such as the 'fringe-finned' mudfish *Ceratodus*. Others, among which the Palaeoniscids were foremost, did not decline and die out but evolved into new types of which *Semionotus* and *Woodthorpea* were examples and with fresh vigour gave origin to the new and varied types of enamel-scaled ganoids that eventually swarmed in the Mesozoic seas (Plate XIV*b*).

The tattered fragments of the invertebrate story found in the British red rocks give no indication of the extraordinary events which were happening among these organisms in the Mediterranean and other regions where marine habitats were maintained, in almost unbroken sequence, throughout this prolonged interlude that was equivalent to nearly one-third of the Mesozoic Era. All the main groups of animal life:—protozoa, sponges, corals, brachiopods, molluscs and the rest—still formed the strands out of which nature wove her tapestry for the new era.

Within each strand the threefold processes of extinction, survival and evolution played their part. One grade of change, that at first sight seems mysterious and inexplicable, may be illustrated from the corals. The Palaeozoic grade of coral with its development and structure based upon a biradially symmetrical plan seems to have vanished completely. Nevertheless its place was taken by a new type which from the outset had a structural plan based upon a six-rayed symmetry. Between these two the fossil record apparently presents no connecting link. It is not unlikely that in Palaeozoic times, as in modern seas, there were polyps which, like the living sea-anemones, did not secrete coral and therefore when they died left no record. It may be that some of these, having six-rayed symmetry, began to secrete lime and build coral just at the time when the Palaeozoic passed into the Mesozoic Era.

The history of the Echinoderms illustrates a more usual type of change. In early Palaeozoic times these creatures had simple sack-like bodies enveloped in a protective mosaic of calcareous plates. Many of these Cystoidea, as they are called, became extinct; others evolved in diverse directions. On the one hand some adopted a stationary mode of life. Of these the stone-lilies or Crinoidea, already described, were the most striking and successful. They flourished in an almost endless variety during the Silurian and Devonian and rose to their climax in the Carboniferous period. During the early part of the Permo-triassic interval they declined with extraordinary and unexplained rapidity and came to the verge of complete extinction. Nevertheless several genera escaped the fate of the others and became the starting point for a minor revival in later times. Other cystoids became able to move and creep about over the sea-floor in search of food. These after a slight setback during the Permo-trias revived and, having entered upon a long and progressive career produced the starfishes, brittle stars and also sea-urchins of present day seas (Plate XIVa). Their fossil remains form one of the most attractive features in many amateur collections.

The general story of the brachiopods is similar to that of the crinoids. For some of them also a period of rapid and varied evolution during middle and late Palaeozoic times was followed by decline almost to extinction. Here again a few types survived and enjoyed a measure of success.

FOS—K

Within the boundaries of the Molluscs all the types of evolutionary record illustrated above are repeated. Normally those cephalopods allied to the cuttlefish do not appear to have produced hard parts that could be preserved as fossils until the Triassic period. They then began to secrete a small internal chambered shell around which films of crystalline lime accumulated and formed those hordes of familiar cigar shaped fossils known as belemnites, which are found in the Jurassic and Lower Cretaceous rocks (Plate XIX). It was noted in an earlier chapter that shells of the nautilus type were common and varied in the Palaeozoic seas. Towards the end of that era they declined until only the closely coiled type remained and still survives in the Pearly Nautilus of the Pacific ocean. The goniatite type of cephalopod on the other hand continued to flourish and gave rise, in the Permo-triassic seas, to amazing multitudes of ammonites. These displayed every degree of complexity in surface ornamentation from perfect smoothness to a chequered pattern of ridges and tubercles. The septal margins likewise varied from the smoothly rounded saddles and finely denticulated lobes of *Ceratites* to the highly labyrinthine suture of *Pinacoceras*.

Towards the end of the Trias some stocks perished even though they had only just reached their prime. In others the shape of the shell reverted to the openly coiled and straight conditions of the earliest ancestral genera, or developed the turreted spirals which usually characterise the gastropods. The septal margins also reverted to primitive simplicity. Finally the nemesis which befell so many other races of organisms smote them also; species, genera and families followed one another into oblivion. Out of this holocaust two generic types alone survived, viz., the closely coiled *Monophyllites* and the more loosely coiled, round whorled *Lytoceras*. Phoenix-like these two

---

PLATE XIII
a. A SLAB OF SANDSTONE CONTAINING FOSSIL FISHES
By chipping away the surface of the slab a swarm of fishes, mainly *Semionotus* was discovered buried in the stone. Lower Keuper Woodthorpe, Nottingham. (*W. Sutcliffe*)

b. AUST CLIFF, GLOUCESTERSHIRE
This cliff alongside the river Severn shows the grey and black shales of the Rhaetic overlying the Keuper Marl. (*H.M. Geol. Survey*)

gave rise to that virile aristocracy among invertebrates—the Jurassic and Cretaceous ammonites.

In general contrast with the cephalopods the bivalve lamellibranchs and the univalve gastropods, which never contributed a striking element to the Palaeozoic faunas, seem to have passed unscathed through those vicissitudes that were apparently so inimical to the other organisms. Like the echinoids, they started off on a career of steady progress that has continued even until now.

Among arthropods the trilobites, which had been steadily declining throughout Palaeozoic times now finally disappeared. The aquatic arachnids, *Eurypterus* and its allies, survived only in the genus *Limulus*, the King Crab and, in a modified form, as the scorpions. Some of the small crustacea continued with little change; others increased considerably in size and set out on a path of change which eventually culminated in the lobsters and crabs.

The generally disastrous influence seems not to have been at work upon the land for terrestrial insects and spiders already present in appreciable numbers in the Carboniferous apparently experienced no serious halt in their progress.

Thus it comes to pass that the fossil-hunter, wandering from the Carboniferous to the Jurassic rocks, finds that there comes into his collections a new look that has a more than fleeting resemblance to that seen by his naturalist friends who today dredge the sea-floor, explore the beaches or go collecting in the fields and on the moors.

PLATE XIV

a. LIASSIC FOSSILS

Left. Slab of limestone crowded with small ammonites (*Promicroceras*). Lower Lias, Marston Magna, Yeovil, Somerset. (*H.M. Geol. Survey*) *Right.* A fossil Brittle Star (*Ophioderma egertoni*) Lias, Lyme Regis, Dorset. (*A. Ferguson*)

b. A GANOID FISH, LEPIDOTUS

Lepidotus minor, about 9 inches long. Note its covering of thick rhombic scales with enamelled surfaces. Middle Purbeck Beds, Swanage, Dorset. (*Pal. Soc. Monograph: 1916-19*) As an illustration of one of the changes that have taken place in the technique of representation compare this figure with Text Figs. 1 and 19 and also with all the other plates in this book, 1959.

CHAPTER 23

THE TRIASSIC CURTAIN LIFTS

A MONG present-day fishes the sharks are pre-eminently marine. This was also true in geological times for their teeth are not uncommonly found as fossils in the marine rocks of Mesozoic periods. Thus for example the pointed teeth of *Hybodus* and the crushing teeth of *Acrodus* are both found in the Liassic clays whose marine origin is beyond dispute (Fig. 20: *1*). What then is the significance of the presence of these teeth in the Keuper of Warwickshire which, in so far as it was of aquatic origin, was laid down in inland waters that might range from being quite fresh to being very saline? It is often explained that this salinity was the outcome of the repeated evaporation of freshwater. If this be the case then how is the presence of normally marine fish in these inland waters to be explained?

Among the familiar fish living today the salmon, eel, three-spined stickleback and sturgeon are all, at some time in their lives, equally at home in streams, rivers or the sea. Did these sharks by any chance sometimes also wander from their haunts in the sea up the estuaries and rivers and find themselves occasionally trapped in lakes? Or were they brought by the sea itself when on some rare occasions it invaded the broad vales of the Keuper landscape? That such invasions did actually take place seemed at one time established for it was reported that shells of the pelecypod genera *Mytilus*, *Thracia*, *Nucula* and *Pholadomya* had been found in the Keuper. Unfortunately they were not well enough preserved for experts to feel certain that these identifications were correct and so judgment on this problem was suspended.

One minor Mecca of English geologists today is Eakring in Nottinghamshire, the centre of a small but valuable oilfield. As recently as 1955 a party of pilgrims from Reading, during their visit, turned aside 'to examine a small exposure of Keuper Waterstones' and 'almost the first hammer blow dislodged a *Lingula*. the first to be found in the British Trias'. The writer of these words and guide of the party goes on to remark that more specimens were added later. About the marine, or at least the brackish-water habits of *Lingula* there is no doubt. This fortuitous find therefore tends to tip the scale in favour of the view that the sea which occupied southern and western Europe did occasionally push its fingers into Britain during upper Triassic times and, like the rippling movements on the curtain, in front of a stage, suggested that the Triassic curtain was just about to be raised. All this shows that no matter how disheartening the search for fossils in the Keuper may be it should be kept up unceasingly.

In the landscape today the low-lying ground occupied by the uppermost Keuper beds is usually bounded, especially on the east, by a low range of hills originating from the presence of the thin but more resistant limestones near the base of the Liassic clays. Though this feature lacks the impressiveness of the Cotswold scarps and the Chiltern hills, there lie hidden within its slopes rocks of especial interest. These may be seen exposed to view wherever the feature is truncated by the coastline as at Penarth, in Glamorganshire and at Watchet, Aust and Westbury along the Severn estuary; and also where it has been traversed by cuttings for canals and railways. In such situations a thin series of black and grey shales is seen interposed between the top of the Keuper and the bottom of the Lias. These yield well-preserved fossils of such marine bivalves as *Pteria contorta, Protocardia rhaetica, Modiola minima* and *Pecten valoniensis.* Precisely the same fossils are found in the topmost beds of the continental marine Trias which are well developed in the Rhaetian Alps. These rocks are accordingly called the Rhaetic Beds. Their presence in Britain shows that at long last the ages of arid climate had come to an end, and that the broad desert plains of Britain had become covered by the sea. Some have been tempted to picture that entry of the sea as a cataclysmic inundation. The rocks with their fossils, however, tell a quite different story.

A very complete sequence of Rhaetic deposits may be seen alongside the Severn Estuary at Watchet and Lilstock, where they have a total thickness of about 80 feet (c.p. Plate XIII*b*). Here the grey-green marls which crown the Keuper have yielded the fossil oyster *Ostrea bristovi*, a sure sign of their marine origin. The absence of any break in the sequence of deposits indicates the quietude with which the sea crept across the surface of the Keuper. This latter, however, was not a perfectly flat plain for slight earth-movements were throwing it into

a series of gentle undulations. Into the broad shallow depressions of the
downfolds the sea entered first and formed long estuaries along its
margins which stretched like fingers across the plains at other places as
well as Watchet. Meanwhile the crests of the upfolds were flattened by
weathering agencies and in their turn were covered by the sea and
buried under dark muddy deposits which ranged in thickness up to
45 ft. The denuded remnants of more ancient uplands could still
be seen as low plateaus and flat-topped islands. Owing to the presence
of the unconformity just described throughout much of the junction of
the Rhaetic with the Triassic, and to the fact that unlike the Triassic
and like the Jurassic it contains a marine fauna, it is customary to
regard the Rhaetic as the base of the Jurassic.

This quiet, but nevertheless comparatively quick, extension of the
sea was accompanied by a varied animal population. Some animals
were borne along as larvae by currents and settling down on the
floor completed their development in these new surroundings. Others
crawled slowly over the sea-floor. Yet others swam freely and followed
the sea wherever its waters flowed. At first conditions were a little
unfavourable and pelecypods like *Ostrea* and *Pteria* were stunted in
their growth. But, as the fossils testify, that phase soon passed away
and a normal fauna became established. This included the gastropods
Trochus, Cerithium and *Natica,* and nearly a score of lamellibranchs
such as *Gervillea, Lima, Arca,* in addition to those already mentioned.
These were not always uniformly distributed through the rocks. For
example *Chlamys (Pecten) valoniensis* occurs in such numbers in one
thin layer that this is known as the 'pecten bed'. In Yorkshire *Schizodus
ewaldi* is equally abundant in some sandy layers, but in this case it
is accompanied by crinoids, whose presence indicates clear water and
slow deposition. The abundance of fossils at such levels is not due
to the multitude of individuals living together at the particular spot
but to the fact that deposition of sediment was slow and the shells
of many generations remained unburied for a long time.

Among the other fossils found in these deposits are the solitary
coral *Montlivaltia;* many spines of sea-urchins; portions of the shelly
covering of *Pollicipes,* the goose barnacle; worm-tubes of *Serpula;* and
even the wings of insects that must have been carried out to sea by
the wind.

Not far above the base of the dark shales occurs a famous deposit
known as the bone bed. This is crowded with fossils among which

are numerous fish scales and teeth. At one time it was thought that these represented a massacre of marine creatures swept suddenly into highly saline lakes by tempestuous marine inundations. But geologists have now developed a more sober frame of mind when interpreting their observations. They have come to realise that all the evidence points, on the contrary, to a peaceful penetration by the sea.

The land that was being submerged was of very low relief, consequently aerial erosion was slow and the formation of sediment slight. In some localities gentle currents in the water wafted the fine sediments elsewhere but could not shift the shells, bones and scales. The remains of many generations then went on accumulating but remained unburied for considerable stretches of time. The bone beds represent such a time of slow sedimentation.

Charles Moore, the discoverer of the Rhaetic in Britain, was a native of Ilminster in Somerset. Like Miller, his interest in fossils was awakened when a casual blow of his hammer split open a nodule and revealed a fish hidden within. This find was the starting point of a large and valuable collection which became the nucleus of the City of Bath Museum. Moore, and others who followed in his trail, also found many vertebrate remains in these Rhaetic Beds. They consisted largely of teeth and scales; that is to say parts of the body which being covered with enamel, the most durable substance occuring in the body, had resisted the action of the digestive juices of carnivorous animals and also the solvent action of natural waters. These remains indicate the presence in this Rhaetic sea of very ancient types of fish, such as *Ceratodus* and *Palaeoniscus,* side by side with the new ganoid types *Lepidotus* and *Saurichthys;* as well as with *Squaloraia,* a relative of the mysterious deep-sea fish *Chimaera.* Bones of marine reptiles are also found including *Saurodesmus,* a primitive turtle; and jaws armed with crushing teeth belonging to *Psephoderma,* a distant relative of the *Plesiosaurs,* about which much more will be said later. Alongside of these were *Zanclodon* and *Gressylosaurus,* forerunners of that great Jurassic group of reptiles the Dinosaurs.

The Rhaetic sea as it extended encroached on a low limestone platform that fringed the Mendip islands. As so often happens in limestone districts, the rocks had been gashed with fissures formed by the prolonged solvent activity of rainwater seeping into and widening the joints. In 1858 Charles Moore in the course of his Rhaetic explorations came to the limestone quarries of Holwell on the flanks of the

Mendips near Frome. Here the quarry face was interrupted by dark vertical walls known to the quarrymen as 'dikes'. These really consisted, in part, of Rhaetic sediments which had accumulated in the fissures. Moore searched through them carefully and records that in one dike alone he found 70,000 teeth of *Acrodus* together with scales and teeth of 15 other kinds of fishes and of 9 reptiles. More amazing still were 29 specimens of small mammalian teeth to which he gave the name *Microlestes* (now *Microcleptus*). Several similar teeth had already been found by Boyd Dawkins in the Rhaetic of Watchet. Unlike the teeth of reptiles, but like those of modern mammals, these teeth had three roots and a large crown. The latter was furnished with cusps arranged in rows, for which reason *Microcleptus* is classed as an early member of the *Multituberculata*, an important order of Mammalia that flourished until the opening of Tertiary times. These little insectivorous mammals shared with the much larger reptiles the living spaces on the limestone islands and the lowlands that adjoined the Rhaetic sea.

CHAPTER 24

AMMONITES IN THE ASCENDANT

THE oncoming of the Rhaetic Sea introduced a long stretch of time during which much of the British area was covered by sea. This lay open to the south and east but was shut in on the north and west by an indented coastline that was on the whole dominated by the same highlands which now overlook the English lowlands. The early half of this stretch, known as the Jurassic period, was brought to a close by a brief general rise of level which converted the area into dry land. The later half, the Cretaceous period, was marked by renewed subsidence which continued until only the topmost portions of the highlands were left unsubmerged.

Magnificent exposures of the Jurassic rocks can be studied in the sea cliffs along the coastlines in the vicinity of Lyme Regis in Dorset and of Whitby in Yorkshire. Here the Lower or liassic portions of the rocks consist mainly of clay. In their Upper or oolitic portions the clay is interspersed with limestones. As these rocks range across the country from coast to coast the outcrops of the clay belts are occupied by lowland plains and vales and those of the limestones by hilly scenery often of great beauty. Inland exposures are mainly limited to artificial openings, to quarries, brick-pits and to cuttings for canals, roads and railways.

Here in the midst of the Jurassic outcrops William Smith lived for many years. The fact that even as a boy he was able to collect fossils is an indication of their abundance. In gardens and ploughed fields when the soil is washed by rain fossils seem to 'grow' out of the ground and their mere abundance and variety creates difficulty for the writer of such a book as this. During the last hundred years many books with such titles as 'The Shells of the Seashore' have been published for the guidance of amateurs. The beaches of the Jurassic seas were not less rich than those of the twentieth century; but into the following pages must be packed some sort of an account of the shells from the beaches, not of one century only, but from those of 300,000 centuries. Under these circumstances the most that can be done is to skim rapidly over the surface and, like a swallow, dip now here now there.

As on a modern beach every type of animal life is represented on the petrified beds and fossil beaches of those ancient seas. Here their remains have lain where they fell and have slept under a blanket of later rocks awaiting the kiss of the student collector to awaken them. Quite often the novice feels overwhelmed by the number and variety of his specimens and at times bewails the fact that he does not know their names. Let him at such times call to mind the fact that William Smith was for some time in like case. But, though at first he did not know their names, he communed with his fossils, and became so familiar with their every feature, that he carried in his memory a complete picture of each and of all the other kinds that were associated with it in the layer in which it was found. As we have already seen, after working in solitude he discovered a kindred spirit in the Revd. Benjamin Richardson who helped him to name his specimens and recognise their affinities. Without laying too much stress upon mere names it must be emphasised that they have one outstanding value; they can be recorded in a note-book and that is much less cumbersome to carry about than bags full of fossils collected from different exposures.

All this is preliminary to discussing a group of fossils which may be thought of as a kind of aristocracy among the invertebrates. These are so abundant and conspicuous that they have long been known to the uninitiated as 'snakestones', for according to one old legend they were once living snakes which became such a plague at Whitby that the Abbess laid a curse upon them; thereupon they lost their heads, curled up and died. In more sophisticated circles they are called ammonites after Ammon, an Egyptian animal headed deity whose horns were coiled like those of a ram. These fossils are present in such numbers throughout the Jurassic rocks and they evolved with such variety of form and ornamentation that they have attracted and still attract a lion's share of attention from students of geology. This has been abundantly justified on practical grounds. Either as living creatures or as dead shells they seem to have travelled, or been transported, quickly over great areas and consequently have proved to be very useful for the correlating of rock formations across considerable distances. By their means more than 40 zones have been recognised in the Jurassic rocks alone.

This special attention has also been justified on purely theoretical grounds by the valuable light they have thrown upon the principles of growth and evolution. Much of the credit for unravelling their complex story, in the course of this century, has been due to the labours of S. S. Buckman, L. F. Spath and W. J. Arkell. Out of the great multitude of different genera and species that these workers have recognised we must be content to let our eyes rest and our thoughts dwell upon only a very few typical examples.

One very attractive type characterises the bottom portions of the Lower Liassic rocks. It was known to earlier workers as *Arietites* (Aries = a ram) Fig. 1: 3). Each coil or whorl is quadrangular in cross section. Its flattened sides are ornamented with stout ridges or ribs which bend forward when they reach the outer or ventral surface of the whorl. This surface is marked by a keel, flanked by two grooves that run longitudinally along the coils. There are numerous ammonites which resemble *Arietites* more or less closely. To these different specific and even generic names have been given. It must suffice here to refer to them collectively as the Arietids. They exhibit striking differencies of shape in cross-section of the outer whorl, due largely to a tendency for this to increase in height and for its outer or ventral portion to become compressed. The climax of these two tendencies is reached in the genus *Oxynoticeras* in which the outer coil is very high and its inner or dorsal margin overlaps and completely hides the inner coils. The sides of the whorl converge towards the ventral margin where they meet in a sharp edge (oxy—sharp). The significance of this progressive change of form is unknown. It may possibly be a case of streamlining that would allow easy and rapid movement through water.

One important feature about ammonites is that, unlike trilobites and arthropods generally but like all shell bearing molluscs, they did not cast aside their shells as they grew but cemented the later formed portions on to the margins of the earlier; and thus, in the fully grown shell, every stage of growth from birth onwards is preserved and is available for study. Even if a novice does not know the name of his specimen he may spell out for himself some portions of its life-story. If he is prepared to sacrifice one of his poorer specimens he may cut it in two across the centre with a hacksaw. By grinding and polishing the cut surface he will see that the whorls change shape with age. In the innermost coils the shape is a depressed oval. In the intervening coils a keel appears and in the outer whorls the sections show some of the changes of shape described above for different genera. Such changes during individual growth give clues to the affinities of species with one another. It is worthwhile also to grind away one side of another specimen on a flagstone or on carborundum powder until the median plane is reached. When this surface is polished it will show a number of interesting and important internal structural features.

Two such sections are shown on Plate XVI*b*; one is of an ammonite, the other a nautilus. In both cases the shell is seen to be a long cone spirally coiled with its cavity divided by thin walls or septa into a succession of chambers. This and other features show how closely related these two types are to one another. Fortunately the latter type is represented today by the Pearly Nautilus of the eastern oceans, and it is reasonable to assume that a study of its structure and habits will give a fair picture of those of the ammonite.

Nautilus has a short stout body housed in the living chamber, the last and largest of the series. All the other chambers are filled with gas which helps to adjust the specific gravity of the whole to that of the water. The creature is thus able to float in the water with the body filled chamber below and the gas-filled chambers above. In the ammonite the living chamber is much longer and occupies a considerable section of the outermost coil. Consequently the opening of the shell with the protruding body faced not horizontally but upwards. That part of the body which corresponds with the foot or creeping surface of a snail is made up of two portions. The front surrounds the head hence the name cephalopod (cephalo = head). It carries a number of tentacles in a circle round the mouth which is armed with horny beak-like jaws. These tentacles can be used for seizing and holding food, worms and other small creatures. The hinder portion of the foot consists of two flat lobes which can be bent down to form a conical tube below the head. Through this the water, from the gill cavity can be forced out as a jet for propelling the animal from place to place As this conical tube is flexible the direction of movement can be changed according to need. No doubt the ammonites had a comparable freedom of movement. It seems certain that they could not descend to any great depth in the sea for the pressure of the water

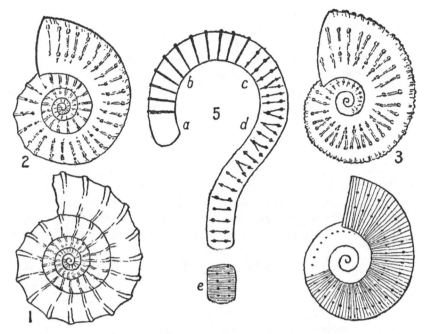

Fig. 15. THE CAPRICORN TYPE OF AMMONITE
AND SOME OF ITS ALLIES

1, A capricorn ammonite. 2, *Androgynoceras*. 3, *Liparoceras*. 4, *Tetraspidoceras*. 5, A diagram showing the stages in ornamentation passed through in the development of some of these ammonites. Which way did the sequence go in the course of evolution: a-e or e-a? For the answer consult the text.

above would have been sufficient to overcome that of the gas inside and to have crushed the shell. Interesting rock specimens which show the mark made by the shell when it touched down, before the recession of the water forced it to turn onto its side, support the description just given of its attitude when floating and indicates that some ammonites lived in shallow water.

In the upper portion of the Lower Lias there is a characteristic and quite different type, formerly called '*Aegoceras capricornus*', commonly referred to as the capricorn ammonite (Plate XV: *13* and Fig. 15). As its name implies this elegant little fossil resembles a goat's horn. It also consists fundamentally of a long thin conical shell coiled closely upon itself into a flat spiral in which all the coils are visible. The innermost coils, secreted in early life, have a smooth surface. The outer become ornamented with stout wrinkles or ribs which cross the sides and the outer or ventral surface. Careful collecting and studying have brought to light the fact that many of these little ammonites were not fully grown individuals but were the inner parts or early stages in the growth of larger ammonites called *Androgynoceras*. In these the outer whorls gradually increased in calibre and began to overlap the inner. In *Liparoceras* this swelling started earlier in development and in some specimens advanced so far that the inner coils were almost hidden from view. When these swollen coils were either accidentally or deliberately broken away it was found that there was no capricorn stage in their development; and that the smooth stage merged into one in which the ornamentation was made up of fine ribs each of which carried two tubercles. A few of these ribs might fork into two branches.

The story of the study of this group of ammonites serves to illustrate a great query which has given, and still gives, rise to much discussion or even controversy among palaeontologists and biologists.

In the early years of this century students believed that the stages seen in the development of *Androgynoceras* illustrated the evolutionary stages passed through by ammonites of this type in the course of their history; that the capricorn young reflected a corresponding adult stage in evolution; that the swelling of the coil and the tuberculation of the ribs represented similar changes in later history. Here then was,

---

PLATE XV

INVERTEBRATE JURASSIC FOSSILS

1-3. Lamellibranchs. 1. *Gryphaea*. Lias, Frethern, Gloucestershire. 2. *Trigonia*. Inf. Ool. Sherborne, Dorset. 3. *Modiola*. Great Oolite. 4-6. Brachiopods. 4. *Rhynchonella*. Anterior view of a species with only a few stout ribs but a strong median fold. 5. *Rhynchonella*, dorsal view showing the many fine ribs. 6. *Terebratula*. 7-9. Echinoderms. 7. *Echinobrissus*. Cornbrash. 8. *Holectypus*. Cornbrash. 9. *Hemicidaris*. Corallin. 10-13. Ammonites. 10. *Dactylioceras*. Lias. 11. *Stephanoceras*. Inf. Ool. 12. *Briarites*. Diameter 2 feet, Portlandian, Upper Jurassic. 13. A capricorn ammonite, diameter 2 inches. This consists of the inner whorls of *Androgynoceras*. Note the tendency for the outer coil to swell and develop two tubercles on each rib. (1, 5, 6, 9, 11, *W. Sutcliffe*. 2, 3, 4, 7, 8, 10, 12, *H.M. Geol. Survey*)

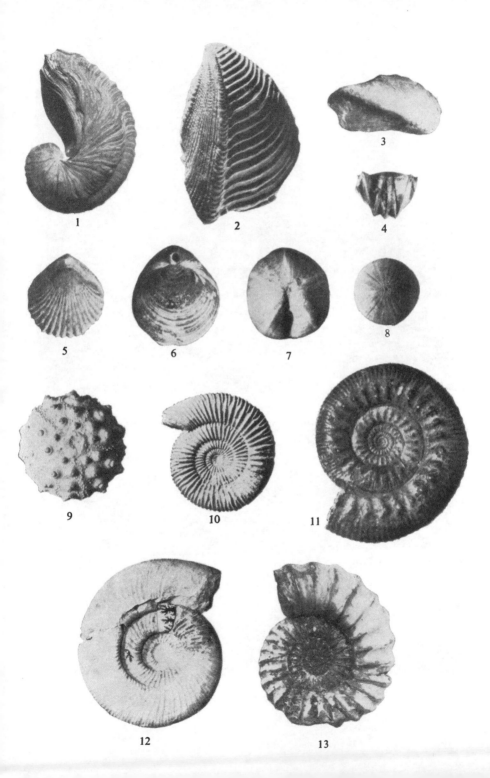

what seemed to be, a typical example of the principle that the development of the individual tended to recapitulate, at least in some characters the successive adult phases in the evolution of the race. According to this principle, known as *palingenesis*, new characters put in their first appearance in late life in succeeding generations.

During the second quarter of this century Spath produced evidence to show that, if careful account be taken of the precise order of occurrence of the fossils in the rocks, the story their development told was quite the reverse of that just described, for in actual fact the *Liparoceras* type was on the whole earlier than *Androgynoceras* and this in turn earlier than *Capricornus*. So then, it seemed, that the capricornus-like young of *Androgynoceras* was not a relic of an ancestral phase but was an anticipation of a phase which blossomed out fully in adult individuals of later generations. Here then was another principle at work known as *proterogenesis*, indications of which have been already noted among the Graptolites. It is natural to ask whence came *Liparoceras?* Spath suggested that its origin was to be found in the less perfectly known ammonite *Tetraspidoceras*. It should be noted, however, that this form is much less inflated than its presumed descendants. This fact suggests that the liparoceratid condition arose palingenetically out of one of the many serpenticone strains that occur in the Lower Lias.

The overwhelming enthusiasm in earlier years for the principle of palingenesis was now followed by a reaction, which sometimes went to the other extreme and led to the declaration by some workers

---

PLATE XVI

a. SEA CLIFFS, LYME REGIS

View looking S.W. from Church Cliff towards Pinhay showing the characteristic appearance of the Blue Lias, mainly Bucklandi zone. (*H. M. Geol. Survey*)

b. MEDIAN SECTIONS OF TWO CEPHALOPOD FOSSILS

Left. Section of *Nautilus* showing the internal chambers separated by septa. These are concave on the front side. The siphonal canal passes through the centres of the septa and chambers. (*A. Ferguson*)

Right. Section of an ammonite also showing the chambers. The septa tend to be convex in front. Here and there traces of the siphonal canal are seen passing through the outer or ventral rims of the septa. (*A. Ferguson*)

In both sections the chambers are lined or partly filled with calcite crystals. Some however are filled with consolidated mud.

that 'palingenesis is dead.' However the more sober appraisal of known facts which is gaining ground indicates that, though proterogenesis seems to play a great part in evolution, the frequent occurrence of palingenetic phenomena is well authenticated. A fuller account of the factors covered by these two terms is out of the question in these pages. This topic is very fully and judically discussed by De Beer (1958). He, however, uses the term *repetition* where the palaeontologist uses *recapitulation*. From the dictionary stand point the latter seems to be the more correct usage.

The fossil hunter returning to town from the beaches near Whitby finds himself looking with envious eyes at ammonites displayed for sale in curio shops. Without appearing to encourage him to step in and buy one it may be remarked that even university professors have been known to enrich their departmental collections from this source; for the natives have the great advantage that they live on the spot and can reap good harvests when the winter storms have done their work of chiselling fossils out of the cliffs.

Many of the fossils that are displayed come from the Upper Lias. Two of the commonest among them are *Hildoceras*, named after St. Hilda, Abbess of Whitby Abbey, and *Dactylioceras* (Fig. 1: *2, 5* and Plate XV: *10*). The Hildoceratids, like the Arietids, have coils that are quadrangular in cross section; but they are higher and more compressed from side to side. The ventral margin has a keel but no grooves and the sides are ornamented with slender ribs. The inner portions of these are short and straight but the outer are long and curved, so that the rib as a whole is sickle shaped. In these ammonites the coils undergo changes of shape similar to those already described for the Arietids. These culminate in the genus *Hyperlioceras*, which bears a superficial resemblance to *Oxynoticeras*. When creatures descended from different ancestral stocks, bear such resemblances to one another they are described as *homeomorphs*. Before the phenomenon of homeomorphy was discovered collectors made many mistakes of indentification,

---

PLATE XVII

EXTINCT AQUATIC REPTILES

a. Ichthyosaurus tenuirostris. Extreme width of specimen 6 feet 3 inches. Lias, Whitby.   (*H. M. Geol. Survey*)

b. Plesiosaurus dolichoderus. Length of specimen 5 feet 9 inches. (*H. M. Geol. Survey*)

PLATE XVIII. THE WEALDEN SCENE

In the centre is *Iguanodon*, a large Dinosaur, with three-toed footprints on the ground close by. Near the tip of its tail is a clump of Horsetails, *Equisetites*, and behind it are two cycadeoids, *Bennettites*. In the lower right corner is the spined dinosaur *Polacanthus* surrounded by tree ferns and ordinary ferns. Above are two coniferous trees, *Sequoia* (right) and *Pinus* (left). The great dinosaur *Brontosaurus*, with its long neck, is seen coming up out of the water, and in the air overhead is the flying reptile *Pterodactylus*. On the left of the picture are shown the massive trunk of *Pinus excelsis* and the less massive trunk of *Araucaria*.

(*H.M. Geol. Survey*)

and even now beginners must be on the alert. In the most advanced Hildoceratids the ornamentation disappeared and the shell became smooth. This feature led to the creation of the term Lioceratid for those many smooth forms which swarmed in the Inferior Oolite waters.

In the Dactylioceratids the coils were round in cross section, as in the capricorn ammonite. Because of the absence of a keel and grooves along the ventral surface the coils of such ammonites are described as round-ventered. In dactylioceratids the ribs forked into two branches, both of which continued across the ventral surface. Notwithstanding the resemblances of some of the later to the earlier ammonites, they were not the direct descendants of these but belonged to separate offshoots of a common ancestral stock, which lived in Mediterranean waters. Evidence from continental rocks indicates that ammonites migrated in successive waves from this ancestral home and, evolving as they travelled, arrived in Britain already possessed of new and distinctive characters. Sometimes these were obscured by a close superficial similarity to the earlier ammonites. The present-day expert, however, with his deeper knowledge of underlying details, and of the principles described above, has been able to separate these homeo-morphs from one another. Of these the stephanoceratids, from the middle oolites, and the perisphinctids from the upper oolites should be mentioned (Plate XV: *10-12*).

In concluding this all too brief survey of the ammonites reference should be made to the two genera *Phylloceras* and *Lytoceras*, examples of which have been found at widely separated levels in both Jurassic and Cretaceous rocks. They remained very constant in their characters throughout and represented two persistent and very stable stocks which have been traced back to the types *Monophyllites* and *Lytoceras* that survived the late Triassic holocaust. These two great stocks gave rise at different times to a number of branches of less stable ammonite types which eventually wandered into the British area.

CHAPTER 25

OYSTERS AND THEIR ALLIES

AMMONITES, as the aristocrats among the invertebrates, tend to draw to themselves the lion's share of the enthusiasm and attention of students. Unfortunately this surfeit of good things is liable to spoil their appetite for the more ordinary fare provided by the seemingly less attractive groups of fossils. Consequently the interest and even the beauty of these may be overlooked for, though they may not have the special value possessed by the ammonites as indicators of time and of stratigraphical level, they may throw much light both on the course of evolution and upon past physical environment.

The oysters and their allies are also mollusca and belong to the lamellibranchs or the pelecypods which, with gastropods were entering into the full flood of their evolutionary careers, and their fossil remains are often more abundant than those of other groups of invertebrates.

These two classificatory names, pelecypod and gastropod imply two quite distinct modes of life. The former live normally with the front part of the shell sunk in the soft mud or sand of the sea-floor. On the underside of the creature's body is a powerful ploughshare-shaped muscular organ (pelecy=plough) the foot which can protrude between the two valves into the mud or sand and by alternately enlarging and extending its tip is used for dragging the shell, with a ploughing action, from place to place. In the gastropods, on the other hand, the foot has a flat under surface by which the animal can cling to or crawl over hard surfaces. Their favourite habitats are therefore along rocky coasts. In both orders the shell is little more than a protective covering for the body and only dimly reflects the evolutionary changes that even these animals have undergone in past ages.

Nevertheless in pelecypods the hinge, which connects the two valves of the shell, exhibits a series of fundamental changes and on that account furnishes a basis for a sound system of classification. The oldest and most primitive shells have no hinge. At its first appearance this consisted of a large number of small teeth and notches arranged in series along the upper margin of each valve. This arrangement has persisted in a few shells of several genera as for example *Nuculana* from the Jurassic and in its modern relative *Nucula* (Plate XXI: *18*). In the majority, however, it was changed by the progressive disappearance of teeth from both ends of the series and by the enlargement and slight reorientation of those that were left, with the result that several relatively stable patterns of hinge eventually emerged.

Independently of this evolution of the hinge many modifications of shellshape took place which were more or less directly associated with the creature's mode of life. These modifications were repeated at different stages in the history of the order and consequently homeomorphs are common. Mistakes in identification can, however, usually be avoided by making a careful examination of the hinge.

As just indicated the bivalves have always been essentially benthic or bottom-living animals and only rarely, as for example in the case of the scallop (*Pecten*), have they been able to rise from the floor and swim through the water in short spurts (Fig. 19: *20, 25*). In order to do this, water is taken in along the margins of the valves and then expelled forcibly through openings near the hinge—an interesting example of jet propulsion. It may be assumed that this was the case also for fossil types having similarly shaped shells combined with similar openings. These shells occur at a number of levels in the Jurassic rocks, as for example in the Liassic ironstones of Cleveland where they are sometimes so abundant that the layers in which they are found are known as 'Pecten seams'. Some species of *Lima*, a relative of this genus, exceeded all other Jurassic bivalves in size.

The study of living lamellibranchs shows that, though the shell is little more than a protective covering, it is remarkably responsive to the creature's mode of life. The forms their shells assume have their parallel among fossil shells. Typically the shell is sharp and wedge-like around its margin, except in the neighbourhood of the hinge. This feature is in itself an adaptation to the necessity for ploughing through the soft surface deposits on the sea-floor. Superposed on this general shape are many differences of ornamentation. In *Thracia* this consists of little more than growth-lines. In *Cardinia* there are broad ribs running parallel to these lines. In *Trigonia* there may be a combination of radiating ribs behind and of concentric ribs or rows of tubercles elsewhere, which gives to the whole an attractive appearance (Plate XV: *2*). *Cardinia* is abundant in some layers of the Lower Lias. *Trigonia* is the main constituent of the Trigonia Grits of the Inferior Oolite limestones. It was a long time thought to be extinct but at the end of the last century it was discovered in Australian waters, yet another example of a 'living fossil'.

Owing to the ease with which sand is shifted about by waves and currents, seaweeds rarely become established in sandy surroundings. But among bivalves the problem of living in such unstable conditions has sometimes been solved by the development of a semiglobular shell, as for example in the living cockle (*Cardium*) (Plate XXI: *16*) and the liassic *Protocardium*. In *Hippopodium*, from the Lower Lias, both valves are of enormous thickness and, as seen in outline, together resemble a horse's hoof as the name implies.

Some fossil bivalves, such as *Pholadomya*, from the Oolite limestones, exhibit features which in living forms are associated with the habit of burrowing. Its valves gape at the hinder end thus providing an exit for a stout tubular prolongation of the mantle known as the siphon. Though the animal descends to appreciable depths in sand and silt this organ stretches up to the surface and thus it is able to draw in and expel the water it requires for bringing food and for breathing. *Lithophagus* belongs to a special type of burrower for it bores into solid rock, coral or thick shells. It furnishes an interesting example of the triumph of living over dead substance. In the act of boring it rotates its shell from side to side around its long axis and by this means the front of the shell abrades the rock but is itself constantly renewed by growth. This rotary movement necessitates a cylindrical form for the shell. Having once started boring at one spot it never moves elsewhere but penetrates more and more deeply as it grows in size. It can therefore never escape through the small entrance it made at first and thus makes itself a prisoner for life (Fig. 19: *23*). The presence of such shells or their borings at any level in the strata is valuable evidence that there has been a temporary cessation of sedimentation during a period of time at least as long as the life of this lowly toiler.

The common mussel (*Mytilus*) illustrates another sedentary mode of life. It lives in large numbers attached to the rocks near to the tide-line where it is subjected to breaking waves and backswilling water. The form of the shell is neatly streamlined for escaping the drag of the water. Close inspection shows that it is anchored by means of a bundle of brown threads, called the byssus. These are secreted by a gland in the underside of the foot and where they emerge the edge of the shell is notched. Among Jurassic fossils the shells of *Modiola* (Plate XV: *3*), *Pteria, Avicula* and others possess similar notches. This fact combined with the shape of their shells indicates that they also were anchored in the same way.

Oysters are also attached, but by means of cement. Inspired by epicurean delights, more attention than usual has been bestowed on these bivalves and their life story has been studied in much detail. In this way it has been learned that the creature starts off as a minute larva. At first this swims and drifts freely about in the sea but eventually it settles down on the floor. By means of two mantle-like folds on either side of the body, it secretes two valves like any normal lamellibranch. Presently the shell falls over on to its left side and as it grows the corresponding mantle-fold, while secreting the valve, simultaneously cements it to the surface upon which it is resting. This process may go on for a short or long time with the result that the area of attachment varies considerably in different individuals. The fully grown shell is always more or less flattened and irregular in shape.

The origin of the oysters is still an unsolved mystery. They appeared first in Britain just as the Triassic period was merging into Jurassic. Their great abundance at many levels throughout the rocks of subsequent periods suggests that they might supply material for a relatively complete account of some part of nature's evolutionary story.

Oysters are, however, less attractive than most other types of shells and are bewilderingly variable. For these reasons they tend to be passed over by collectors. Nevertheless even they are worthy of careful study. Though the palaeontologist cannot himself carry out genetic experiments with his material and thus decide whether or not any given variation is heritable (genotypic) he has before him the results of nature's own experiments on unnumbered generations. If in his carefully collected series of fossils from successive levels he finds that some variations are not only transmitted but undergo progressive change he may legitimately conclude that they are genotypic and not merely phenotypic.

The dominant variable in *Ostrea* is the shape of the shell. In outline this may be circular, elongate oval or even triangular, symmetrical or excentric. Normally the shell is flat but the left valve may be more or less convex. As already seen the area of attachment has a great range in size.

Though the shells as a whole vary considerably they do so only within strict and constant limits. This is indicated by the fact that, apart from size, the varieties met with in collections of *Ostrea irregularis* from the lowest beds of the Lias can all be matched from among those cast up in such abundance at the present day on some beaches. This constancy in variability, if such an apparently contradictory phrase may be allowed to pass, can only mean that the genetic make-up of the long succession of oyster populations through the aeons of post-triassic time has been broad and stable.

From time to time, however, for reasons not yet understood, some restraining influence was withdrawn and sections of the stock started off on a sequence of changes leading to the development of new series of species and even genera. An illuminating piece of work, done by Trueman showed that within the early half of the Lower Lias one such series starting as *Ostrea irregularis* culminated in *Gryphaea incurva* (*arcuata*) (Plate XV: *1*). Fossils of these are so common that any collector may gather enough specimens to illustrate the main steps in the series. In some specimens of this oyster the left valve was slightly concavo-convex. During a stretch of time lasting some 250,000 years or so, the factors which controlled this feature strengthened in influence and extended to all sections of successive generations, with the result that the curvature became more and more widespread and affected *all* the varieties; and also increased until the left umbo curled over towards the right valve. It did not, however, as some have stated, ever press upon and lock this valve even in the oldest individuals.

A study of the umbonal portions of advanced shells of *Gryphaea incurva* is exceptionally interesting. This is the part which is formed in early life and, when examined in a large number of specimens, a striking fact emerges. It is found that they exhibit closely similar ranges of variation in shape of outline, symmetry, curvature and size of area of attachment to those seen in the original *O. irregulare* stock; an excellent example of Palingenesis on a wholesale scale. This shows that the successive communities studied were indeed linked together genetically and that the populations of which they were samples interbred freely.

This increase of curvature, continuing over a long period of time, is a very good example of a TREND. This term was introduced by

W. D. Lang who showed that this gryphaeoid trend was repeated several times during the Jurassic period in later offshoots of the oyster stock. A similar tendency, leading to the production of homeomorphs, has been noted above in the ammonites and earlier among the late palaeozoic corals. With the gryphaeas also the later homeomorphs are sufficiently distinctive in some details for them to have some value as time indicators and as zonal indices. The term *iterative evolution* has been suggested for this recurrence of the same trend at different periods in contradistinction to parallel evolution shown in more or less contemporaneous stocks as already noted among the diplograptids which lead to various monograptids (v. Fig. 5).

W. D. Lang also showed that this *Ostrea* stock provided starting points for other trends. Thus the slightly asymmetrical twist seen in some varieties of *Ostrea* became strongly developed in *O. acuminata*. Combined with a gryphaeoid curvature this produced the genus *Exogyra* which lasted through the late Jurassic and, combined with an increase in size, culminated in the large species of the Lower Cretaceous.

Though bivalve shells as a whole are characterised by what has sometimes been mistakenly spoken of as 'merely adaptive modifications' the examples just described show that over long stretches of time they have exhibited changes which must be regarded as deeply seated and genuinely evolutionary; changes which must reflect some corresponding alteration in genetic control.

CHAPTER 26

FOSSIL DEPUTIES

LOOKING at the face of a cliff or a quarry is like looking at a closed book lying on a table. The edges of many layers of rock are seen piled one upon another, like the leaves of the book. We may, by picking away at the edges of the layers, find fossils now and then; but these are merely odd syllables or words; small fragments, torn from the leaves bearing meaningless traces of a thrilling story that is hidden away in the volume. It is only when the book lies open, when the layer whose edge we have chipped is uncovered that an appreciable portion of the story is revealed. Occasionally a collector is fortunate enough to strike an exposure where some industrial undertaking has done this uncovering for him.

Away down in Wiltshire there was one such exposure near to that lovely little Cotswold town, Bradford on Avon. Resisting the temptation to explore the beauties of the town we may wander along the canal side in the direction of Trowbridge and reflect on the fact that William Smith sometimes traversed this same path. Presently we come upon a flat space which in his time was hidden under a covering of clay suited for puddling the floor of the canal and making it watertight. Even at the opening of this century the clay was still being used for the same purpose, and the pit whence it was being dug was a paradise for fossil collectors. The clay has now all been removed and its fossils have been dispersed to museums in Bristol and many other places. As the student studies them lying on exhibit, with their faces washed and each carefully docketed, he can imagine the thrill felt by past generations of collectors when they gazed for the first time at the floor of that little pit and read in detail the story of one eventful moment in the primeval history of the west country. The limestone surface upon which the clay rested was the floor of a shallow sea swarming with a rich variety of animals enveloped in clear water and bathed in sunshine. There they lived and dying left their remains upon the limestone surface to rest in peace for ages until William Smith and his many followers rescued them from oblivion.

Almost the first fossil that caught the eye was a stone lily, *Apiocrinus*, familiarly known as the 'pear encrinite'. Its tall cylindrical stem was built up of numerous beadlike rings lying one upon another. Near the top it became pear-shaped owing to a rapid increase in the size of the rings. The topmost ring carried five branching arms, the lower portions of which formed part of the pear.

Along with this crinoid lived many brachiopods of two kinds known to early collectors as *Terebratula* and *Rhynchonella* respectively (Plate XV: *4-6*). In the former the larger or ventral valve has a prominent umbo the apex of which appears blunted because it is perforated by a hole through which in life a fleshy stalk passed and anchored the animal to some solid object. Thus, like the encrinite, these creatures spent their lives fixed in one spot; a fact which emphasises the clarity of the water and its freedom from sediments that might have engulfed them. The fossil brachiopods that lay around on the quarry floor were sufficiently numerous to represent the remains of many generations. Some were encrusted with various kinds of Polyzoa with their minute chambers arranged in single file or crowded together in compact circular colonies. All these features combined to produce the impression of peaceful conditions lasting for a considerable time. Then, almost suddenly, calamity came in the form of clouds of mud which, settling down, buried all these remains under several yards of clay.

The passing of time at this spot, as indeed at many other levels and localities where similar conditions existed, must be pictured not by the thickness of rock layers but in terms of the life stories of many generations of creatures that lived during an interval when little or no sedimentation took place. Behind all this lies a lesson. It is that those who go about merely picking up and choosing the best specimens they can see miss much of the glamour of the story fossils can tell. Even poor specimens have their extrinsic as well as intrinsic value. Moreover, the value even of the best specimens may be greatly enhanced if the collector carefully notes their precise location and any details that might throw light upon the conditions in which the creatures lived. Only by doing this will he be able to make his full contribution to the great task of reconstructing the history of the earth and of understanding the cause and the course of evolution.

Other elements in this Bradford fauna include occasional samples of the sea-urchin *Cidaris* and of the attached bivalve *Avicula (Oxytoma)*. The absence of ammonites is noteworthy and accords with their general scarcity in the limestones among which the Bradford clay is situated. This fact serves as a reminder that a zone ammonite is after all only one member of the fauna which, in its absence, assumes its stratigraphical function of index. Thus for example the Bradford clay fauna as a whole has been found also at many other places between the Mendips and Oxfordshire. Though the clay itself may be absent the fauna is often present in the upper part of the Great Oolite limestone and the lower part of the Forest Marble. This shows that, while at Bradford deposition halted, it continued more or less rapidly elsewhere and sediments accumulated to a thickness of about 50 feet, a figure which gives some impression of the length of time which elapsed while the fossils assembled on that quarry floor.

The identification of a fauna depends, however, upon the determination of the various species which compose it. Some like the pear encrinite *Apiocrinus parkinsoni*, though very distinctive belong to a group, in this case the crinoids, which is rare at other stratigraphical levels. Others again, like *Terebratula* and *Rhynchonella*, belong to the brachiopods, a group which has so many representatives in other strata that they can be linked together in a time series the members of which may deputize for the ammonites when these are absent.

Brachiopods of the Terebratula type vary in general outline from being almost circular to being oval or even triangular. The profile also varies from plano-convex to spheroidal. The surface of the shell is smooth and marked only by lines of growth. But *T. coarctata*, a characteristic member of the fauna, is exceptional in that its surface is ornamented with a delicate network.

In young terebratulids the junction between the two valves lies in a flat plane and shows in profile as a straight line. As growth proceeded the margins of the two valves became wavy with a median trough and two side-crests, as in *T. (Epithyris) bathonica*. With advancing knowledge these external features have proved inadequate for precise identification and attention has been turned increasingly to the important task of elucidating the internal structure. Normally the mud in which the shell was buried, entered the shell through the opening for the stalk or between the edges of the valves when these gaped, and the filling hardened into rock. Occasionally this did not happen and consequently the fossil was left hollow. By carefully opening the cavity of such a specimen the internal details may be examined. But such examples are rare and recourse must usually be had to cutting the solid fossil into a series of thin slices or to grinding it away slowly taking care to photograph or draw successive polished surfaces. This procedure has resulted in the discovery of many internal structural details. Upon the basis of these many species formerly included in *Terebratula* have been shown to belong to other new genera and species. This increased precision has made it possible to use these brachiopods as valuable adjuncts to the ammonites for defining and correlating subdivisions of the Oolite rocks as well as for evolutionary studies.

The name *Rhynchonella* suggests a little snout and refers to the small and pointed appearance of the umbo of the ventral valve. Here also the margins of the valves are folded into one broad central crest. In addition, however, the shell is delicately pleated, a feature which makes it an attractive little object. This type lacks most of the internal structures found in the terebratulids, but on the inside surface marks have been discovered which were made by the attached ends of the muscles that opened and closed the shell. S. S. Buckman, who did so much valuable work upon the ammonites, turned his attention to the brachiopods also and devised an ingenious method for studying these markings. He found that by judiciously heating the shell in a flame he could flake it away without damaging the impressions left by the muscle markings upon the stony cast. This led to the discovery of details by which to distinguish new genera and species.

Though the Jurassic brachiopod fauna consisted mainly of forms related to these two main types there were others which, as long ago as Middle Mesozoic times, merited the designation 'living fossils', for even then they were the sole relics of types which reached and passed their climax long ages before. One of these, *Spiriferina* was the last of the great race of spirifers which attained their climax in Middle and Late Palaeozoic times. This genus includes a series of species— *S. walcotti, S. venustia,* etc., which were limited in their vertical range and therefore also have value for the correlation of strata. *Lingula* and *Discina* were survivors from still earlier times but they are with us still and, being comparatively unchanged, are examples of types in which evolution has been for long ages almost at a standstill.

CHAPTER 27

CORALS AND THEIR
ASSOCIATES

A T the opening of this century the student of zoology, entering the laboratory found himself confronted day after day and week in week out by a succession of dead specimens ranging from earthworms to rabbits. These he dissected until he was familiar with every hidden recess in their bodies. In the lecture theatre he caught a vision of the value of applying the method of comparison to the results of his laboratory studies, and thereby increased his understanding of the changes of structure by which one type gave rise to another.

In recent years, however, there has been a revival of the methods of Darwin and the other great naturalists who concerned themselves mainly with the living animal, its habits and its living conditions. Fossils are all dead and he who studies them therefore seems to be outside the pale of this revival; but this is not entirely true.

From time to time creatures turn up in the fishing net or are seen by the hunter which have been dubbed 'living fossils'. Having long outlived all their relatives they portray for us almost exact replicas in flesh and blood of creatures that were thought to have become extinct long ago. But even they do not necessarily throw light upon the habits and habitats of the fossils themselves for in most cases they seem to have survived by fleeing from the arena to some place of refuge in the depth of the sea or in the heart of the great forests. As suggested in previous chapters, however, indications of the homes and way of living may be fossilised not only in shell forms but in the rocks themselves for those to interpret who have been on the outlook. This method of approach, which has developed in recent years, is the palaeontological equivalent of that zoological revival.

Some types of animals, especially among the freely moving vertebrates and the arthropods, cannot be relied upon as indicators of any particular kind of environment. This seems not to be the case for the coral-forming polypes. These seem to live abundantly only in seas which have an average temperature above 20° centigrade and a salinity slightly above normal; in depths of less than 25 fathoms and situations where the sea-floor, owing to the clarity of the water and its freedom from sediments, is bathed in sunshine. This last condition is imposed upon them by the presence in their tissues of algae living symbiotically with them. From the abundance of corals and even reefs in the Oolite Limestones, which range from Dorset to Lincolnshire, it may be inferred that during Jurassic times such conditions prevailed over south and central England.

As pointed out by W. J. Arkell, though coral rock is there widespread it is found only in sheets up to 10 feet thick. This is in marked contrast to the modern reefs some of which go down to depths more than ten times as great. In the Jurassic Oolites these sheets are separated by normal limestones that evidently represent times during which the depth of the sea was too great for the growth of coral reefs.

Among the liassic rocks only one patch rich in reef corals is known. This was found by A. E. Trueman among the lower zones in Glamorganshire. There the coral polyps must have lived in shallow waters where the sea washed round islands of Carboniferous limestone. These were too small to supply enough sediment to cloud the surrounding waters. Here corals flourished upon a limestone floor cluttered with boulders. Everywhere else the liassic sea was befogged with sediment coming from the mainland in such quantities as to prevent the growth of coral reefs. Here and there, when the waters were temporarily free from sediments, the simple coral *Montlivaltia* grew (Fig. 16: *1, 2*).

In a general way *Montlivaltia* bore the same relationship to other Jurassic corals as did *Zaphrentis* to the carboniferous corals, for it also illustrates the simple structural basis from which many compound reef-building corals developed. There was, however, a fundamental difference between these two simple types. *Zaphrentis* was biradially symmetrical with its septa arranged in four quadrants (Fig. 12: *2, 3*). *Montlivaltia* had a six-rayed symmetry which was maintained no matter how many septa were later interposed between the first six. Hitherto no satisfactory evidence has been forthcoming which directly links the Mesozoic with the Palaeozoic types. It is unlikely that the former descended directly from the latter. As already suggested they may have arisen from a strain of coelenterate polyps which, like the modern sea-anemones, did not secrete lime, but first began to do so, and to build up coral, in the early part of the Mesozoic era. On the other hand there is evidence that the embryo of *Zaphrentis* had a six-rayed symmetry. Such embryos may have foreshadowed, proterogenetically the Post-Palaeozoic type of coral.

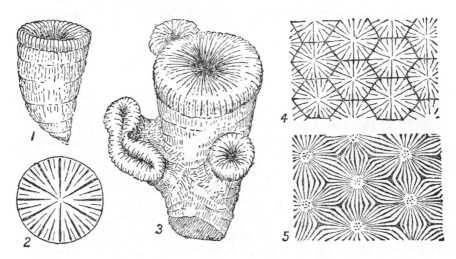

Fig. 16. CORALS FROM THE JURASSIC SEA

1, *Montlivaltia*. 2, Cross section of *Montlivaltia* showing the six rayed arrangement of the septa. 3, *Thecosmilia* showing a simple branching colony of the same type. 4, A section of *Isastraea* a compound coral in which the individual corallites are separated by definite walls. 5, A similar section of *Thamnastraea* in which the separating walls have disappeared and the septa of the adjoining corallites flow into one another.

By the beginning of Liassic times this new type of coral had already made good progress towards forming compound colonies; for corals of this type were found in Glamorganshire. *Thecosmilia* was a simple branching colony with only a few corallites. *Isastraea* had numerous corallites so closely packed against and fused with one another as to form a solid imperfect sphere with a coarse honeycomb surface pattern. The same genera are found also in the reefs of the Inferior, the Great and the Corallian Oolite limestones. In these a further evolutionary stage is found in *Thamnastrea* in which the thin wall that separates the adjoining corallites has disappeared and the septa flow across the boundaries; thus giving to the surface of the coral a pattern of considerable beauty (Fig. 16).

It was pointed out by Arkell that ammonites are usually absent from formations in which corals are common. This is an interesting example of the varying environmental needs of different creatures that suggests a brief enquiry into the other fossil organisms found in association with corals and presumably preferred the same general living conditions.

The coral reef occupied only one belt of the sea-floor which, as it sloped away from the shoreline down to greater depths, furnished a variety of minor habitats. Across this slope was spread the debris produced from the dead parts of the reef broken up and pulverised by both the mechanical action of waves and the solvent action of the water. To this may perhaps be added the work done by those fishes which possessed powerful jaws and strong crushing teeth which enabled them to browse on the living garment—polyps, molluscs and echinoids —of the coral reefs. This debris was distributed far down the slope upon which other animals lived, singly or in communities. Some of these lived also on the reef and their fossil remains are found in the reef rocks. Others are found mainly or exclusively in the rocks formed from the debris.

The subsidiary habitats within this beautiful and varied underworld of the sea, with its floor of deposits and its carpet of seaweeds enlivened by creeping and swimming animals, were not static, for the whole area was subjected to gentle up and down movements. This necessarily brought about a horizontal shifting of different habitats to and fro across the several localities. At any one of these there was consequently a sequence of conditions varying from shallow to deep water and back again; accompanied by corresponding changes of inhabitants, now corals and gastropods, then bivalves or brachiopods or sea-urchins or even stone-lilies.

This is not merely a fanciful live television description for in any one of those localities there may be today a quarry, a cutting, or a cliff, in which the succession of rock layers, with their contained fossils, may be studied and a mental film constructed showing the successive changes of scenic conditions and of the inhabitants in that ancient coral sea. None of this is perceived by the collector who merely hurries round collecting 'good' specimens. Nature tells her story only to those who sometimes 'stand and stare.'

As already indicated sea-urchins or echinoids formed one constituent in this complicated association. Some lived in the reef itself,
some in groups out on the submarine slope. Occasionally one such
group may be dramatically displayed as, for example, in a quarry at
Calne in Wiltshire where the Corallian Oolite was worked during the
latter part of the nineteenth century. In it the surface of one layer
of rock was seen to be crowded with hundreds of urchins:—*Cidaris,
Hemicidaris, Acrosalenia, Stomechinus* and so on. Evidently when that
layer was being formed sedimentation was temporarily at a standstill.
Meanwhile the generations of urchins followed one another and their
limy skeletons or tests lay for a while unburied. Normally, however,
sedimentation proceeded simultaneously and the tests were distributed
through the layers in succession as they were being formed.

Cidaris florigemma, the full name of one of these urchins, implies
that it is an object of great beauty. In shape it is like a sphere slightly
flattened above and below (cp. Plate XX: *3*). It consists of a regular
mosaic of polygonal calcareous plates arranged in 20 vertical rows
radiating from the apex, where the vent is situated. After descending
the sides they converge towards the mouth in the middle of the base.
These rows are in pairs. In alternate pairs the plates are pierced by
minute pores through which, in life, the tubular organs that functioned
as minute limbs emerged. At the end of each was a sucker by means of
which the creature could hold on to any solid object and drag itself
along. The surfaces of the other plates are beset with tubercles. In
ordinary urchins each of these carries a long sharp spine; but in *Cidaris*
this was stout and club-shaped and its surface highly decorated.

In all Echinodermata this armour-like framework, which protects
the body, lies wholly within and is interpenetrated by living substance,

---

PLATE XIX
LOWER CRETACEOUS BELEMNITES

1. *Acroteuthis lateralis.* 2. *Acroteuthis subquadratus.* 3. *A. subquadratus.* This
specimen was found split in two longitudinally. Note the alveolus, a conical
cavity which during life enclosed a chambered shell, the phragmocone.
4. *Hibolites jaculoides,* still attached to its clay matrix. At the upper end the
phragmocone is seen in the alveolus. 5 and 6. *Hibolites jaculoides,* two
varities. 7 and 8. *Neohibolites ewaldi.* Slim variety and stout spindle shaped
variety. 1-6 from Speeton Clay, Yorks. 7, 8, from Sutterby Marl. Lincs.
(*Palaeontographical Society Monograph*)

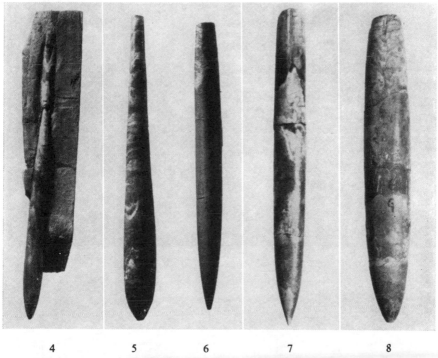

1   2   3

4   5   6   7   8

1   2

3   4   5

6   7   8   9

as is the case also with our own bones. In echinoids it is therefore not called a 'shell' but a 'test'. In it each plate grows as the body grows and new plates are inserted at the apex of each column.

Hemicidaris is only less beautiful than *Cidaris* (Plate XV: 9). Its hemispherical shape is due to an extensive flattening of the lower surface.

Many kinds of radially symmetrical or *regular echinoids* are found in the Jurassic rocks. Associated with them are others exhibiting varying degrees of bilateral symmetry. These are known as *irregular echinoids*. In *Holectypus*, while the mouth remains in the centre of the underside, the vent has shifted from the apex towards the hinder margin (Plate XV: 7, 8). It would seem therefore that while *Cidaris* and the regular echinoids moved freely in all directions, *Holectypus* and the other irregular echinoids moved usually only in one direction. In *Clypeus* (the pundstone) of the Inferior Oolite the mouth, having moved forward from its central position, was also excentric. This loss of radial symmetry was accompanied externally by a reduction of the spines and the tuberculate ornamentation; and internally by the degeneration and disappearance of the complex jaw mechanism carrying 5 teeth and known as Aristotle's lantern.

Though among the Mollusca the free swimming Cephalopods are usually absent from this association the gastropods and pelecypods, which are almost ubiquitous in other formations, are present here also. Their broken and pulverised shells make considerable contributions to the building up of the limestones. Some species of the bivalve genera *Ostrea, Chlamys, Lima* and *Lithophaga* were closely associated

---

PLATE XX
CRETACEOUS FOSSILS

1. This thin slice of Chalk shows that it contains numerous complete and fragmentary shells of Foraminifera. 2. Apical portion of *Micraster* showing the detailed structure of the ambulacral areas. 3. *Cidaris* side view showing its stout spines attached to tubercles and also a number of tubercles from which the spines have fallen off. Note the narrow wavy ambulacrum. 4. *Holaster*, ventral view. 5. *Schloenbachia*. 6. *Inoceramus*. 7. *Marsupites*. Test showing the large plates which enclose the body. 8 and 9. *Micraster*, ventral and dorsal views. Classification: 5, Ammonite. 6, Lamellibranch. 2, 3, 4, 7, 8, 9, Echinoderms. (1, 2, *W. Sutcliffe*. 3, *A. Ferguson*. 4-9, *H.M. Geol. Surrey*)

FOS—M

with the reef itself. The name of the last genus signifies 'rock eater' and is most appropriate, for the animal spent its life boring into solid coral. Some gastropod genera also lived on the reef as for example *Littorina* (the winkle) and the tall turreted forms *Cerithium* and *Turritella*.

Belonging to this coral association, but not usually living on the reef itself but on the adjoining floor of sediments, were other bivalves of which *Trigonia* should be mentioned. As its name implies it is broadly triangular in shape and has a stout thick shell with a clear-cut ornamentation of ribs and sometimes tubercles. Its remains were at times so abundant as to make an important contribution to rock-formation as in the Trigonia grit.

The submarine slope must have been extensively covered with coralline seaweeds. These coated their surfaces with lime which, when they died and perished, made powdery contributions to the deposits. In this connection reference may be made to *Solenopora* which, because its limy coat was firm, built up solid masses of lime which are occasionally found in the rocks. Within the limestone are many round grains which together resemble the roe of a fish. These are described therefore as oolite (oon=egg) grains which, as shown by thin sections, are often built up of delicate tubules produced by the filamentous alga *Girvanella*.

CHAPTER 28

MESOZOIC VEGETATION

JET black! Could anything be blacker or take a more beautiful polish than Whitby jet? No wonder, that from later prehistoric times onward, this was so highly valued for making beads and other personal ornaments that it was traded across Europe and as far as Egypt.

Early in this century Professor A. C. Seward proved by microscopic examination that jet was the fossilized wood of some kind of conifer which had been drifted out into the Liassic sea. There it became waterlogged and, sinking to the sea-floor, had been buried in mud and eventually carbonised like coal. The presence of fossilised branches in the rocks at Whitby and Lyme Regis; and of twigs, leaves and various other plant fragments in the Stonesfield slates and Jurassic rocks elsewhere; also showed that though much of Britain was covered by sea, land lay not far away.

Near Whitby fossil tree-stumps have been found enclosed in yellow Inferior Oolite sands standing where they grew with their roots branching downwards into the clays of the Upper Lias. Similar stumps and prostrate trunks of coniferous trees may be seen also in the Purbeck beds of Portland Bill and the Isle of Wight. One great log, four feet long and three feet thick is exhibited in the British Museum (Natural History). Similar timbers, often referred to under the name of *Dadoxylon*, have been found in other Jurassic and Lower Cretaceous rocks. Quite often the wood is silicified so that its microscopic structure has been preserved. This reveals a close resemblance to that of *Araucaria*, the Monkey Puzzle tree, which today makes up extensive coniferous forests in Chile.

Fortunately we are not wholly dependent for our knowledge of the Jurassic woodland upon these scattered woody fragments. While the Inferior Oolite limestones were accumulating in the clear seas of South and Midland England, rivers flowing from off the northern continent were pushing out their deltas southwards as far as Yorkshire. Here under the influence of the genial climate of those times the flat often swampy deltaic surfaces became overgrown with luxuriant vegetation. In some localities this state of affairs continued so long that considerable depths of vegetable debris accumulated. This was eventually changed into thin seams of coal which may now be seen cropping out in the cliffs along the Yorkshire coast north of Scarborough; and also at Brora in Scotland. Of much greater interest than the coal are the innumerable fossilised leaves and other plant fragments which, having been caught up by the rivers as they flowed through the woodlands or crossed the swamps, were at last deposited along with ordinary sediments on the outskirts of the deltas. The sorting out of this mingled assemblage of fossil plant fragments from various sources has now given us the first really comprehensive picture of British vegetation since the decline and disappearance of the Coal Measure forests of Carboniferous times. In this picture several general features of interest should be noted.

In the first place no traces have been found of those giant Lycopods *Lepidodendron* and *Sigillaria*, whose foliage filled the uppermost storey of the Coal Measure forests; nor of those giant horsetails the *Calamites* that were so prominent among the trees of the middle storey. Nevertheless these two types of plants survived in their smaller relatives *Selaginellites* and *Equisetites*, which were ancestral to but larger than the present day *Selaginella* and *Equisetum*. Fossil remains of *Equisetites* have been found standing upright as they grew from their underground rhizomes. The latter infested the soil of the drier areas in and adjoining the deltas and covered broad expanses of the landscape with a shimmering veil of horsetails.

In the second place those seed-bearing ferns, the Pteridosperms, which played so prominent a part in the undergrowth of the Coal Measure forests, had also disappeared. But the ordinary spore-bearing ferns, with their richly varied and beautiful fronds, were even more conspicuous. To the eyes of any who have wandered through the hot houses of Kew Gardens or of similar places in other great cities many of these fossil fronds from the Yorkshire coast will seem familiar for they included a number of types such as *Marattiopsis*, *Matonidium* and *Todites*, of which representatives still live in warm temperate forests.

Finally by far the most prominent elements in the Jurassic landscape were the Gymnosperms. For the better understanding of this fascinating assemblage of Jurassic plants it is necessary to consider briefly certain features connected with the reproduction of higher land plants in general. In all of them the microspore or pollen grain, carrying the sperm cell, is borne by the wind or insects and is thus brought into close proximity to the macrospore which contains the egg-cell. The pollen grain then sends out a long structure the pollen tube from which a non-motile sperm-cell is released that enters the egg cell and fertilises it. This then develops into an embryo which with the surrounding tissues and protective coverings forms a seed.

In the Gymnosperms (gymnos = naked) the pollen grain and its tube have direct access to the ovule or unfertilised seed for this lies exposed on the surface of a leaf-like scale.

In the Angiosperms (angeion=vessel) which later became the dominant plants the pollen grains do not have direct access to the ovules for these are contained in a closed capsule, the carpel. The grain settles on the stigma or outer end of the capsule and the pollen tube must traverse the tissues of this before it can reach the ovule.

In Gymnosperms the scales carrying the reproductive organs are usually arranged spirally around a short axis in the form of a *cone* and there are separate male and female cones. In the Angiosperms these structures are congregated in a *flower*. At the centre of this lie the carpels surrounded by stamens which contain the pollen. Beyond these are whorls of coloured leaf-like petals and green sepals.

Among the fossil plant remains are found twigs bearing leaves and even male and female cones, similar to but not identical with those of *Araucaria, Cupressus* (Cypress) and *Taxus* (Yew). Intermingled with these important coniferous Gymnosperms are two other not less important groups. On the one hand is the Maiden Hair tree, *Ginkgo* the sacred tree of the Buddhists. Judging by the number of varieties of the leaves, Ginkgos formed a considerable section of the trees in the Jurassic woodlands. They had affinities with *Cordaites* of the Coal Measure forests. Ginkgo retains in its reproductive processes an interesting primitive feature for, unlike all the higher types of plants, the pollen tube in the act of fertilising the egg cell releases a sperm cell that has vibratile hairs and is *motile*. This feature it shares with the cycads as well as with the lower plants, including the Pteridosperms.

Cycads live today in the subtropical forests of the southern hemisphere. Though fossil remains of them are not abundant they are found as low down as the liassic rocks in Britain and the Rhaetic and Trias elsewhere. They are in fact living fossils. In cycads the reproductive organs are carried on leaves or scales that are grouped together in cones.

By far the most prominent element among the fossil fragments found in the Yorkshire Oolites are large leaves closely resembling those of the cycads. Each leaf has a central rib bearing a series of long narrow leaflets feather fashion on either side and it may be as much as three feet long and nine inches wide. On the basis of the leaves alone it is tempting to think of these plants as cycads but, as will be seen presently, their reproduction organs differ sufficiently to justify classifying them separately from the cycads or Cycadales as cycadeoids or Cycadeoidales*, i.e., plants which resemble cycads. They were the dominant plants of Mesozoic times; indeed it has been estimated that they formed two fifths of the vegetation so that the period may be described as the Age of Cycadeoids which may be thought of as the counter part of the Age of Dinosaurs.

Some of these leaves are associated with the long slender stem and branches of the small tree *Williamsonia*. Among them are also found curious objects popularly known as 'Cliff Roses'. These have a diameter of about 4 inches and are like a star with a round central disc and ten or a dozen rays. Each ray originally carried two vertical rows of 'stamens' on its inner surface. This arrangement bears a closer resemblance to that found in a true flower than to that of the cone in Cycas and the conifers. A female 'flower' bud about 4 inches long was found by Hugh Miller in the Upper Jurassic of Eathie, Cromarty. This was carefully investigated by A. C. Seward. In it were numerous ovules not shut up in a close case or carpel but attached at their lower ends to a convex surface or receptacle. Each ovule was surrounded by tall scales but its outer end was left uncovered so that pollen had direct access to it as in typical Gymnosperms and not as in Angiosperms.

Another small tree, *Williamsoniella* had narrower simpler leaves. In it both male and female elements were present with the ovule bearing receptacle in the centre, surrounded by the 'stamens' as in a flower. This grew on a short stalk and was situated in the angle between two branches. The resemblance to a flower was, however, only in the arrangement of the parts for closed carpels were absent

*Synonymous with Benettitales, a term often used in Britain.

and the tips of the ovules were exposed at the surface so that pollen had direct access to them as in other Gymnosperms. Nevertheless in both genera nature seems to have been feeling her way to the production of a true flower. Though this attempt may be described as a near miss it scored considerable success in Lower Cretaceous as well as Jurassic times.

In 1925 H. H. Thomas described the remains of some small but very interesting plants from Gristhorpe, Yorkshire. They were referred to the new genera *Caytonia* and *Gristhorpia*, which had a similar type of floral structure to those just described but the ovules were enclosed in a carpel-like case bearing at its lower end a lip which was at first thought to be a stigma for the reception of pollen grains as in the Angiosperms. It has, however, since been proved that a small opening appeared close to this lip through which the pollen gained direct access to the ovules inside the case; thus showing that their resemblance to the Angiosperms was only superficial. Apart from this their affinities appear to be more with the Pteridosperms than with the Gymnosperms.

Towards the end of the Jurassic period gentle uplifting earth-movements converted nearly the whole of Britain into dry land. In the south-east this was so low-lying that it was subject to occasional submergence by the sea and burial under marine deposits. Generally, however, this area was an ill-drained countryside crossed by rivers and partially occupied by swamps and bodies of freshwater in which the snails *Paludina* and *Limnaea*, together with minute crustacea known as Ostracods, abounded. The shells of the former accumulated in such masses as to form limestones some of which, known as Purbeck marble was extensively used in medieval times for decorating the interiors of Salisbury and other Cathedrals and churches.

On the drier rises of ground in this part of the country rich soils developed and abundant vegetation grew. Here reptiles, mammals and insects found food and shelter. The rocks formed from the deposits laid down under these varying conditions, are well exposed along the coast of Dorset, especially in the Isles of Purbeck and Portland and the Isle of Wight. This closing phase of the Jurassic period in the south of England merged into the opening phase of the Cretaceous when the bodies of freshwater expanded into a large lake known as the Wealden Lake. This was fed by several large rivers which built out deltas along its margins. Under these circumstances the Jurassic flora and fauna continued to flourish practically unchanged except for a new element which will be discussed later (v. Page 225).

Plant fossils have been found at different levels in both sets of rocks but they are relatively more abundant in association with the fossil soils, the so called 'dirt beds', of the Purbeck rocks. Here once more the cycadeoids are the most conspicuous element. Unlike their predecessors in the Jurassic rocks these have short stout stems not unlike old-fashioned straw beehives in shape. Occasionally their stems can be seen standing where they grew in such numbers as to merit the popular description of Fossil Forest. Good examples are to be found near Lulworth and on the Isle of Portland. They are, however, only miniature forests for even the tallest stems were only a few feet high. One good example is on exhibit in the British Museum (Natural History). As with living cycads, their stems carried a crown of large pinnate leaves which uncurled as they grew from the apical bud. When these faded and fell away their stalks were broken across just above the bases, which were surrounded by brown scales, and together formed a protective covering for the whole stem. Numerous 'flower' buds grew in the midst of these leaf-bases and are supposed to have come into blossom all at one time. If it may be assumed that these 'flowers' had rich colours then we may picture each plant closing its career in a sunset glory of considerable beauty.

The Cycadeoidales came into being during the Triassic period. They reached their climax in the Jurassic and continued to flourish in the Lower Cretaceous. Fossil evidence, from the Gault of Folkestone, indicates that they died out about the middle of this period. They represent one of nature's most interesting and temporarily successful experiments in producing a fully efficient terrestrial flora.

CHAPTER 29

A MAID GOES FISHING

A T THE close of the eighteenth and the opening of the nineteenth centuries, as Jane Austen's novel 'Persuasion' testifies, Lyme Regis was a fashionable seaside resort. Here there lived a cabinet maker, Anning by name, whose skill as a craftsman was accompanied by a natural flair for finding and collecting fossils, an interest in which he indulged on Sundays and holidays. Though his wife ridiculed him for wasting his time thus she allowed him to display his finds for sale alongside the fish that she sold, for the family was very poor. He often took his little daughter Mary with him on his forays along the beach and cliff. Though no more than a child she learned from him how to spot fossils in the rock, how to extract and clean them—in other words how to go fishing in the Liassic sea.

When Mary was only ten years old her father died. Being the oldest it fell to her lot to help in supporting the family. But how? That was the problem that now distracted her. Returning from the beach one day she was stopped by a lady who, after looking at an ammonite she held in her hand, offered half a crown for her find. In accepting her offer Mary got more than the money, she got a solution to her problem. She realised that though she was so young she could earn money by collecting and selling fossils. Not long after, while carrying out her purpose she discovered in the rocks the skeleton of an *Ichthyosaurus* and extracted it. This, as Dr. Lang tells us, was the first to be found in anything like a complete condition. The news of its discovery came to the ears of the Lord of the Manor who purchased it from her for the sum of £25. Unfortunately this historically interesting specimen has since been lost.

Mary Anning became more than a mere collector for she spent time in carefully dissecting different animals in order that she might gain a fuller understanding of the extinct creatures she was handling, which included fishes, crustacea, starfish and belemnites as well as reptiles. Rumours of her fame as a collector penetrated to geological circles in London and many distinguished geologists visited her. Under her guidance even Buckland and Murchison learned more about the art of collecting fossils. Such was the value of her work that, though she was not a Fellow of the Geological Society, the President included an obituary and generous appreciation of her in his annual address in 1848.

On the basis of specimens collected by Mary Anning, and subsequently by others, *Ichthyosaurus* became more fully known than any other fossil reptile (Plate XVII*a*). Like the whale and the porpoise among mammals it was a land animal that had become perfectly adapted for living in the sea. Such close approximation in structure or appearance in unrelated or distantly related lines of descent is described as *convergent evolution*.

Fossils in which the fleshy outline of *Ichthyosaurus* has been preserved show that its body was as streamlined as that of a fish for slipping rapidly through water. The tail was its main organ of propulsion and in this connection had developed a fin. This, however, was situated upon the upper and not the lower side of the tail as in fishes. The discovery of this explained why the back bone was bent down sharply at the tip of the tail in so many specimens. The limbs, no longer needed for supporting the weight of the body, had been converted into flippers or paddles that could serve the purposes of steering and braking. They were secondarily broadened by the development of extra digits, the bones had also changed shape and fitted together like the tesserae in a mosaic. *Ichthyosaurus* had a large head which merged into the trunk without the intervention of a neck, and its long pointed snout was split from end to end by a horrible mouth armed with sharp teeth. It had large eyes surrounded by a ring of bony plates believed to have been part of a mechanism for rapidly adjusting the focus during swift movements in the pursuit of prey. The presence in some specimens of the remains of embryos within the body shows that, in contrast with other reptiles, the young were not hatched from eggs but were born alive.

Mary Anning's most astonishing find was the almost complete skeleton of *Plesiosaurus* (Plate XVII*b*). This was removed with great skill and labour and was sold to the Duke of Buckingham for £200.

Gazing at the remains of such marine monsters as these, now displayed on the walls of the fossil reptile gallery in the British Museum (Nat. Hist.), creates a vivid sense of this woman's energy and initiative; and it is appropriate that a portrait of her should have been placed alongside of one of the largest.

Plesiosaurus was less fully adapted for aquatic life than *Ichthyosaurus*. Like the turtle it probably returned occasionally to the beach to bask in the sunshine or to lay its eggs. It had a small head, a long only slightly flexible neck, a broad flat body and short tail. Both pairs of limbs had become large flattened paddles and were used for propulsion. They were less specialised than those of the *Ichthyosaurus,* for each paddle still enclosed only five digits but the bony elements of these were multiplied and elongated. This reptile occupied an important place in the fauna of the Lower Liassic waters.

Another exciting find made by Mary Anning revealed the remains of a flying reptile that had been drowned in the sea. It was the opposite extreme of the monsters already described not only in its habitat but also in size. Moreover it was the first specimen of its kind to be found in Britain. Its arms were greatly elongated and the fingers more so. As in modern bats these supported two folds of skin which extended from the sides of the body and were attached posteriorly to the much shorter hind limbs. These folds served as wings and had a span of three and a half feet from tip to tip. The toes of the hind feet, like those of the bat, had strong claws which enabled this flying reptile *Pterodactylus* to come to rest by hanging upside down from a projecting ledge of rock or from the bough of a tree. As in birds their bones were very light for they were hollow and filled with air. The skull, though large, was also light for it consisted mainly of a framework of thin bones. The mouth matched the skull in size and was furnished with long piercing teeth which no doubt were effective for capturing insects on the wing.

Such were the more outstanding fossils which this remarkable woman found; but she also collected ammonites, belemnites, corals, starfish and ganoid fishes. Among the last named *Dapedius* should be mentioned. It had a deep laterally compressed body, like that of a John Dory, but was enclosed in an armour of rhomboidal bony scales covered with enamel. These varied finds were exposed for sale alongside the fresh fish in her mother's shop and yielded a precarious income. As she grew older rheumatism curtailed her activities. In later years she was saved from dire poverty by the generosity and influence of her local and scientific friends. She died at the age of 48, and her memory was perpetuated by a stained glass window in Lyme Church.

CHAPTER 30

ON THE INDUSTRIAL TRAIL

SINCE Mary Anning's day the work she did so indomitably has been continued along the coast and at inland exposures. Leaving Lyme Regis behind we come to its northern counterpart Whitby. Hereabouts for two and a half centuries the Upper Liassic shales were worked for the extraction of alum and, in later years yielded to fossil-hunters many fishes and remarkably complete skeletons of *Ichthyosaurus, Plesiosaurus* and other reptiles belonging to types long since extinct. Here was found the skeleton of *Steneosaurus* one of the early forerunners of the crocodiles. As in these creatures its nostrils were situated at the tip of a greatly elongated snout; but their internal openings lay in the roof of the mouth close to its front end. Fossils of related forms found in other countries show that, with the passing on of Jurassic times, these internal openings were gradually shifted backwards by the formation of a false roof to the mouth. This developed until they lay so close above the throat that air could be passed straight to the lungs, even when the mouth cavity was filled with water. This was of course a great convenience to the crocodile while it was holding the snout of its prey submerged.

In these days when the fossil-hunter leaves the sea cliffs and goes inland he must, like the crows and sea-birds following the plough, keep in the trail of such industrialists as those that excavate material from the ground for making bricks and hydraulic cement. As late as the opening years of this century many villages situated on the Jurassic clay-lands had their own brickfields; and opportunities for collecting fossils were widespread. The advent of brick-making machinery, about the year 1860, however, led eventually to the extinction of the little local works and the concentration of the industry in those great concerns that have forested the countryside around Bedford and Peterborough with tall chimneys. This concentration was accompanied by an afterglow of this type of collecting before it suffered a further curtailment by the onslaughts of mechanical diggers. For a time the increased demand for clay was met by digging with pick and shovel to deeper layers than were reached in village pits. With the new opportunity offered by more extensive digging there fortunately arose the right quality of collector to match the occasion.

At Eyebury, near Peterborough, there lived a farmer, Charles Thurlow Leeds, who had two sons Charles and Alfred. When the latter was only four years old the father died and the farm was left in charge of trustees. In 1865 Charles went to Oxford to study mathematics. There he came under the influence of the Professor of Geology, John Phillips, nephew of William Smith, with the result that he spent his vacations searching for fossils in the surrounding clay-pits; and thus started the formation of what became a famous collection. After a brief spell at engineering he took up law as a profession in 1873 and left home to practise elsewhere. In 1887 he migrated to New Zealand.

When Charles went to Oxford, Alfred had to take charge of the farm and to give up his own ambition to become a doctor. Nevertheless the natural aptitude, which might have made him a successful surgeon, found an outlet in setting and mending the broken and splintered bones of extinct reptiles rescued from the attacks of clay-diggers' tools and crowbars. His official surgery and museum was in the attics at the top of the house; but numerous operations were performed in the living room downstairs where all available resting places were frequently occupied by patients in various stages of recovery under the watchful eyes of his wife and children as helps and nurses.

With the exception of Professor H. G. Seeley this collection remained unknown to the scientific world until 1885. In that year Dr. Henry Woodward, from the Department of Geology of the British Museum, visited Eyebury. On seeing the collection his first remark, as recorded by R. Thurlow Leeds, was: "Are you aware, Mr. Leeds, that there is not another such private collection as this in Great Britain?" After that, like bees around a pot of honey, vertebrate palaeontologists, both British and American, came to inspect the treasures here preserved. In 1890 the attics were cleared and all the specimens transferred to the British Museum. Alfred Leeds, however, continued the work and enriched his own and the Museum's collections almost up to the time of his death in 1917.

In addition to fossil sharks and chimaeroids the fishes found by the Leeds brothers included a representative series of ganoids that was in keeping with the general transitional character of Mesozoic forms of life. The stage attained in the Triassic *Semionotus* had been carried to a climax in the closely related but much larger *Lepidotus* with its small mouth, its complete covering of ganoid scales and a tail which, notwithstanding its symmetrical form, still retained marked traces of the uptilted end of the vertebral column (Plate XIV*b*). Another close relative, *Mesturus*, was proportionately much more deeply-bodied even than *Dapedius*. In both these fishes the teeth had rounded crowns suitable for crushing shells and seaweeds (Fig. 20: *3*.)

Among the other fishes were lithe swiftly swimming forms, such as *Caturus* and *Hypsocormus*, ranging in size up to that of a fully grown salmon. Like this fish they also had large mouths with sharp teeth. Their scales were, however, no longer thick and rhomboidal, fitting together like the tesserae of a mosaic, but were thin, rounded in outline and overlapping. In these respects they approached present-day fishes. Nevertheless, the exposed portions of the scales were still covered with thin enamel. The most extraordinary fish found was *Leedsia*, of which only fragments were rescued. These indicate that it was 30 feet long and had a forked tail with a vertical span of 10 feet from tip to tip; a truly royal meal for some of those great reptiles that lived in the same waters. At the other extreme was *Pholidophorus*, only 9 inches long, but it exhibited features which brought it into yet closer relationship with modern fishes.

The remains of reptiles found by the Leeds brothers include complete skeletons of marine types already described and of others such as *Ophthalmosaurus*, a new kind of Ichthyosaur that had no teeth. They included also various relatives of *Plesiosaurus*. One of these was *Pliosaurus* a fierce and agile swimmer with a much shorter neck and larger head. The clay-pits also yielded many primitive crocodiles.

As already noticed the Jurassic seas of Britain were marginal and were bounded by extensive areas of land covered with vegetation sufficiently luxuriant to support a large population of land animals. At times some of these were caught by flooded rivers and their carcasses were carried out to sea. Their flesh rotted and the bones, falling apart, were scattered over the sea-floor. It is not surprising therefore that usually only fragmentary remains of land animals have been found in the British Jurassic and Cretaceous rocks.

Fortunately other parts of the world, especially the Western States of North America, have yielded many complete skeletons, on the basis of which specialist artists have been able to portray the creatures as they appeared when alive. Chief among these were the dinosaurs (dino = terrible) whose fantastic dimensions and shapes still capture the imagination of popular writers to the exclusion of smaller but equally entrancing fossil fry. The dinosaurs were superficially similar to lizards but many were bipedal; like their miniature triassic fore-runners, and their equally miniature descendants, the birds. In many of them the forelimbs were small but the hind were powerfully developed, for they had to support the whole weight of the body when this was poised upon them and lifted clear of the ground for running.

Primarily the smallest dinosaurs must have been insectivorous. The larger were either herbivorous or carnivorous. Some of the latter eventually adopted the herbivorous habit and reverted to the primitive fourfooted gait. Some grew to sizes that gave them a place among the largest creatures this world has ever seen. The carrying of such huge masses of flesh and bone naturally posed a serious problem, which seems to have been partially solved by the adoption of an amphibious habit. Those that remained on land were usually of normal sizes but developed protective devices, horns, spines and body shields.

With the background of wider knowledge thus gained experts have been able to deal intelligently with the isolated teeth, vertebrae, legbones and other fragments which make up so many of the British fossil remains; and to identify more or less precisely the reptilian types to which they originally belonged. In a few instances, however, almost complete skeletons have been found.

Long before these important discoveries were made in America traces of kindred animals had been found in England. Among the earliest of these were sundry fragments from the Inferior Oolite beds, which were being worked for roofing slates in the quarries of Stonesfield in Oxfordshire. These fossils came into the hands of Professor Buckland about the year 1826. They included a thigh bone 2 feet 4 inches long which must have belonged to a correspondingly large creature, to which he gave the appropriate name *Megalosaurus*. It is now known to have been a carnivorous dinosaur about 30 feet long.

Another equally early find was a strange-looking tooth picked up by a lady when out for a walk in Ashdown forest, Sussex. Her husband G. A. Mantell, a medical doctor with a keen interest in geology, searched for and found other specimens in the Wealden of that district. Recognising that it had points of resemblance to the grinders of a herbivore he showed it to Sir Charles Lyell and to Baron Cuvier but it baffled both of them. He then made a systematic search through the series of teeth kept in the Royal College of Surgeons. His search was on the verge of proving quite fruitless when the Curator, as a matter of mere interest, showed him a newly discovered lizard from America called *Iguana*. A glance at its teeth showed Dr. Mantell that these bore an extraordinary resemblance to his fossil. The tooth was subsequently described by W. D. Conybeare who created the name *Iguanodon* for the reptile that once owned it (Plate XVIII).

Since those early days other bones and even almost complete skeletons of dinosaurs have been brought to light from the Jurassic and Cretaceous rocks. It may be inferred therefore that those parts of Britain which now form the highland regions of Wales and Scotland, together with an adjoining North Atlantic landmass, were inhabited by these great reptiles.

Cetiosaurus, of which an imperfect skeleton was found in the Oxford Clay of Peterborough, was about 60 feet long and represents another section of the carnivorous dinosaurs that had become herbivorous. Related forms found in North America attained even greater dimensions as may be seen in the cast of *Diplodocus* which is on exhibition in the fossil reptile gallery of the British Museum. With it there are also attractively displayed many of the reptilian remains referred to in these pages.

Another important series of dinosaurs were herbivorous from the outset. Of these almost complete skeletons have been found in England as well as scattered fragments from various levels in the Jurassic and early Cretaceous rocks. *Camptosaurus*, a near relative of *Iguanodon*, was 17 feet long. It was of clumsier build than the carnivorous forms for its hind limbs were shorter and stouter and its fore-limbs larger. The front teeth had been lost and replaced functionally by a horny rim not unlike that seen in tortoises and was no doubt used in the same way for cropping soft leaves. *Hypsilophodon*, from the Wealden of the Isle of Wight, was 4 feet long. Its habits seem to have been similar to those of the present-day Tree Kangaroo. An almost complete skeleton of *Iguanodon* was found in the early cretaceous rocks at

Atherfield in the Isle of Wight. It belonged to the same type as these last two genera but was larger, for it stood 12 feet high.

Scelidosaurus, from the Lower Lias, was a smaller and earlier member of this branch of the dinosaur stock. It had resumed the habit of walking on all fours and had developed a protective armour in the form of two rows of bony plates and spines arranged along the whole length of the back.

Though it is the great size of the giant dinosaurs that has captured the imagination it must not be forgotten that there existed diminutive strains, of which *Scleromochlus* from the Upper Trias of Lossiemouth is an example (Plate X*a*: *13*). The great dinosaurs have now been completely extinct for three score millions of years, but some diminutive descendants of the original stock such as the one just mentioned, lived on in a greatly changed state and now, in the form of birds, swarm over the land and triumph in the air.

As we watch a hen fleeing from pursuit with its head and neck stretched out and its wings flapping it is easy to catch its resemblance to some of the artistic reconstructions of running dinosaurs. In this connection it is profitable to visit the British Museum once more and inspect the fossil remains of *Archaeopteryx* from the lithographic lime-stone of Germany. This creature, which was about the size of a pigeon, has been pithily described as an 'avian reptile or a reptilian bird'. It was however definitely on the bird side of the boundary for in it the scales of the reptile had become feathers. With these along its arms, legs and tail we may picture it, as it ran fleeing from an enemy, presently becoming sufficiently airborne to glide upwards out of reach, and to find refuge on the boughs of a *Ginkgo* or to nestle in the foliage of a *Williamsonia*. When danger did not press it could take the more leisurely course of using its strongly clawed fingers and toes for scrambling up the rough trunks of these small trees. After resting it could launch itself like a bat into the air and with gliding and flying movements pursue the insects upon which it probably fed.

CHAPTER 31

LILLIPUTIAN FOSSILS

FROM the foregoing pages it is evident that the student of fossils is much indebted to the activities of industrialists; but, as the remarks on coal resources showed, he is able sometimes to repay part of his debt. This is true also in the world-wide search for oil, which has been accompanied by an almost unbelievable advance in the technique of boring; for operations which formerly took months and years are now completed in days and weeks, and penetrate to 10 or even 20 times the depth. Under the old conditions a solid core was brought up from which fossils could be collected. These were, however, very few compared with the number that could be obtained from surface exposures which gave access to much more extended portions of the rock-layers. With the new methods the number is still fewer for they necessitate the smashing of much of the rock and the pulverisation of the larger fossils. Owing to their very small size the Foraminifera generally escape this destruction and, after being separated from the debris, can be used as substitutes for the larger forms in zoning the rocks.

After dealing with giant reptiles it is a pleasant change to turn to the contemplation of their lilliputian companions; especially to the Foraminifera, some of which are so minute that they are only just visible to the naked eye. During the last war one investigator turned his attention to a bed of clay that had been exposed many years ago in a railway cutting near Byfield, Northamptonshire. In it he found many Foraminifera, especially in two thin layers separated by an interval of only 2 feet. These included numerous specimens of the genus *Ophthalmidium* which he made the subject of a special study.

The shell of *Ophthalmidium* consists of a small spherical chamber in the centre surrounded by a series of long chambers arranged in a flat spiral, slightly oval in outline. These chambers extend from one end

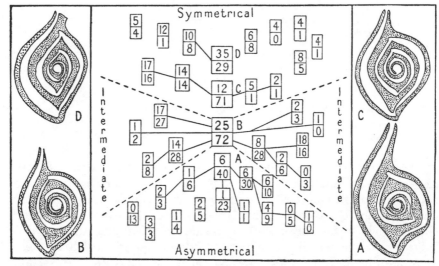

Fig. 17. STRUCTURE OF AND VARIATION IN OPHTHALMIDIUM

A-D. Four important varieties of *Ophthalmidium northamptonensis* showing differencies in structure. Note the changing direction of the axis in the central portion of the shells. The main part of the figure is a modified scatter diagram showing the distribution of variation in two communities of shells collected from two distinct layer. Those from the lower layer are represented by the lower number in each rectangle ; those from the upper layer, by the upper number. (Adapted from Alan Wood and Tom Barnard).

of the oval to the other, and the line joining their points of union may be called the axis of the shell (Fig. 17 D). Closer inspection, however, showed that the axis for the inner chambers was not always in a line with the main axis but made angles with this varying up to 90°.

Other points of difference were also noted, for example, the elongation of the last chamber beyond the outline. These differences were taken into account and some 40 varieties were distinguished. Specimens of these are represented diagrammatically by the figures in the accompanying modified scatter diagram. This is divided into three sections based upon the degree of symmetry of the whole shell— symmetrical, intermediate and asymmetrical. The varieties were, of course, not so sharply marked off from one another as the rectangles enclosing the figures might suggest; but were often linked together by a continuous series of variants suggestive of evolutionary changes which are known as *clines*. In each rectangle the lower and upper numbers correspond respectively to the specimens found in the lower and upper layers.

The total number of specimens of *Ophthalmidium* collected from the lower level was 1659. Looking at the lower figures it will be seen that the maximum of 72 is situated at B in the intermediate section; and close to it comes the figure 71 at C in the symmetrical section. Here then is the core of the population. Radiating from this are clines along which the numbers tend to decrease, though occasional local increases may occur.

The number of specimens collected from the upper level was 615. They also tend to decline radially outwards. At this level the core of the population has two parts; a smaller which has remained at B, and a larger which has shifted along a cline to D. The latter represents a change of numerical proportion which has shifted along a cline to D, with the passage of time. The series of variants which link B 72 through time to D 35 may be called a *chronocline* and is apparently approaching some new type not unlike the genus *Spiroloculina*. The combined scatters for the two assemblages of specimens thus illustrates how, by a reshuffle of numbers, a new variety may in time become a new species or even a new genus. In the outlying portions of the diagram indications may be seen of other possible chronoclines.

Since the middle of the nineteenth century the beauty of Foraminiferal shells, fossil as well as living, has attracted the attention of microscopists, and the mere list of the genera and species they have described and named would fill a book. With them, as with *Carbonicola* and other larger organisms, the emphasis was originally laid upon the detailed description of species types, a very valuable kind of work that has resulted in the laying of a solid foundation of fixed points from which to set out on other exploratory researches. This initial importance attached to the establishment of types reflects that stage in the development of knowledge when creation by fiat was the dominant conception of the origin of species.

But such work as that upon *Ophthalmidium*, briefly outlined above, illustrates a method of approach to the systematic study of organic nature which has come increasingly into vogue, since Hutton and Lyell opened the eyes of students to the fact that creation was not a magical act but an understandable process that they may investigate.

To Darwin, who acknowledged that Lyell was his teacher, belongs the credit for first showing this to be the case for the organic as well as the physical world.

The realisation of the value of Foraminifera as guides to the interpretation of strata passed through in borings, has given an impetus to the study of their distribution in the rocks. The material for such work may be obtained from surface exposures or from borings. In any case great care is taken to link up the minute micro-fossils, with the zonal time-scales already established in terms of the large macro fossils; so that, where these are absent, the Foraminifera may be used as 'deputies'. Work done upon the Lower Liassic rocks in the cliffs near Lyme Regis may be taken as an example. Thanks to the work of W. D. Lang and others the zonal time-scale for these rocks is exceptionally well established in terms of macro fossils, especially ammonites. Sample material from many known levels has been sifted and species belonging to over 20 genera have been identified (Fig. 18).

In general terms the Foraminifera have exhibited the same behaviour as do other groups of organisms. Some forms are of little value for stratigraphical work, either because they are so rare that too much time would be wasted in searching for them, or because they ranged through too many zones. Of greatest practical value are those which, in addition to being common, have a limited range and are therefore good markers of time or of zones.

Though the practical value of short-ranged forms is high the others have a considerable theoretical interest. Thus the lenticuline foraminifera have a moderately long range but, like *Ophthalmidium* are very variable. The study of the zonal distribution of their varieties has thrown an interesting light upon foraminiferal evolution. Even though sexual reproduction seems at first sight to play a much less important part in the succession of generations than in higher animals it does plan an essential part. Their story has therefore much in common with that already studied in corals and *Gryphaea*. In the Lenticulinae also there appears to have been a radicle stock which had a long range through time and changed but little. In this the shells are closely coiled. From it there arose, even within the limits of a subzone, a series of forms in which the shell uncoiled in later life and the chambers followed one another in a straight line (Fig. 18: *4*). The same sequence of changes was repeated in succeeding zones, thus producing homeomorphs. Other changes also took place, as for instance in the shape and

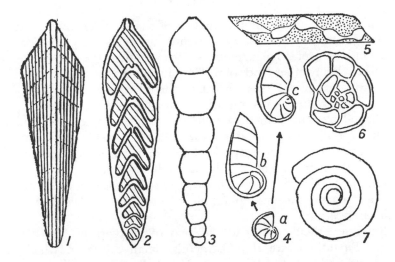

Fig. 18. FORAMINIFERA FROM THE LOWER LIAS

1. *Frondicularia.* 2. A section of the same showing the chambers in the megalo-sphaeric generation. 3. *Nodosaria.* 4. *Lenticulina* showing variation trends *ab, ac.* Similar trends are repeated in other layers. 5. *Bullopora* adhering to the surface of another object. 6. *Epistomina.* 7. *Spirillina.* (After T. Barnard).

relative sizes of the later chambers. These took place independently of the uncoiling so that superficially similar shells could be distinguished and therefore had some value as zonal indices.

The contemplation of the amazing plasticity of these single-celled animals creates a feeling of wonder that, though the period of their existence on this earth must approach 2000 millions of years, they have not become stereotyped; and the resources of the biochemical and genetic processes within them are still far from becoming exhausted. Even in the later phases of geological time the output of new forms within the limits of their inheritance is phenomenal.

But the Foraminifera are by no means the only element that makes up the micro-fauna of the rocks, for the remains of other single-celled types also make an appreciable contribution. The shells of Radiolaria are still smaller and much more beautiful; for they consist of glassy silica woven into exquisite network patterns. *Coccoliths* have been familiar objects since the early days of microscopic studies. They are exceedingly minute calcareous discs which play an important part in the make-up of the fine matrix of chalk. Their mode of origin was for a long time a mystery; but now, it seems, they are produced as a kind of protective armour in yet another type of unicellular organism. Many other kinds of single celled forms occur in the plankton or micro-fauna of the seas. Most of these produce no resistant substances and consequently perish completely. A few, such as the Dinoflagellates, are clothed in a delicate but tough cellulose cell wall which is slightly less perishable and, under favourable conditions may be preserved. Thus for example the Kimmeridge clay, as the result of very careful treatment, has been made to yield such cell walls in a fossil state. The finding of these raises the hope that the remains of other equally delicate planktonic organisms will eventually be forthcoming.

Reference should be made to two other types of larger microfossils. First there are the Ostracods, small crustacea which have the whole body enclosed in a bivalve shell strikingly like that of a minute lamellibranch. Their remains have been found in marine deposits dating from palaeozoic times onwards up to the present. Some of them, however were abundant in freshwater deposits and have proved useful for zonal purposes, as for example in the Purbeck Beds. Then there are those puzzling minute fossils, only about one millemetre long, known as *Conodonts*. Their shapes, together with their sharply denticulated edges, have recalled to the minds of various workers such structures as the jaws of carnivorous worms, the tongue-like rasping organs (radulae) of gastropods, the hooks on the suckers of the *Octopus*, or even the horny 'teeth' which arm the suctorial mouths of such fish as the lamprey. They seem to be characteristic of the Palaeozoic rocks.

So far only the remains of marine organisms have been described; but others occur which were of terrestrial origin, such as spores and pollen-grains. At times, when the wind swept over the Carboniferous forests, the air carried golden clouds of spores which settled down into the swamps in sufficient quantities to produce layers of spore coal. Similarly in recent geological times pollen-grains, picked up by the spring breezes from woodlands were scattered far and wide over the landscape, and deposited on the peaty surfaces of moor and fen. In the last few years these have been, with infinite patience, extracted; and have added greatly to our knowledge of the history of the present British vegetation (Plate: XXIII*a*).

By the same means these minute plant fragments have been carried out to sea and settling down have become mixed with sediments which are now rocks. The search for them in pieces of rock is like hunting for a needle in a haystack; but the ingenuity of the 'palynologist', to give the investigator his specialised cognomen, has evolved a technique for destroying the stack and rescuing the needle. Having pulverised his rock sample, he removes all the lime that may happen to be present, by digesting the dust with hydrochloric acid. The sand and other siliceous constituents are then dissolved in hydrofluoric acid having a concentration of 60%. The unwanted vegetable matter that is left behind is then oxidised by being boiled in nitric acid and its residue is removed by treatment with potash. Out of this fierce trial the spores emerge unscathed; a marvellous illustration of nature's ingenuity in providing protection for vegetable organisms at this vital reproductive stage in their life-history. Thus extracted from the rock these micro-fossils make their valuable contribution to the correlation of rocks and to our knowledge of the progress of life upon the earth.

CHAPTER 32

THE EARLIEST MAMMALS

THE geologist, being himself a mammal, is naturally deeply interested in any fossils that might throw some light upon the history of these, the highest vertebrates. The first finding of such a fossil took place about the year 1764 but, strange to relate, it reposed unrecognised in private collections for more than half a century. It was at last noticed in 1828 by Professor Phillips who recognised it as a small mammalian jaw imbedded in Stonesfield slate. Through his influence it found a permanent home in the Museum of the Yorkshire Philosophical Society and was given the generic names of *Amphilestes*.

Meanwhile other fossil bones of mammalia had been found in the quarries of Stonesfield, 10 miles north of Oxford. The first of these came into the hands of W. J. Broderip, a law student at the university, whose interest in Natural History had led him to join Professor Buckland's classes in geology. About the year 1812 an old stonemason brought to him two small jaws imbedded in slate from those quarries. He and Buckland both agreed that these were mammalian lower jaws. In coming to that conclusion they broke loose from the commonly accepted view that no mammals existed before Tertiary times. They received support for their opinion from the great French palaeontologist Baron Cuvier, who went so far as to link it with that primitive living mammal the opossum of the American continent. These and other specimens found subsequently, were carefully described by Cuvier's counterpart in Britain, Professor Owen, in 1836 and 1842.

The strength of the prejudice against the existence of mammals in Mesozoic times is reflected in the name *Amphitherium* given in 1838 to one of Broderip's specimens by a French savant, de Blainville. Relying only on a drawing made by Buckland he hoped that, by giving it this name, he would dissociate it from any affinity with the opossum and peg it down definitely as a reptile. It is a curious irony of advancing knowledge that this name fits in remarkably with the now established view that, while retaining traces of a reptilian ancestry, it was well on the way to being a full-blooded mammal.

This jaw, unlike that of a reptile and in common with those of all mammals, consisted of only one bone. In it also the teeth were differentiated into incisors, canine, premolars and molars. Each half of the jaw had 16 teeth a number which with the passage of time was reduced to and stabilised at 11. The cheek teeth had all the main elements of the mammalian molar in its simplest form. These included three stout roots, a broad crown carrying a triangle of sharp piercing cusps or tubercles in front and a crushing surface behind. This combination of features indicates that *Amphitherium* lay near the main line of descent of modern mammals. Nevertheless, it lies so far back along that line that the gap which separates it from such a lowly living type as the opossum seems in imagination relatively much greater than that which separates the earliest Old Stone Age man from a twentieth century aristocrat.

Two other types of mammalia have been found in the same quarries. The triconodont type is represented by *Microlestes* and *Phascolotherium*, in which the molar teeth are armed with three sharp cusps arranged in a straight line from back to front (Fig. 20: 5). This is not a pattern from which any modern mammalian tooth could have been derived. From this and other features of jaws and teeth it is inferred that these fossils represent a side branch from the main stem of mammalian evolution. It was, nevertheless, a successful branch for it included no less than half of the specimens yielded by the Stonesfield quarries.

The third type is represented by fragments of both the upper and lower jaws of *Stereognathus*. In this the cheek teeth have more than three roots and their crowns carry six cusps arranged in longitudinal rows. This multituberculate type of tooth is characteristic of the earliest known mammal *Tritylodon;* of which an almost complete skull was found in the triassic rocks of South Africa. The Stonesfield quarries have also yielded limb-bones. These have been shown to possess characteristics that lie between those of the mammal-like reptiles from the South African Trias and those of the duckbilled platypus, *Ornithorhynchus* of Australia, the lowliest of living mammals which still lays eggs. This emphasises the greatness of the gap which lies between the mid-Jurassic and present day mammals.

With the exception of the insectivore *Amphitherium* these Jurassic mammals probably belonged to the pouched mammal or marsupial grade. The facts just given about the limbs, however, may indicate a possibility that they had not yet advanced much beyond the egg-laying or monotreme grade.

The Stonesfield slates are also rich in marine molluscs, brachiopods and fishes. Along with these are the bones of terrestrial as well as aquatic reptiles; and also fragments of ferns, cycadophytes and conifers. Evidently they were deposited on the floor of a shallow sea not far from a land drained by rivers which, when in flood, swept the carcasses of larger animals out to sea along with the plants in whose foliage the little mammals had sought refuge. This assemblage of facts and fossils throws an indirect light upon the environment in which these land animals lived. They are like a spotlight that brightens up for one brief moment the darkened stage of mammalian history then, fading out, leaves this enshrouded in darkness for 15 millions of years, when the spotlight was switched on once more.

Near the close of the Jurassic period the scene shifts from Oxfordshire to the Isle of Purbeck in Dorset; and we must transfer our attention from the quarries of Stonesfield to the neighbourhood of Swanage, to the cliffs of Durlston bay where may be seen a remarkable series of rocks some 400 feet thick. These show that, whilst most of Britain had become dry land, the south-east of England was a low-lying region over which the sea flowed occasionally. More usually it had a badly drained landscape occupied by marshes and freshwater lagoons, interspersed with rises of drier ground overgrown by low woodlands of cycadeoids and other tree-like plants. Small mammals lurked in the branches or scurried through the undergrowth and fed upon cockroaches, beetles, dragonflies and other insects. The soils formed under these conditions were in time covered up and together with rootlets and organic debris became fossilised.

Our knowledge of the facts upon which that description is based is due in part to the labours of naturalists living in the vicinity of Swanage. Two of them, the Revd. P. B. Brodie and Mr. Wilson, found a number of small bones in the fossil soils and sent them to Professor Owen in 1854. Among them he discovered the jaws of a mammal, *Spalacotherium* the molar teeth of which have a large central cusp, with two smaller ones symmetrically placed in front and behind on the inner side. Another worker, S. H. Beckles, carried out extensive excavations over a period of years and was rewarded by a rich haul of mammalian bones now housed in the British Museum. These included no less than six new genera closely allied to, but slightly more advanced than *Amphitherium*, with which they are now classed in a new order of primitive mammalia known as the Pantotheria, that come near to being the common ancestors of all existing mammals.

In the same collection is *Peralestes*, a relative of *Spalacotherium*, also *Triconodon* and *Triacodon*, relatives of the earlier *Amphilestes*. The two orders represented by these genera were offshoots from the main line of mammalian descent. They also attained a measure of success, but the records from other countries show that they died out shortly after the close of the Jurassic period.

Second in interest only to the Pantotheria were several multi-tuberculate genera of which *Plagiaulax*, from the Purbeck and Wealden, is the most fully known. Unlike the types mentioned above these were vegetable feeders and had the usual large incisors separated by a wide space from the cheek-teeth. The latter carried on their crowns two longitudinal rows of tubercles.

On the premolars the inner row of these was raised into a sharp cutting edge.

The Multituberculata are a mysterious group. There is no doubt that they were mammals but apparently they had no direct link with any other known group. They must have separated from the main line at an exceedingly early date. Indeed it is possible that they may have arisen independently from the same mammal-like reptilian stock. They were evidently very successful, for they range in time from the Triassic period to the opening of Tertiary times; a stretch of time much longer than the period of existence of any other mammalian order.

CHAPTER 33

THE GREAT TRANSGRESSION

A T THE time when, in the south of England, *Iguanodon* cropped the foliage of cycadeoids, and furry little mammals hunted for insects among the ferns and horsetails, great physical changes were beginning to take place over the British area as a whole. Further north, in the region between Suffolk and Durham, these involved slow irregular sinking movements which resulted in the formation of downfolds north and south of an east-to-west axis running across central Yorkshire. While the latter remained for a while above sea-level and suffered erosion, the former became submerged. The sea first entered the southern downfold over Lincolnshire and brought with it the earliest marine Cretaceous fauna known in Britain. This included ammonites, of which the earliest had features reminiscent of Jurassic types. They were, however, speedily replaced by primitive species of the Lower Cretaceous genus *Subcraspedites*.

At first deposition was very slow and the sediment consisted of fine sand rich in glauconite grains. This formed, at the base of the Spilsby sandstone, a bed that was only 2 feet thick but was crowded with ammonites and large belemnites. As there are no cliffs along the Lincolnshire coast and the rocks inland are masked under a covering of cultivated soil, exposures have been seen only in small excavations and in the cores of borings. The rest of the Spilsby sandstone was more rapidly deposited and attained a thickness of about 70 feet. The fossils which are scattered throughout it include a stout belemnite, *Acroteuthis lateralis*, together with several species of the ammonite *Subcraspedites*.

While the Spilsby sandstone was being formed the sea also gained access to the northern downfold in which muddy deposits nearly 300 feet deep were laid down. These now crop out on the beach and in the cliffs between Filey and Flamborough in the vicinity of Speeton, and are accordingly known as the Speeton Clays. Unfortunately, as is often the case with clay cliffs, the face is smothered under minor landslips; so that this very important exposure is, as one Yorkshire geologist described it, 'a mess'.

About the year 1872 there came to Bridlington, six miles south of Speeton, a widow and her son G. W. Lamplugh, a mere youth of 13 years. It was his lot to share in the upkeep of the home by going into business, first as a shop assistant. In his spare time wanderings his attention was attracted by the fossils that lay strewn along the beach. These aroused in him an enthusiasm for geology and an ambition to become a geologist. At the age of 21 he began to explore the Speeton clays on the beach, and at the foot of the cliff where the sea at high tide had washed away the slipping clay. On summer evenings, after the shop shutters had been put up he hastened off to Speeton to spend the remaining hours of daylight examining the clays, distinguishing the layers, measuring them inch by inch; collecting fossils and recording precisely the positions where these were found. When the sun began to set he curled himself up in some sheltered spot and slept. Rising with the sun he continued his work until it was time to trek back to Bridlington. By the end of five years he produced and read to the Geological Society of London a paper which has become a classic in the geological literature of the Cretaceous rocks.

In the vital task of zoning these clays he relied mainly upon the belemnites, which were abundant and frequently almost complete. Ammonites, on the contrary, were scanty and usually only fragmentary. Among the belemnites he recognised four main types, that provided him with clues by which he could recognise four separate groups of layers known respectively as the zones of *lateralis, subquadratus, jaculum (jaculoides)* (Plate XIX) and *brunsvicensis*.

B. lateralis is a stout form more than 6 inches long and almost 2 inches wide, with a broad groove along its under side.

B. subquadratus is nearly as long but is narrower and almost cylindrical, with only a slight trace of a groove on the under side.

B. jaculum (now *jaculoides*) is a long slim elegant fossil having, as its name implies a shape like that of a javelin.

B. brunsvicensis is a smaller form 3 inches long by ½ an inch wide, with a slightly flattened cylindrical shape.

The four types have apparently no direct relationship to one another. Having evolved elsewhere they came into Britain in successive invasions: some from the north, others from the tropics.

Some of the qualities that made Lamplugh a good geologist also made him a successful business man able to afford time and money to travel to North America in pursuit of his hobby. In 1893, at the age of 33, Archibald Geikie, Director of the Geological Survey offered him a junior position on his staff. Though the remuneration was low, he evidently preferred to be a doorkeeper in the tabernacle of geology than to dwell. . .

In Lincolnshire the Spilsby Sandstone was succeeded by a variable series of deposits ranging from ironstone through clay to limestone and back again. In these the same sequence of belemnites has been found, and has made it possible to correlate these rocks with those at Speeton. On the other hand recent work upon the spores found at certain levels in the Lincolnshire series, has made it possible to correlate these marine rocks with certain layers in the freshwater Wealden deposits, a uniquely interesting achievement.

Though ammonite remains are scanty and often fragmentary, those that have been found have been precisely identified by Spath, and their position fixed in a zonal series which he had recognised in other lands. This enabled him to detect the presence of some breaks in the sequence of deposits both in Yorkshire and Lincolnshire, a fact which, together with the varying nature of the Lincolnshire rocks, reflects the instability of the region as well as the variability of the conditions usually found along and near to the shorelines of submerging areas. The fossil record, just briefly summarised, favours the reflection that the problem of peopling such areas tends to be solved, less by the evolving of new generations on the spot, than by invasion from more stable living spaces situated in deeper water further from the coastline where continuous evolution could more readily occur.

The general subsidence which led to the deposition of the Speeton clays and the corresponding rocks in Lincolnshire, affected the south of England also; with the result that at last the sea gained access to the Wealden Lake, and began to transgress across the surrounding lowlands. The marine deposits which were then laid down and which immediately overlie those of the freshwater lake, have long been known as the Lower Greensand. As with the early Cretaceous deposits in the northern basins these also exhibit breaks in succession and vary in character from one locality to another. For this reason they have received a variety of names. Though they are normally porous and therefore unsuitable for the preservation of shells and the like, fossiliferous patches do occur; such as the so-called gravels at Faringdon in which, as often as not, the pebbles are fossils, sponges, brachiopods or echinoids. Some of these are fragments of ammonites and are 'derived' fossils, for they were washed out of the underlying Kimmeridge clay outcrop before it was finally submerged. A number of belemnites have been preserved in these rocks at Sevenoaks and Godalming; and occasional specimens have been found as far north as Upware, near Cambridge, and possibly at Arlesey. These belong to the species *Neohibolites ewaldi* which is abundant in the Sutterby Marl, at the top of the Lincolnshire series; and in the Ewaldi Marls, at the top of the Speeton clays. A few ammonites belonging to the genus *Deshayesites*, found at restricted levels in association with *N. ewaldi*, occur also in the Atherfield clay which lies at the base of the Lower Greensand. All this fossil evidence serves to confirm the inference that the inundation of the Wealden Lake by the sea took place at the time when the uppermost beds at Speeton and in Lincolnshire were being formed. It fits in also with the conclusion, derived from the distribution of still more northerly patches of Lower Greensand, that transgression continued until these two new embayments of the sea became joined together by a strait lying north of London and west of the Mercian upland, over the present south-east midlands.

The Lower Greensand is succeeded by the Gault Clay and Upper Greensand. This clay attains its maximum development in the southeast where it ranges in thickness up to 300 feet; and represents those equable conditions that, as noted above, are situated further from the shore-line. Westwards and nearer to the shoreline, the clay gives way first to a silty rock, the malmstone, and then to greensand. This last may be seen capping the cliffs near Lyme Regis and the hills beyond. Evidently the 'Great Cretaceous Transgression' was now well on its way, and the sea was spreading as far as (and ultimately beyond), the former Jurassic coastline.

The chalk, which succeeded the Gault and Upper Greensand passed beyond the boundaries of these in northern Ireland and in Scotland. At its maximum extension the chalk sea must have covered all but the highest lands of Great Britain. In England the chalk is usually about 1,000 feet thick and is remarkably, though not absolutely, uniform in character throughout. Though it consists to a large extent of precipitated calcium carbonate in thin slices, examined under the microscope it is often seen to consist largely of foraminiferal shells and their debris (Plate XX: *1*). The similarity of its composition to that of the deep sea foraminiferal ooze led some nineteenth century workers to the opinion that it was of oceanic origin. The continued exploration of the chalk in the field has, however, brought to light a wealth of larger fossils, which points to water of more normal depths. Except at a few levels the quantity of sedimentary material derived from the land is remarkably small. It has therefore been suggested that the climate of the adjoining lands was very dry and that the general level of the land surface had been lowered almost to sea-level. Under such circumstances the rivers would be greatly reduced and able to transport only the very finest sediments. Conditions of life in the chalk sea appear to have been remarkably equable and favourable throughout that prolonged spell of time reflected by the great thickness of these almost impalpable sediments.

CHAPTER 34

AMMONITES IN DECLINE

T HE recession of the sea from off Britain at the close of the Jurassic period, in addition to bringing about a minor break in the sequence of the rocks, led to a corresponding gap in the story of marine life in this region. There were, however, ample living spaces, in other parts of Europe and of the world, where evolutionary processes continued to unfold a complex story; in which various streams of organisms pursued their diverse and separate courses. When the sea returned to Britain these streams came flowing back, and the different types of organisms came in whensoever and wheresoever conditions suited their needs. In the early stages, when the sea was creeping westwards across the area, the conditions resembled those of the Jurassic in that they varied considerably from place to place and from time to time. But later, when the main shoreline had shifted beyond the former western boundaries of the Jurassic sea, conditions became relatively uniform everywhere and remained so for a long period.

Once more, as during the Jurassic, ammonites were common, and their remains have furnished the geologist with the usual valuable basis for dating and correlating the strata. Once more therefore they merit our full attention.

It must be assumed that the Cretaceous ammonites descended from those of the Jurassic but direct evidence is not forthcoming from the British rocks; partly because of the break in the sequence already mentioned, and partly because Britain, instead of being a home or centre for evolution, was at first only a reception area for emigrants. Nevertheless, on the basis of the principle that similarity of structural character implies relationship, the several strains already studied may be recognised in a modified form among the Cretaceous ammonites.

Derivatives of the round-ventered Stephanoceratids and Perisphinctids are represented at the outset in the Speeton clays by isolated genera such as *Subcraspedites, Polyptychites* and *Simbirskites,* and later in the Lower Gault by the strongly ribbed and tuberculated *Douvillieceras* and, as late as the base of the Upper Chalk, by *Puzosia* and *Lewesiceras.*

At the top of the Speeton series, in the Ewaldi marls, appears *Deshayesites,* a moderately closely coiled form in which the inner coils are partially hidden by the outer. The latter are slightly compressed and elevated and decorated with ribs that meet at an angle on the venter. This ammonite has a double interest. On the one hand it is found also in the Sutterby marl of Lincolnshire, and in a peculiar bed of rock, which crops out on the beach at Hunstanton, Norfolk; and again in the Atherfield Clay at the base of the Lower Greensand in the South of England. Its range in time is much shorter than that of the belemnite *Neohibolites ewaldi;* and therefore marks still more precisely the geological moment when the sea broke into and dispelled the peacefulness of the Wealden Lake, and finally established a link with the northern embayment across the midlands.

Deshayesites is also an early representative of another and important stream of ammonites which made up practically half the ammonite population of the quiet Gault waters. The contemporary deposits extend far and wide over south-eastern England, and have always been available for examination in the classical cliff exposures at Folkestone. The ammonites found here were familarly known to the collectors in the nineteenth century under the generic name of *Hoplites.* This name, however, included such a great range of variation in the degree of compression and height of the outer whorl, as well as in

---

PLATE XXI

MARINE FOSSILS OF THE QUATERNARY

Early Tertiary: 1. *Xanthopsis,* a crab like crustacean. 2. *Pectunculus.* 3. *Lamna (Otodus).* 4. *Panopaea.* 5. *Crassatella.* 6. *Calliostoma. (Trochus).* 7. *Odontaspis.* 8. *Turritella.* 9. *Fusinus (Fusus).* 10. *Volutospina.* (1, 2, 3, 4, 7 are from the London Clay. 5, 6, 8, 9, 10 are from Barton Beds, Barton, Hants.)
Late Tertiary: 11. *Neptunea.* 12. *Buccinum.* 13. *Natica.* 14. *Nassa.* (All from the Ked Crag, Walton on Naze.)
Pleistocene: 15. *Macoma.* 16. *Cardium.* 17 and 18. *Nucula,* outer and inner views.
Classification: Vertebrates — 3, 7, Sharks' teeth. Arthropod, Crustacea — 1. Molluscs — Lamellibranchs. 2, 4, 5, 15, 16, 17, 18, Gastropods. 6, 8, 9, 10-14. *(Photographs by H.M. Geol. Survey)*

PLATE XXII. AN EARLY TERTIARY LANDSCAPE

This imaginary picture is set in the South East of England when the London Clay was being formed. On the left *Magnolias* are in bloom. Below these little ancestral horses, *Hyrachotherium* run around. Above, Ostrich-like birds are seen on the coastal flats. Left centre is a group of Palm trees and on the flat beyond is *Coryphodon* a hippopotamus-like mammal. Right centre crocodiles wallow in the swamp. On the right is a cluster of trees including *Gingko*, Oak, Walnut, Breadfruit and tall swamp cypresses.

(*H.M. Geol. Survey*)

ornamentation, that a number of species became recognised. From 1920-40 L. F. Spath turned his attention to them; and by combining careful collecting and precise recording of levels, with detailed examination of great numbers of specimens, he traced their gradations into one another. He thus came to distinguish several evolving lines, and crystallised his knowledge in a series of new generic names of an almost ideal type. In each of these he retained the familiar old name of *Hoplites*, but distinguished the line and successive evolving stages by such prefixes as *Proto-, Eu-, Epi-, Ana-;* take for an example the name *Euhoplites*.

The fact that he was able to do this with British specimens shows that, during the Gault period, equable living conditions favourable to the ammonite's mode of life persisted for some time; and southeast England became a home, or at least part of a home, where evolutionary development proceeded with but little interruption. With the close of the Gault period the Hoplitids disappeared almost completely from British waters. *Schloenbachia*, from the Lower Chalk, was probably their last representative (Plate XX: *5*). Evolving alongside with the Hoplitids were the less numerous keeled types, of which *Mortoniceras* is perhaps the best known representative. Spath considered that both these streams originated through the genus *Desmoceras* from the long-ranged *Phylloceras* stock to which reference has already been made.

Living alongside these normal ammonites were a number of others which, because they exhibit unusual peculiarities of form are known as heteromorphs. These evolved elsewhere and are represented in the British Cretaceous rocks by sundry immigrants many of which were apparently derived from the Lytocerates. *Lytoceras* itself did not appear in the British seas, but *Crioceras*-like forms made an important section of the ammonite population. As in *Lytoceras* their coils were round in cross-section but they were no longer in close contact with one another for the spiral had loosened and opened out. They had therefore ceased to give mutual support; consequently they were easily broken apart, and their fossil remains are usually fragmentary. Differences in ornamentation make it possible to distinguish species and genera, some of which have proved useful as zone fossils.

In *Macroscaphites* from the Lower Gault, the early growth stages resemble *Lytoceras* sufficiently to suggest that it also was a derivative of that genus. In later life the outer coil grew straight for some distance and then bent back upon itself like a hook. Towards the end of the Lower Cretaceous it gave rise to *Scaphites* and was replaced by this for the remainder of the Cretaceous period. The long range in time of *Macroscaphites* testifies to the stability of this abnormal type, which may also have given origin to even more striking and likewise stable forms having points of resemblance to *Bactrites,* that far-off ancestral ammonoid of the Devonian period. There is an interesting parallelism between the histories of the Triassic ammonites and those of late Mesozoic times. In both cases in some sections the factors which governed the main characteristics, coiling, ornamentation and sutures, remained in control until the end while in others their influence weakened and set free tendencies that gave rise to abnormal heteromorph types and culminated in the straight *Baculites.* That flourished in North America until the close of the Cretaceous period, but is represented in Britain only by *Cyrtochilus.*

Another and more abnormal form, arising from the same stock, was *Turrilites* in which the shell-coil became helicoid or turreted like that of the gastropods. One specimen of especial interest was found by L. F. Spath in the Gault clay. This was *Engonoceras,* which exhibited a very different kind of abnormality. In general appearance it looked like an ordinary ammonite but its suture line had lost the complicated folding and frilling which characterised the ammonites throughout their long history, and had returned a long way towards the simplicity of the Goniatite in the roundness of the upfolds. The downfolds, however, showed incipient frilling like that seen in the Permo-Triassic *Ceratites.* This rare form must be regarded as a stray migrant from its North American home.

With the close of the Cretaceous period the great race of ammonites disappeared completely, not only from British seas but from those of the rest of the world. These facts show how even the tattered records of the British rocks reflect the major events in world history.

The reason for the extinction of the ammonites still remains an unsolved mystery. Many of the abnormal types appear to have lived quite happily in the same waters and under the same conditions as the vigorously evolving Hoplitids. The progressive changes manifested in one, and the implied recession to earlier structural features in the other, can hardly be ascribed to changes in environment; for this seems to have remained constant during the deposition of the Gault clay in which their remains were entombed.

The passage from Gault to Chalk must have been accompanied by some changes in the character of the environment during which, however, the Hoplitid stock still survived in the genera *Schloenbachia* and *Hypohoplites*. It is interesting to note, that while the index fossils for all the main zones recognised in the Lower Cretaceous rocks have been selected from among the ammonites, this is not the case for the Upper Cretaceous. Out of the 11 zones recognised in the English Chalk only one, and that the lowest, is named after an ammonite. This fact reflects the relative scarcity of these cephalopods in the Chalk. Nevertheless the presence of immigrants such as the giant *Prionotropus*, of species of *Scaphites*, *Turrilites* and of baculite forms, shows that the conditions, though not very favourable, were not entirely inimical to the ammonites. It would seem therefore that the causes for their slow decline and extinction must be sought for within and not solely outside these organisms.

CHAPTER 35

EVOLVING IN PEACE

AMONG the many and varied types of landscape which make up the British countryside, none is so peaceful as that of the Chalk downlands, with their gently curving skylines and smooth open valleys untorn by rocky cliffs and gorges. Not less peaceful were the conditions in that sea wherein, ages ago, the chalky foundations of that landscape were laid down. Then as now the surface waters of the sea may have been lashed into fury by passing storms, but even at depths only a few fathoms down the influence of these storms was practically unfelt. In those shallower waters into which the sunshine penetrated myriads of minute foraminifera lived, died, and sinking settled like dew upon the floor below. Today vast areas of the ocean floor are covered with such foraminiferal ooze. Nineteenth century geologists, examining samples of chalk in very thin slices, saw in them a close resemblance to consolidated ooze, and concluded that it also had been formed in profound oceanic depths; and formed so slowly that one inch alone corresponded to a hundred years, a mere moment in the vast period during which were formed the 1200 feet of chalk which underlie the Downs.

As indicated earlier this rock has yielded a rich variety of fossil remains of creatures belonging to every section of the animal kingdom, from minute foraminifera and polyzoa, to large ammonites and bony fishes and even giant marine lizards. The presence of all these shows clearly that the chalk sea was not oceanic but epicontinental, probably much of it less than 1000 feet deep and therefore more comparable with the Mediterranean.

This chalk sea, however, differed markedly from the Mediterranean in both its internal and surrounding conditions. This is indicated by the general paucity of all but the finest sediments derived from the land; a fact which suggests that the surface of the adjoining lands had been reduced by prolonged denudation almost to sea-level, so that the gradients of all the rivers were very low. Furthermore it seems that the climate was dry and consequently the quantity of water small. On both counts the flow of the rivers was so slow that they could transport only the finest sediments. The rocks themselves show that, while the lowest layers reflect littoral conditions, and the base of the Middle Chalk a temporary return to shallower waters, an over-whelming proportion of the remainder was probably deposited in depths of 1000 or even 1500 feet.

The variety and healthy development of many different animal types reflects the favourableness of the conditions under which they lived. Though these conditions had a stability quite unknown on land, the successive generations were far from being stationary in physical structure. While no great waves of new immigrants invaded this sea, faunal changes were brought about by the evolution of the organisms within the area. It is not surprising therefore that fossils from the chalk have supplied material for many interesting evolutionary invest-igations. Several of these have been carried out upon the Echinoderms, which are relatively common, often remarkably well preserved, and comparatively easy to extract from the rock.

Among the regular echinoids the ancient genus *Cidaris* (Plate XX: 3) still survived and was accompanied by others, such as *Salenia* and *Phymosoma*, which have a similar decoration but a flattened test, and their simple ambulacral plates show a tendency to unite and become compound.

The irregular echinoids, which became established during the Jurassic period, were quite numerous. One section of them is typified by *Conulus* which still retained some features characteristic of its regular ancestors, such as a centrally placed mouth armed with jaws, but these had become vestigeal. The test had a smooth surface and a conical form. The several species of this genus, found at different levels in the chalk, varied in height; those from the layers formed in shallow or in deep waters were respectively low and high. To what extent this is really indicative of the influence of environment in stimulating an evolutionary trend is a matter for speculation.

In another section, represented by the genera *Echinocorys*, *Holaster* and *Micraster*, bilateral symmetry had become well established; the mouth had shifted forward and the jaws had disappeared (Plate XX: 2, 8, 9). In the closing decade of last century the limelight of interest was concentrated upon *Micraster*. This heart-shaped urchin is relatively common at many levels from the Middle Chalk upwards. The interest was aroused by the work of A. W. Rowe; a medical doctor practising at Margate, who found respite from his many professional and public activities in collecting and examining fossils from the chalk exposures along the Kentish coast. In addition to keeping accurate records of the positions in the chalk where his specimens were found he cleaned them with the greatest care and subjected them to the minutest scrutiny. Much of this work was done at the end of the day after finishing his other duties, and was often carried far into the midnight hours.

The test of an echinoid is a miniature but wonderful building made up of a multitude of calcareous plates differing in size and shape but fitly joined together in perfect harmony. Looking at an echinoid, as it reposes in a museum show-case, it is difficult to realise that it was once a little living cosmos, in which new plates were being continually produced near the apex of the test. As the creature grew, these plates travelled slowly outwards across the upper surface, descended beyond the ambitus or circumference and arriving on the lower surface, moved slowly towards the mouth. Throughout this journey the size, outline and surface curvature of each plate was being adjusted to fit in close accord with its fellows, and in harmony with the shape of the test as a whole.

In the quiet hours of darkness Dr. Rowe must often have been thrilled, while he examined his numerous and carefully docketted specimens and followed the course of the many evolutionary changes that had taken place in this *Micraster* cosmos as the long ages of the Cretaceous period unfolded. He traced these changes not merely in the organism as a whole but in a score or more of the small structural parts of the test. Each of these, as it changed in harmony with the whole, passed independently through its own sequence of changes. It is out of the question here to follow Dr. Rowe through all the developmental and evolutionary stories as he spelled them out for every part; but two examples may be outlined as typical of the rest.

In the regular echinoid the mouth, as seen from below, is round and its margin lies wholly in a horizontal plane. In *Micraster* the mouth is situated well in front of the centre, and in the earliest species is transversely oval in outline. Later the hind margin of the oval bent down below the level of the front. In this way a lower lip was formed which, acting as a scoop, directed a stream of nutritious mud into the mouth as the animal moved slowly over the surface of the oozy sea-floor. Dr. Rowe found that in later species this lip gradually grew forwards and became a still more effective scoop.

The second example is taken from the ambulacral areas near the top of the test. These lie in concave furrows radiating like petals from the apex. The floor of each furrow is made up of narrow plates arranged transversely and having their inner ends in contact along a zigzag line down the middle. In the earlier species, the outer surfaces of these are flat and smooth. In later species, at the inner end of each plate, the surface becomes inflated and decorated with granules. In the latest the swellings become separated by a median zigzag groove which was eventually steep-sided and trenchlike. These systematic featural changes seem to have no functional significance, they just happened. It has been suggested that they provided a miniature dumping ground for an excess of lime-secretion. But this need was already met by a progressive thickening of the test as a whole. More-over these changes were merely passing phases in the development of the individual plates for, as each of these grew and migrated from the apex, inflation and decoration first rose to a climax and then declining finally disappeared before the plate left the upper surface of the test.

On that vast sea-floor with its uniform and stable conditions, its inexhaustible store of food, and apparent absence of competition, the precise influences which stimulated these serial changes must have been largely internal and genetic. No doubt they originated primarily as combinations of mutations in the gene-complex but their expression was guided by selection. From Dr. Rowe's detailed studies of these and many other features in the *Micraster* there seems to be no evidence that the steps in these changes occurred at random. On the contrary, as judged by his very full records, they seem to have been related to one another as systematically as the links in a chemist's chain series, when he is building up new molecules with new properties. What then is a mutation? Is it the starting point of a new series, or is it each step in the sequence?

The stability of the hereditary make-up and the steadiness of its progressive changes, as indicated by the physical features in the test, received support from the large communities of interbreeding individuals; each endowed with a closely similar if not identical hereditary equipment. In such communities fresh changes would not be swamped, but strengthened and distributed, and so become in their turn the springboard for further changes.

The total result of all these developmental and evolutionary changes was a progressive modification of the test as a whole; which made it possible for an experienced collector to identify the zone from which he was gathering his specimens. Dr. Rowe's detailed studies have therefore proved to be not only of deep theoretic interest, but of real value to the economic and industrial geologist.

The Asteroid or Starfish division of the echinoderms has received very careful attention from W. K. Spencer, for whom such study proved a pleasant diversion from his duties as a Royal Inspector of Schools. Of special interest is the *Pentagonaster* group. This name well describes the shape of these asteroids; for in them the central area of the body extended, and encroached upon the five rays of the star, until these were represented only by the angles of the pentagon. Its upper and lower surfaces were composed of a mosaic of thin calcareous plates and enclosed the body cavity. The plates which formed the margins of the two surfaces were much thickened, in accordance with the depth of the body cavity which, with the passage of time, became deeper and more capacious. This change was reflected in these marginals, for they underwent a corresponding increase in height and change in shape. Complete specimens of these asteroids are rare but the separate marginals are relatively common and can also be used for zonal purposes.

Evidence for the existence of crinoids is usually rare in the chalk. Nevertheless for a brief period they were represented by the two genera *Uintacrinus* and *Marsupites* (Plate XX: 7). Conditions were far from favourable for attached crinoids but these two, which had evolved

---

PLATE XXIII

a. SUB-FOSSIL POLLEN GRAINS

1. *Quercus* (Oak). 2. *Alnus* (Alder). 3. *Corylus* (Hazel). 4. A patch of algal remains. Ehenside, Cumberland. (*H. Godwin*)

b. BLAKEMERE NEAR ELLESMERE

This North Shropshire landscape is typical of a countryside that has been smothered under hummocky glacial deposits. The hollows are occupied by lakes and meres with marshy and peaty margins, and are surrounded by wooded hills. (*H.M. Geol. Survey*)

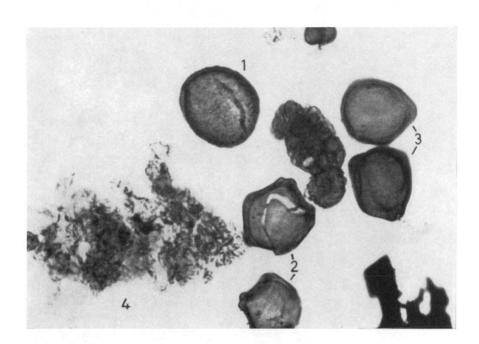

1   2

3   4   5   6

elsewhere, had lost their stalks and had adopted a free-swimming habit in which the arms, with a waving movement not unlike that of the bell of a jellyfish, wafted the creature with stately motion through the water. It was at this advanced stage in their history that they came swarming into British waters. In both of them the body was capacious and enclosed by numerous small plates in *Uintacrinus* and only a few large ones in *Marsupites*. These exquisite creatures vanished as quickly as they came but the presence of their remains is very characteristic of zonal horizons near the top of the chalk.

Among the Mollusca the Pelecypoda are represented in the chalk by many genera but more especially by allies of *Pecten*. While this genus and *Lima* retained their freedom of movement others adopted a sedentary habit. *Plicatula*, like *Ostrea*, became attached by cementation. *Spondylus* on the other hand was anchored in the mud by long spines. Two other non-related genera may be mentioned: *Trigonia*, because in the chalk sea it made its last appearance in British waters; and *Inoceramus* (Plate XX: 6), because it formed the subject of an interesting evolutionary study by H. Woods, lecturer in Palaeontology at Cambridge. After playing an insignificant part in the faunas of the Jurassic seas, this genus blossomed out into two actively evolving stocks in early Cretaceous times. These flourished throughout the time of formation of the chalk and eventually produced species of great size. Detailed descriptions of the changes traced by Dr. Woods cannot be given here; but reference may be made to the reappearance of two trends of development, one of which was seen in the *Ostrea—Gryphaea* series during the Jurassic. In the late species *Inoceramus involutus* the left valve became greatly thickened and the umbo curved. This species,

---

PLATE XXIV

SAMPLES OF PREHISTORIC MAN'S HANDYWORK

Palaeolithic: 1. Acheulian handaxe, 6-7 inches long. Ruskington, Lincs. 2. Acheulian handaxe, 4·4 inches long, Salmonby, Lincs.

Neolithic: 3. 'Rough out' of stone axe, 8 inches long, from the Great Langdale axe factory.

Bronze Age, Early: 4. Flint 'Beaker' dagger, 4 inches long. Osgodby, near Market Rasen, Lincs. 5. Polished Flint axe, 8·5 inches long. Cold Hanworth, Lincs.

Bronze Age, Early Middle: 6. Polished Stone axe, 6 inches long. Bishop Norton, Lincs. (*Photographs by F. T. Baker*)

like *Gryphaea*, must have rested permanently in the mud on this valve. Meanwhile the thin right valve functioned as a lid or operculum which opened and shut according to the needs of the organism. In one variant of the species *Inoceramus inconstans* both valves were enormously thickened, and they reproduced the conditions already seen in the liassic genus *Hippopodium*, the significance of which is still a mystery.

Other equally interesting studies were made by Dr. W. D. Lang on the simple coral *Parasmilia*, and the little colonial organisms the *Polyzoa*. But these cannot be described here for this chapter has already exceeded its proper limits.

All these studies emphasise the impression already made that, despite the quietude and uniformity of the conditions in the Cretaceous sea, a constant pressure towards evolutionary change was maintained, peacefully and without strife, in all sections of the animal population. In the samples described above the urge seems to have come initially from within the organism but it nevertheless must have acted to some extent under the directive influence of the creature's needs and surroundings; that is to say of natural selection.

Part Four

AN ERA OF
CULMINATIONS
THE CAINOZOIC

CHAPTER 36

THE EMERGENCE OF BRITAIN

IN LATE Cretaceous times uplifting movements of the earth's crust brought about the withdrawal of the sea, and the conversion of the British region into a broad expanse of chalk downlands. These events marked the opening of the Cainozoic Era (kaino = recent) which has lasted some 70 millions of years and embraces the age in which we live (v. Table p. 31). It therefore includes that stretch of time usually known as the Tertiary Era, together with the last brief span of one million years called the Quaternary Era. This little snippet of time during which man has existed on the earth is, on that account, regarded by some workers in some moods as of equal importance with the other and immeasurably longer eras.

In early Tertiary times great rock folding forces developed across Central Europe and culminated in the upheaval of the Alps. The ground-swell of these movements affected the south of England and produced minor upfolds along the axis of the Weald and of the Isle of Wight, together with complementary downfolds which gave rise to the London and the Hampshire basins. These latter became submerged, and in them were laid down a varied assortment of deposits —marine, estuarine and freshwater—the differing facies of which are named after the localities where they are best known, e.g., Thanet Sands, London Clay, Bracklesham Beds and Bembridge Limestone.

Uplifting movements then resulted once more in the complete retirement of the sea from off the British area which was then, for a long time, no more than the core of a spacious peninsula extending from Europe westwards beyond the confines of Ireland into the Atlantic.

In late Tertiary times the sea returned once more and, by flooding the low-lying land between Britain and the continent, began to institute the North Sea. On its western margin this sea trespassed across East

Anglia and covered much of it with richly fossiliferous sandy deposits known as Crags.

The marine faunas preserved in both the early and the late Tertiary deposits, present a striking contrast to those yielded by the Chalk. The most obvious differences are due to the physiographic revolutions described above. These abolished the stable conditions that had prevailed for so long in the Cretaceous seas; and had substituted minor intrusions and recessions of marine waters which, being mainly coastal, were accompanied by conditions that changed rapidly from place to place, and by correspondingly changeable faunas. The more fundamental differences of the latter were, however, due to the stately progress of evolution, which was pursuing its course uninterruptedly in distant and more stable areas, from whence occasional waves of emigrants swept into the British seas.

In the Tertiary deposits, as in all the earlier rock systems, molluscs filled a prominent place in the fauna, but they were represented by different categories. Among the cephalopods the ammonoids after losing their supremacy had disappeared. The nautiloids survived only in the genus *Nautilus*. The belemnoids had also gone but were represented by close allies which, though they left behind them only scanty traces of fossil remains, lived on and, continuing to evolve, carried the cephalopod type to a fresh acme in the familiar cuttlefish and *Octopus*.

On the other hand the Gastropoda and Pelecypoda, which had been relatively inconspicuous in Palaeozoic times, when the nautiloids were at their zenith, went on evolving and producing new genera and species even into the present epoch. Thus for example among the Gastropoda, during the age of ammonites, were *Turritella* and *Natica* in the Trias; *Nerita* in the Jurassic; *Fusinus* and *Neptunea*, in the Cretaceous (Plate XXI). Though some of these reached their maximum of development during the Tertiary and have since begun to decline, they still have relatives living in existing seas and rivers. The inception of new genera continued throughout the Cainozoic Era; *Conus* appeared in the Eocene; *Trochus*, in the Miocene; *Nassa* and *Buccinum*, in the Pliocene. In this way both these great divisions of the Mollusca went on increasing, and rose to that prominent position they hold in the world today.

It is not surprising that molluscs fill so large a place in any collection of Tertiary fossils. Thus for example the deposits exposed at Bracklesham, on the coast of Sussex, are said to have yielded no less than 500 species. These are in almost as perfect a state of preservation as shells found on modern beaches. Naturally therefore these Tertiary shells were among the first to attract the attention of both British and continental workers. The latter, however, had the great advantage that they had access to a much fuller succession of deposits.

As the result of their collecting it soon became evident that, though Tertiary genera survived into existing seas, many of the species became extinct. The French scientist Deshayes made a statistical investigation of the species found at different levels; and established the fact that, in advancing from lower to higher horizons, the number of species that are also living today increased. Sir Charles Lyell, who spent much time on the continent studying the Mollusca, soon grasped the value of Deshayes' discovery for classifying the Tertiary formations on the basis of the living species they contained. He therefore suggested the divisions shown on the accompanying table.

TABLE

THE DIVISION OF TERTIARY TIME

Percentage of molluscan species living today	Divisions suggested
35% — 50%	Pliocene (more recent)
17%	Miocene (less recent)
3.5%	Eocene (dawn of recent)

Another division, the Oligocene (slightly recent), was subsequently interposed between the Eocene and the Miocene. At a later date Lyell added the Pleistocene (most recent) for those Post-Tertiary or Quaternary deposits in which practically 100% of the marine species exist today. On the basis of this scheme the Tertiary strata of the Thames and Hampshire basins have been allocated mainly to the Eocene and the Oligocene; and those of East Anglia to the Pliocene periods.

One striking feature about the Lower Tertiary molluscan faunas of Britain is that some of their elements, though they are no longer present in British seas, resemble those now living further south in Mediterranean or even tropical seas. As examples of this the following genera may be mentioned; among the Pelecypoda, *Crassatella;* among the Gastropoda; *Conus, Voluta* and *Fusus.* Along with these Nautilus may be quoted for it lives in the Indo-Pacific waters. Complementary to this retirement of Eocene faunas to southern seas was the entry

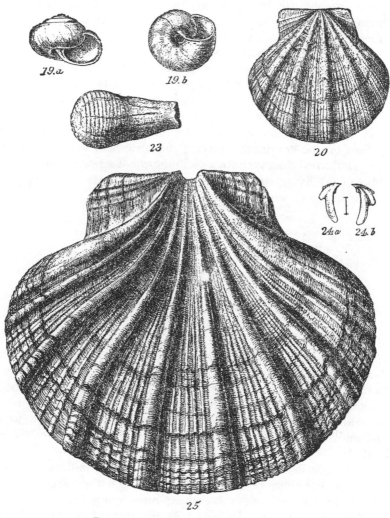

Fig. 19. FOSSILS FROM THE CRAG

19. *Helix fructicum*. 20, *Pecten polymorphus*. 23, *Pholadidea,* cast of cavity formed by a boring mollusc. 24, *Aplysia*. 25, *Pecten maximus* var *larvatus*, abnormal ½ correct number of ribs. (Reproduced from Searles V. Wood *Monograph of the Crag Mollusca. Pal. Soc. Vol. II, Appendix, Plate XXXI. Publ. 1851-61. Compare Fig. 1, page 4.)

into the British area, during late Tertiary times, of genera from the colder northern regions. These included the pelecypods *Glycimeris* (*Pectunculus*) and *Yoldia;* and the gastropods *Neptunea, Buccinum* (whelk) and *Littorina* (winkle).

In 1900 F. W. Harmer published the results of a statistical study he had made of the extinct, the southern, and the northern species found in the different stratigraphical horizons of the East Anglian Crags. His summary is given in the accompanying table, in which the strata involved are named according to the district in which they occur.

TABLE

CONSTITUTION OF THE FAUNAS
IN THE PLIOCENE OF EAST ANGLIA

Stratal Horizons	Species now extinct	Southern species	Northern species
Norwich Crag	11%	7%	32%
Butley Crag	13%	13%	23%
Newbourne Crag	32%	16%	11%
Walton Crag	36%	20%	5%
Gedgrave Crag	38%	26%	1%

From this table it will be seen that two types of progressive faunal change were going on simultaneously. First there was an evolutionary one involving the disappearance of species either by actual extinction or by transformation into new species. Second there was a geographical one resulting from the departure of less hardy species to more genial climes, and the entry of hardy species from colder northern seas. Taken as a whole these facts point to a gradual worsening of the climatic conditions. This change was, however, probably enhanced by the closure of the southern entry to the North Sea and the opening of the northern. Thus the path was blocked for the entry of southern and opened for that of the northern forms. Among the latter special reference may be made to the genus *Yoldia*, species of which now characterise the Arctic waters.

Other elements in the British Tertiary marine faunas must now be more briefly mentioned. In rocks of all ages Foraminifera occur and are normally inconspicuously small. In Lower Tertiary times one section blossomed out into giant individuals often more than one inch in diameter. These flourished greatly in Mediterranean seas and built up massive limestone, blocks of which were used in the Pyramids. They were essentially warm water organisms and the presence of several species in the British Eocene supplies yet further evidence that the climate of Britain was at that time more genial than now. Corals and Echinoids tell a similar story. While both groups flourished in Mediterranean seas they had their representatives in the British Eocene; nevertheless these were small in size and few in numbers of individuals and of species.

In the Jurassic rocks some crustacean arthropods show a tendency towards a broadening of the carapace, or the fore part of the body, and a reduction of the abdomen or so called 'tail'. This culminated in the production of the Brachyura or crab-like forms of crustacea such as *Xanthopsis* which is found in the London Clay (Plate XXI: *1*).

The climatic changes indicated by the successive Pliocene faunas lead our thoughts on to the last great series of events which gave the final touches to the face of Britain. Overlying the uppermost members of the Crag series of deposits are others which indicate that the delta of some great river on the continent had encroached upon the North Sea even as far as the East Anglian coastlands. Here some twenty feet of deposits accumulated which are now known as the Cromer Forest beds. These were laid down in an estuary into which fragments of trees and of land animals had been swept. With these occur the shells of indigenous species of the pelecypod genera *Mya* and *Cardium*. There also occurs *Macoma balthica,* which as its name indicates is a northern form (Plate XXI: *15*). Beneath and above these estuarine deposits occur fossiliferous peaty beds known as the Lower and Upper Freshwater beds. These are in turn succeeded by marine deposits whose mineral grains have been shown to have been derived from boulder clay, and therefore indicate the proximity of a great expanse of ice known as the Scandinavian Ice Sheet. This fact introduces us forthwith to the first of a series of Ice Ages which afflicted Britain during the next 500,000 or possibly one million years. Records of that series are to be seen in the cliffs of the Norfolk Coast, including those which overlook the foreshore upon which the Cromer Forest Beds have been exposed and examined.

These cliffs are made up largely of deposits laid down by glaciers and ice-sheets coming from the north and north west; they consist of boulder clays, and of gravels and sands washed out by the waters that issued forth from these as they melted. The cliffs exhibit only the truncated edges of widespread sheets, which make up a relatively thin covering over much of Britain and hide from view the rocks which, according to ordinary geological maps, should be exposed at the surface. A careful study of this Glacial Drift, as it is called, leaves no doubt that, during Quaternary times, Britain was extensively occupied by ice-sheets and glaciers for several brief spells of time, each lasting about 20,000 years. These spells are known as glaciations.

The intervals between these glaciations were warmer and are called Inter-glacials. At the onset of each of these the winters were severe, and snow accumulated over the whole landscape. In summer the temperature rose sufficiently high to melt all the accumulated winter snow, together with some of the ice. At that season innumerable streamlets of escaping water spread gravel and sand over broad areas of the lowlands. Coming together these streamlets swelled the rivers into mighty floods laden with stones and gravel, with which they were able to scour out and deepen their channels into wide trench-like valleys with flat floors such as those of Trent and Severn. Later, as the climate ameliorated, the winter snows were replaced by showers of rain, and consequently the run-off of water took place steadily. The rivers, now reduced in volume, meandered on their way down to the sea all the year round, and carpeted the valley floors with gravel, sand and alluvium. During these genial interludes plants, animals and even men, lived happily upon these river plains; and, when they died, left their remains upon the ground where they usually perished, but sometimes they became buried and fossilised.

After each glaciation a similar sequence of events was repeated. The sub-arctic summer floods excavated new trench-like valleys within the floor of the previous ones. Usually fragments of the old floor were left as terraces along the flanks of the new valley. Thus it comes about that, alongside the Thames and other large rivers, series of terraces occur at different levels, silent witnesses to the recurrence of glacial and interglacial intervals. They are valuable as storehouses for the remains of man, of his handiwork; and of fossilised plants and animals that were contemporary with him.

The stretch of time during which these final touches were being given to the surface of Britain, is called the Pleistocene. The 10,000 years or more that have elapsed since the last glaciation is called the Holocene (completely recent). These together make up the whole of the Quaternary.

CHAPTER 37

BIRDS AND FISHES

AT FIRST sight it may seem that the bringing together of these two extremes into one chapter is incongruous; for, apart from being vertebrates, they appear to have nothing in common in ancestry and descent. Fancy may, however, link them together by analogy. Thus for example, both these types live with triumphant success in elements from which man has been completely excluded until recent years. Again from a mechanical point of view, it is not too absurd to say that a bird swims through air and a fish flies through the sea. In performing these operations they have both been so successful that they are now in the heyday of their evolutionary history, and at their peak both in numbers and variety. That fact makes it difficult to deal with that history concisely in a few pages, a difficulty that is enhanced by the scantiness of the fossil record in British rocks.

As seen above we owe more abundant records of the terrestrial reptilian story to the fact that these creatures must often have been caught unawares by great riverine floods. We also pictured the early mammals as being more alert. But, though many of these could find a refuge in trees from rising floods, in a few cases these leafy citadels were swept away and their mammalian refugees perished with them. No doubt the birds also sought safety in trees but, when these fell crashing into the waters, they merely flipped their wings and escaped disaster.

An old fossil fragment or two, named *Enalliornis*, has been found in the Cambridge Greensand, and is the only bit of evidence that true birds already existed in Britain during early Cretaceous times. It has been classed with *Hesperornis*, of which complete remains had been found in the Upper Cretaceous of Kansas, U.S.A. These show that it combined a diving habit with strong powers of flight. Geologically speaking, the lapse of time between *Archaeopteryx* from the Jurassic of Bavaria and *Enalliornis* from the Cambridge Greensand was relatively short; and fits in well with the view that, once the mechanical principle of flight had been expressed in bone and muscle, adaptive development proceeded rapidly. Here is a palaeontological parallel to the rapid. progress in the development of the aeroplane during this century.

Like *Ichthyosaurus* among reptiles, seals and porpoises among mammals, and fisher folk among prehistoric peoples, most of the known early birds gained a living by catching fish. Thus among the fossil remains of birds, especially from the London Clay along the coast of Sheppey, *Proherodius* was a heron; *Odontopteryx*, which had sharp points along its horny beak, and *Argillornis* were related to the cormorants; *Prophaeton* was allied to a large present day tropical sea bird; finally a fragment of the skull of *Halcyornis* has been compared with that of the kingfisher.

Among living birds some, such as the kiwi of New Zealand, and the ostrich, have given up flying and have become groundlings. Such birds are exposed to the same hazards from storm and flood as other land animals. It is interesting to note therefore that *Gastornis*, from the Lower Eocene of Croydon was a long-legged running bird. With it may also be associated *Dasornis* from the London Clay of Sheppey.

The finding of these birds shows that their association with an aquatic environment, and the cessation of the flying habit, led to more opportunities for the accidents of life to be followed by burial and preservation in the fossil state. *Ibidipsis* was an ibis from the Oligocene, *Aetornis* was another cormorant from the Oligocene of Hordwell, Hampshire; and *Diomedea* was a Pliocene albatross, from the Red Crag of Norfolk. The more recent deposits of the fenland and of Glastonbury Lake village have yielded pelicans. Nevertheless fragments of *Lithornis*, a bird of prey from Sheppey, and of *Palaeocircus*, another of the same kind from the Oligocene of Hordwell, shows that even flying birds may at times be caught in the net of geological disaster, a fact which raises hope for future extensions in the knowledge of Bird History.

Turning now to the fishes the great interest, indeed excitement, caused by the recent catching of a live coelacanth, *Latimeria*, is almost a palaeontological version of 'rejoice with me for I have found that which was lost'. For until that event the last known representative of that very ancient Devonian type of fish was *Macropoma*. This fossil fish, nearly two feet long, was found in a remarkably well-preserved state in the English chalk, and therefore lived about 100 million years ago. It was described by Sir Arthur Smith Woodward of the British Museum who, during the early part of this century, did such a great work for vertebrate palaeontology in general and fossil fish in particular.

As the glamour of fresh discovery fades away from *Latimeria* it will be relegated, as a new recruit, to the ranks of living fossils alongside with the already familiar *Ceratodus* from Australia, and *Polypterus* from the rivers of Africa. These are three of the last survivors of that great Palaeozoic stock, the fringe-finned fishes, from which all terrestrial vertebrates, including man himself, have descended; and of which the Coelacanths were merely one specialised offshoot.

Another 'living fossil' is the Port Jackson shark, *Cestracion*. As with sharks generally its skeleton consists mainly of cartilage, a perishable material having about the same consistency as a rather tough radish. Consequently, apart from teeth, these fishes are rarely preserved in the fossil state. Nevertheless an almost complete skeleton of *Drepanophorus*, a close relative of *Cestracion*, has been found in the chalk of England. Fossil teeth, however, show that sharks of the same type also lived as long ago as Carboniferous times; along with many other primitive types of fish which succumbed to those antagonistic influences already noted that brought so many animal types to the verge of extinction at the close of the Palaeozoic Era. The presence of the teeth of *Hybodus* and *Acrodus*, even in British triassic rocks, is part of the evidence which shows that cestraciont sharks survived the general holocaust, possibly because, like the Port Jackson shark, their jaws were equipped with two types of teeth. Those situated on the front of the jaws were sharp and suitable for holding active prey; but the hind teeth had flattened crowns and could be used for crushing either soft seaweeds or the hard shells of molluscs. A jaw of *Synechodus*, with a remarkably complete set of teeth, was found in the chalk of Sussex. It differed from *Cestracion* in that each of the front teeth carried a series of small sharp cusps, while the hind teeth were much less modified for crushing food.

In Jurassic times there arose from this *Cestracion* stock two divergently modified types which culminated today, in swiftly swimming predaceous sharks, and in depressed and much flattened bottom-living skates and rays. Teeth belonging to both these types of cartilaginous fishes are not uncommonly found in the Chalk and the Eocene clays, as well as in the earlier Mesozoic rocks. The shark's teeth are attractive

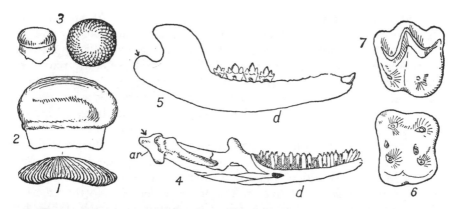

Fig. 20. FOSSIL TEETH AND JAWS FROM VARIOUS PERIODS

1, *Acrodus*. Lias. 2, *Ptychodus*, Chalk. 3, *Lepidotus*, Jurassic. 4, *Iguana*, Present. Shows the many bones seen in a reptilian jaw. *ar*, articular. *d*, dentary. 5, *Phascolotherium*, Stonesfield slate. Inner view of the lower jaw of a very primitive mammal with only one bone, the dentary *d*. The arrow in 4 and 5 indicates the surface of articulation. 6, *Hyrachotherium*, Lower Tertiary. 7, *Anoplotherium* Tertiary.

fossils with shiny enamelled piercing points and cutting edges. Those of *Notidanus* have long crowns carrying a graded series of pointed cusps based on a long deep root. In *Odontaspis* there are two minute cusps separated by a tall, often dagger-shaped cusp, all set on a deeply forked base. In *Lamna* the central cusp is short and broad (Plate XXI: *3, 7*). This latter type reached a maximum size in *Carcharodon* some individuals of which, found in other parts of the world, are said to have had a mouth with a horrifying gape, 6–7 feet wide.

From the same rocks come also fossil teeth of the second type. Those of *Ptychodus* are not uncommon (Fig. 20: *2*). They have a flattened almost cubical body crowned with coarse enamelled ridges. One rare specimen from the Lower Chalk shows a lower jaw with a complete array of teeth closely packed together, forming a solid crushing surface. This type culminated in *Myliobatis* in which the teeth are more flattened and fitted together so closely that they form a perfect mill roller. Remains of this are found in the Middle Eocene Beds of Bracklesham, Sussex; and it still lives in present-day seas.

During Jurassic times the majority of fishes had their bodies enclosed in a flexible armour of rhomboidal ganoid scales, which to some extent served the purposes of a supporting skeleton. As already seen there was an increasing tendency for these scales to overlap one another and to become thin. This weakening of the external support was accompanied by a strengthening of the internal skeleton; partly by the replacement of the cartilage by bone, partly by the insinking of bony plates derived from the surface armour, especially on the head. These changes brought into being the perfected bony fishes or Teleostei.

Ganoids of the Jurassic type persisted through Purbeck times; but decreased in numbers and, in such genera as *Neorhombolepis*, survived into the Wealden and the Lower Chalk waters. Two genera of especial interest still live in the fresh waters of North America. One, the gar-pike, *Lepidosteus*, with its armour of ganoid scales has been found fossil in the Oligocene rocks of Hordwell, Hampshire. The Bowfin, *Amia*, which resembles the Jurassic *Eugnathus* is also found in the freshwater beds of the Lower Eocene, in the Isle of Wight.

Among Jurassic fishes *Pholidophorus*, from the Lias of Lyme Regis and Whitby, and *Leptolepis* from the Upper Lias had, in several respects including the thinning of the scales and of their enamel covering progressed a long way towards becoming teleosteans. Both also lived in the Wealden Lake.

From Gault times onwards teleosts became increasingly dominant. Today they are as numerous and varied as the birds of the air and the flowers of the field; but they are not as conspicuous, for they are hidden from view down in the chambers of the sea. In all of them there is an air-bladder, the presence of which gives to their bodies the same specific gravity as the water; so that they need not always descend to the floor to rest, but may rock comfortably as in a cradle or swim with ease at any level. In more primitive teleosts this bladder is connected with the gullet by means of a tube because it originated like a lung, but in the more specialised there is no such link. On the basis of these and other differences, these fishes are divided into two classes, the Physostomi and the Physoclisti respectively.

The more primitive Physostomi include such types as the smelt, herring, trout, and salmon. Fossils of the two former, and of a number of their relatives, have been found in the chalk and early Tertiary rocks of Britain. With such good hunting provided, it is not surprising that the pike and its fellows also came into being; for their remains have also been found in the Chalk, and conjure up less peaceful scenes in those quiet waters. Fossils from the chalk and the London Clay show that eels had come into existence.

One small section of this same division include the carps and goldfish, which possess an apparatus that links the air-bladder to the surface of the body and serves to detect vibrations coming through the water. This makes them sensitive to the footfall of any fisherman who approaches his pitch too carelessly. Fragmentary fossils of this kind of fish have also been found in the London Clay near to Croydon.

In many of the Physoclisti the front rays of the dorsal fin became strong and spiny, like those in the familiar perch and stickleback. Such fishes are well represented in the chalk by fossils closely allied to *Beryx*. These fossils used to be known to quarrymen as John Dory because, like this fish, they had deep laterally compressed bodies. The mackerels also rose to importance during the Eocene, and the large tunny appeared during the Pliocene. Remains of both the cod and the swordfish have been found in the London Clay of Sheppey.

This brief and scanty survey of the fossil bony fishes found in Britain suffices to show that, as with flowers and birds, after the main features of their organisation had been established, they evolved rapidly throughout Cretaceous and Tertiary times; and diverged into a multitude of types, often of great beauty, familiar only to those who study marine life by keeping aquaria or better still go exploring the sea itself with the aid of modern diving equipment.

CHAPTER 38

EARLY FLORAL HISTORY

FOR a period of some 50 million years the chalk sea spread even beyond the bounds of the former Jurassic seas, and overflowed all but the topmost levels of the British Highlands. The area of land that remained was insufficient to support a large flora and fauna; or to supply rivers large enough to carry copious deposits into the sea. For us therefore the chalk rocks hang like a white curtain across our view, and hide from us a long section of the evolutionary history of terrestrial organisms.

Beyond the curtain, in other parts of the world, vegetation underwent important changes. It is necessary therefore to glance at those changes, if we would fully appreciate the limited evidence that is forthcoming from subsequent British Cainozoic deposits.

The earliest and most striking evidence bearing upon this story comes from beyond the Arctic Circle, from Disko Island and other places along the western coastlands of Greenland. There deposits of about the same age as the Wealden have yielded many fossil leaves. Caution must be exercised in trying to identify such remains, for a cursory inspection of the foliage of any living tree or bush suffices to show how wide is the range of variation in shape that they exhibit. Nevertheless a sufficient number of distinctive features may be recognised to make possible the identification of many of the fossils. When this has been done the astonishing fact emerges that, shortly after the opening of the Cretaceous period, forests flourished no less than 300 miles north of the Arctic circle; and nearer to the present pole than the most northerly forests of today. Not only so, but they were more luxuriant than these, and included a much richer and more varied assortment of trees. These facts do not necessarily imply that the climate of the polar regions was then much warmer. On the contrary it is now becoming increasingly evident that the position both of the land masses and of the poles may have changed during geological time.

As might be expected these early Cretaceous forests (Plate XVIII) resembled the Jurassic woodlands in the presence of Cypress, *Araucaria*, *Sequoia* and of sundry relatives of *Ginkgo*, together with several groups which, because they resemble the living cycads are conveniently spoken of as Cycadophyta. The undergrowth consisted largely of ferns. Alongside these Jurassic survivals, which were mainly Gymnosperms, a new and important element had appeared in the form of true flowering plants or Angiosperms. These included such familiar trees as the Plane (*Platanus*), Oak (*Quercus*), *Magnolia* and others now growing in tropical and sub-tropical regions, including the Breadfruit tree (*Artiocarpus*), the Camphor tree (*Cinnamonum*), *Persimmon*, and a laurel (*Sassafras*).

In England at Ightham and Maidstone, Kent; and also in Bedfordshire and the Isle of Wight, the Greensand, which overlies the Wealden, has yielded fragments of wood referable to several genera of flowering plants.

The existence of well developed flowering plants in early Cretaceous times suggests that they must have had a long previous history during the Jurassic period; evolving possibly in upland areas where conditions did not favour the accumulation of sedimentary deposits or the preservation of fossil remains. Their presence in later Cretaceous rocks in North America and Europe shows that these, together with other flowering plants, had begun to migrate southwards from their original home in the far north.

In the apparently rapid development of flowering plants insects must have played an important part. For many ages they had fed upon the microspores and pollen of the evolving Gymnosperms. Incidentally, no doubt, they carried pollen from male to female flowers and thus replaced the uncertain activity of the wind in the vital function of pollination and so became benefactors to the plants they had raided. The latter, under the guiding influence of natural selection, evolved devices for attracting insects including nectar, scents and brightly coloured petals.

Compared with the dearth of remains in the Cretaceous rocks, the records of flowering plants from the early Tertiary rocks of Britain are relatively copious. They come from scattered exposures both inland and along the coasts of Kent, at Sheppey; of Hampshire, near

Bournemouth; and in the Isle of Wight, at Alum Bay. Reference should also be made to two outlying localities; to the Pipe clays of Bovey Tracey, in Devon; and to freshwater deposits in the Isle of Mull. In the latter area, soon after the opening of the era, there was an outburst of volcanic activity when sheet flows of lava were poured out across the landscape. The lapse of time between the flows was sometimes sufficiently prolonged for the surface of the lava to disintegrate into soil and for trees to grow. Occasionally a lava flow blocked the passage of rivers and consequently minor freshwater lakes developed. In these, sediments and plant fragments were deposited, and were subsequently buried under later lava flows. An exposure of these fossiliferous beds, discovered at Ardtun in the Isle of Mull, has yielded numerous leaf impressions.

Perhaps the most striking feature about the flora revealed by all these deposits was its close affinity to that of the world of today; an affinity so close that not only orders but families, and even genera, were the same then as now. This does not mean that plant evolution was at an absolute standstill but, taking into account the vast stretches of time involved, it was extraordinarily slow. It should, however, be remembered that effective search has been going on for only a century, and broad spaces of the earth's surface still remain unexplored. Future discoveries will no doubt pin point the times of appearance of new genera and even new species. None of those discoveries can, however, alter the truth of the facts already summarised.

But while evolution was persuing its leisurely course great changes were, and indeed still are, taking place in geographical distribution. In this connection one factor, the human, has come into rapid action especially during recent centuries. This may be realised by anyone as he wanders round the countryside. In our hedgerows and in our woodlands, now alas so depleted, may still be seen trees that are native to Britain:—poplar, oak, willow, ash, elm, birch, beech and so forth, all of which will be found mentioned in any standard British Flora. But in parks, private gardens, botanical show-pieces such as those at Kew and in most great cities, many strange trees may be seen that are not mentioned in those works. These are exotics that have been brought from overseas; and they will be found described, and their places of origin indicated in good books on gardening. Some are Gymnosperms which link our present landscape with that of Jurassic times:—*Ginkgo*, from the far east; *Araucaria*, the Monkey

Puzzle tree, from Chile; *Cryptomeria*, a cedar from Japan and North America; *Sequoia*, the giant redwood from the western seaboard of North America. Among the Angiosperms are the Plane (*Platanus*) which gives a touch of greenery to our more sombre city streets; the *Magnolia* whose blooms give so much pleasure in the early summer season. Both these hail from North America and the Orient. Then there is the Sweet Gum (*Liquidamber*) the Tulip-tree (*Liriodendron*), and the Indian Bean (*Catalpa*) also from North America.

Fossil evidence from the London Clay brings out the striking fact that these exotic trees, and others no longer native to Britain, flourished here also in early Tertiary times (Plate XXII). We may picture them as clustered together in forests and woodlands, beautified in spring and early summer with blazes of blooms rivalling in beauty the cherry orchards of Kent. Wandering alongside the rivers or out over the downlands they quietly invaded and occupied every new landscape as, with passing ages, it was being moulded by the deft fingers of Nature.

Many of these exotics, so recently re-introduced here by man, were brought from warmer regions. This fact suggests that the British climate was in early Tertiary times more genial than it is now, and is supported by the presence of fossil leaves of the Breadfruit *Artiocarpus;* of the fig, *Ficus;* of the fan palm, *Sabal;* and of the fruits of other tropical palms, including *Nipa* which today is limited to the southeast Asian seaboard.

The general absence, even of traces of smaller plants, of herbs and grasses does not necessarily imply that they did not exist. It is more likely that they died down and perished where they grew. Unlike the trees they did not hold their leaves aloft to be caught by the breezes as they fell and wafted away into streams and lakelets. Moreover they did not grow thick woody stems that would rot only very slowly. Nevertherless conditions existed here and there which favoured their preservation as fossils. Such were the conditions under which, towards the end of early Tertiary times, the Bembridge beds were deposited. In exposures near Cowes, Isle of Wight, additions to the types already mentioned occur; fossil remains of smaller plants such as Poppies, together with others of aquatic habit; a Water Lily, *Brasenia;* a Water Soldier, *Stratiotes;* a Burweed, *Sparganum;* and Water-fern, *Azolla.* Of particular interest is a semi-aquatic insect-eating plant allied to the Sundews, *Drosera;* a reminder that insects were everywhere, some of them still playing their beneficial parts in fertilising the flowers of herbs, shrubs and trees.

Evidence from West European deposits shows that this rich and varied flora, so closely allied to that existing today on the eastern sides of the American and Asiatic continents, continued to flourish here also throughout Middle Tertiary or Miocene times and on into the late Tertiary or Pliocene period. But in Britain there is at this stage a wide gap in the record of the rocks that appropriately brings this chapter to its close.

CHAPTER 39

EARLY BRITISH MAMMALS

THE name of Richard Owen has already cropped up several times. He was born in 1804. In his youth, like so many English boys, he hankered after a seafaring life and for a time actually served as a midshipman in the navy. Early manhood, however, found him studying medicine and in 1827 he qualified as a member of the Royal College of Surgeons. About this period he lived for a time in Paris and augmented his studies by attending a course of lectures by Baron Cuvier. This distinguished scientist, in addition to playing an important part in many public activities, found time to do much towards laying the foundations of the science of Comparative Anatomy. In addition to dissecting individual animals with great care he went on to a detailed comparison of the anatomy of the types he had dissected. This comparative method led him to a much more precise knowledge of the differences and resemblances of animals, and therefore to a more correct interpretation of their relationships to one another. At that time the present conception of genetic relationships was unknown, and similarity of structure became the accepted basis upon which classification should be built.

Not far from Paris were limestone quarries from which fossil bones of mammals had been obtained for some years. Cuvier turned his attention to these and, with his friend Brogniart, initiated the modern method of collecting by carefully recording, not only at the level at which the bones was found, but also the exact position of each bone in relationship to its fellows. Thus as the quarry face advanced and more bones were brought to light he was able to link up the later with the earlier finds. Into this apparently jumbled mixture of bones thus collected he brought order, partly by the use of his records but mainly by the application of a principle he had discovered, the principle of the correlation of parts. Most people at some time make unconscious use of this principle. By it they distinguish the parts of a bicycle from those of a motorcar or of a sewing machine; for in each case the parts have shapes and peculiarities more or less suited to the purposes of the respective machines. This is true also for the bones of mammals and other animals. No one would mistake the jaw of a cat for that of a lamb, nor a claw for a hoof. By studying the skeletons of existing mammals Cuvier familiarised himself with the shapes and peculiarities of the bones of many mammals, and with the ways in which they were related to their modes of life. Thus equipped he brought order into the most chaotic mixture of bones from the quarries. Gradually he assembled those which belonged to the same individual animals, fitted them together in their correct positions, and finally rebuilt the original skeletons. These reconstructions were often so complete that he could in imagination clothe them with flesh and blood and draw portraits of them as they appeared when alive (cp. Fig. 21: *11*).

Owen was so fascinated by Cuvier's teaching that, turning aside from his medical studies, he devoted his skill as a surgeon to the study of fossils; and in subsequent years became the Cuvier of British Paleontology. On his return to England he was appointed to the curatorship of the Hunterian Collection at the Royal College of Surgeons. From thence he eventually passed on to the superintendency of the Department of Natural History in the British Museum. The enormous volume of his researches, especially on extinct reptiles and mammals; combined with his skill as a lecturer and his considerable social gifts, brought him into positions of great influence. The building in South Kensington that houses the Natural History section of that Museum, is a fitting memorial to his 20 years of untiring efforts to secure a worthy home for the great national collections.

His deep knowledge and skill, combined with his official positions, made him the natural centre to which vertebrate remains were sent; and consequently the great advances in the knowledge of British fossil vertebrates made during the first half of the nineteenth century, are closely associated with his name. But it must never be forgotten that the multitudes of specimens he handled were found at different places by isolated collectors too numerous for mention here. Nevertheless, as the result of their observation, interest and generosity, each made a definite and valuable contribution to the progress of knowledge.

Owen was a cautious thinker and his main contribution to thought was the distinguishing and clarifying of the principles of homology and analogy. Thus for example the wing of a bird, in fundamental position and structure, is the same as or *homologous* with the leg of a horse or even the flipper of a whale. On the other hand it differs in these respects from the wing of a butterfly, with which, though it has the same function, it is merely *analogous*. In early life, in common with the majority of other naturalists he believed in the miraculous creation of species. As his abundant researches on fossils extended they brought to light forms which showed that one species did pass into another. Thus he made an important contribution to the doctrine of evolution which was coming into vogue. He, however, did not describe this as evolution but as transmutation. After the publication of 'The Origin of Species' he cautiously admitted that secondary causes may have played a part in bringing these changes about.

Those arms of the sea which in early Tertiary times invaded the downfolds north and south of the Wealden axis, were extensions of larger basins which occupied Belgium and the region around Paris. It was from the deposits laid down in the latter area that the mammalian remains investigated by Cuvier were collected. Similar but much less abundant remains have been forthcoming from the contemporary deposits in Britain. Though the material found in England is scanty compared with that obtained from the Paris Basin and from North America, it suffices to illustrate some of the main features revealed by those more ample collections.

With the disappearance of the great and varied groups of reptiles that dominated the world scene during the Mesozoic Era, a relatively clear field was left open for exploitation by the mammalia. Much of their early history is still locked up in the rocks of regions not yet explored. A few of the threads have been picked up in rocks of about the same age as the Thanet sands, which lie at the base of the Tertiary series in the Paris basin. Many more have been obtained from similar basins situated along the eastern flanks of the Rocky Mountains, U.S.A.; and have revealed a much richer mammalian fauna than any yet found in the Mesozoic rocks. Though small forms still played a prominent part there was a general increase in size up to the stature of an ordinary dog. This increase necessitated a more bulky supply of food than could be supplied by a diet of insects, Some gained this by becoming vegetable feeders; others fed on vertebrate flesh. All of them were characterised by small brains; and by feet that had a full complement of five toes, and were placed with the sole full length upon the ground (plantigrade). The legs were correspondingly short. Because of this combination of lowly features they are usually referred to as Archaic Mammals.

The gradual evolution of modernised mammals is partially revealed by the fossils found in the Paris Basin and in North America. These have provided a good basis for interpreting the scanty records found in Britain, which unfortunately consist only of odd bones, teeth, jaws and exceedingly rare and imperfect skulls. These have come from the Eocene and Oligocene rocks exposed at various places scattered about south-east England; in Essex; at Herne Bay, in Kent; at Brackle-sham and Hordwell, in Hampshire; and Binstead, in the Isle of Wight. Thanks to the labours of many experts, more especially of Owen, these fragments have been described, identified and correlated with the more complete remains that have been found abroad. All this has made possible a more or less connected story of mammals in Britain.

At the time represented by the earliest fragments found in Britain, the archaic mammals had passed their zenith; and only a few types lingered on to fight a losing battle in a world increasingly dominated by modernised forms. Here at least four archaic types are represented. *Platychoerops* was an insectivore about the size of a weasel. *Didelphys* was a small pouched mammal, or marsupial, which even today still carries on the struggle cheerfully in the person of the Opossum, a familiar sight today on the American continent; and a flourishing example of a 'living fossil'. *Coryphodon* was a much larger and bulkier type (Fig. 21: *9* and Plate XXII). As indicated by its teeth it was a herbivore. It was clumsily built, with stout limbs and short feet bearing a small hoof on each toe. It is believed to have descended from the very early Eocene *Pantolambda,* but it became extinct by the close of the Lower Eocene. *Pterodon* on the other hand was a flesh feeder belonging to that large group of archaic carnivores, the Creodonta. Nevertheless it held its own until far into Oligocene times.

Along with these archaic types lived many slightly modernised hoofed mammals or Ungulates. These are classified into two great groups, the Odd-Toed and the Even-Toed ungulates respectively. The former, or Perissodactyla, had already appeared in Lower Eocene times. In these the middle or third toe of each foot was already slightly larger then the others, and carried a greater share of the weight of the body. Two genera, *Lophiodon* and *Palaeotherium,* were similar in

Fig. 21. LAND LIFE IN EARLY TERTIARY TIMES

Plants. 1, *Metasequoia.* 2, Palm. 3, *Ginkgo.* 4, Oak. 5, *Vitis.* 6, Sedges. 7, Ferns. Mammals. Artiodactyles: 8, *Anoplotherium.* 9, *Coryphodon*; both of these were amphibious in habit. Perissodactyles: 10, *Hyrachotherium.* 11, *Palaeotherium,* Archaic carnivore or Creodont. 12, *Pterodon.*

appearance and clumsy gait to the Tapir, which survives still in the forests of South America. The former was dominant in Europe during the Upper Eocene. The latter appeared in the Middle Eocene and, rising to a prominent position during the Upper Eocene, declined towards extinction in the Oligocene.

Belonging to a quite distinct branch was the genus, *Hyracotherium,* from the London Clay, the relative size of the brain was greater then in the earlier mammals. It thus exhibited a tendency which has since then characterised the more modern types of mammals. It was about the size of a sheep but was much lighter in build than the mammals mentioned above. This together with its slender limbs shows it to have been a swifter runner than any of them. The number of its toes was reduced to four on the front foot and three on the hind. It was almost if not quite identical with the American genus *Eohippus*, the first of that wonderful series of remains which exhibit a sequence of changes in feet and teeth that culminated in the horses. This series is almost entirely unrepresented among British fossils. Nevertheless some of the changes passed through are strikingly similar to those seen in the feet of the Eocene perissodactyles referred to above; and those in the teeth of certain artiodactyles described below. Here then are two illustrations of parallel changes taking place in separate lines of descent. This phenomenon is known a *parallel evolution*.

One skull from the London Clay was identified by Owen as *Hyrachotherium leporhinus*. Comparison of this with the American series shows it to have been slightly more primitive even than *Eohippus*. *Hyracotherium* disappeared from Europe at the end of the Eocene.

From the Middle and Upper Eocene of Hordwell, Bracklesham and Binstead has come a fuller record of the history of the Artio-dactyles or even-toed ungulates. In these the third and fourth toes became enlarged at the expense of the others, which were reduced; the first was quickly lost. The cheek-teeth, or molars, passed through an interesting series of changes tending towards greater efficiency in crushing and eventually grinding food (Fig. 20: 6, 7). In the most primitive of these herbivores the crown of the tooth was armed with four blunt cusps. This type, which is described as *bunodant*, is suited mainly for crushing soft herbage. Such was the condition in *Dichobune* a small mammal which, according to Cuvier, closely resembled the mouse-deer (Chevrotain) a little animal, not as large as a hare, which lives in the East Indies. Even in this genus there was a tendency for the two outer cusps to develop crests shaped like a crescent. This tendency became more marked in the slightly larger *Anthracotherium*, a light-limbed and rapid runner that could travel far, and was widely dis-tributed over Europe. It was for a long time the dominant herbivore, and ranged from the Middle Eocene far into the Oligocene. In the closely allied *Hyopotamus* the molar crown was longer. *Anoplotherium* was larger, being about the size of a donkey but, having shorter feet and legs, its body was not raised so high above the ground. Its molars had advanced to the *selenodont* (selen = moon) condition in which all the cusps were crescentic. As in all the herbivores so far considered, the molars had low crowns, a feature which indicates that they still fed on soft vegetation, and not on dry grasses. In harmony with fossil records of other semi-aquatic animals the presence of a powerful tail combined with short limbs suggests that *Anoplotherium* haunted swamps and rivers, a mode of life that tended to shield it from the attacks of carnivores. It arose near the end of the Eocene and died out in the Lower Oligocene. *Chaeropotamus* belonged to the pig type of artiodactyle. It bore some resemblance to the Peccaries of the South American forests.

With a slight exception, that will be referred to later, the story of the British Mammalia during the Miocene and Pliocene is almost a blank. How great was the progress that took place meanwhile will become apparent when the records for the Pleistocene period come up for consideration.

CHAPTER 40

THE LAST FLORAL PHASE

EAST of the Pennines the outcrop of the Magnesian Limestone must, in Pliocene times, have been intersected by valleys with steeply sloping sides, interrupted here and there by rocky exposures. Most of the leaves and seeds shed by the vegetation growing here fell to the ground and perished; but a few were caught by the streams and, being carried away, were ultimately buried in the alluvium lower downstream. During the Pleistocene a great glacier flowing from the north or north-east, acting like a titanic bull-dozer, pushed the newly formed soil and ancient alluvium before it, rammed portions of them into fissures in the limestone, and buried them under boulder-clay. Since the retirement of the ice the sea has carved cliffs out of the limestone, with its covering of glacial deposits, and has exposed to view the earthy plugs which filled the fissures. Some of these were discovered and explored by C. T. Trechman along the coast of Durham near Castle Eden. Fortunately he found and extracted many seeds together with other plant fossils. The seeds he submitted to Mrs. E. M. Reid of Cambridge who, having previously made an extensive study of modern seeds, was exceptionally well qualified for dealing with them. She succeeded in identifying 70 species, including small plants such as Nightshade, *Potentilla argentea* (Hoary potentil) and *Erica* (Heath); together with shrubs and small trees, Bramble and Birch, Hawthorn and Oak. Though some of the genera were the same as those living today in Britain the species were exotic. Other genera and species, though now extinct in Britain still have a place in the East Asiatic and American associations of plants.

Summarising the history of vegetation in Europe during the latter half of the Tertiary era, Mrs. Reid pointed out that, while in Miocene times the whole flora belonged to the *Liriodendron*, *Magnolia* assemblage, at the opening of the Pliocene, plants with these affinities made up only 64% of the total flora. By the Middle Pliocene, as shown by the Castle Eden flora, this figure had dropped to 31%. These facts indicate a progressive worsening of the climate of Western Europe, including Britain.

The story of this decline is carried still further by the plants found fossil in the uppermost Pliocene deposits, represented in Britain by the Cromer Forest beds. These contain the remains of trees and other plants that had been brought from upstream by the Rhine and its tributary the Thames when in flood, and deposited in one of its western estuaries that happened to trespass across East Anglia. These beds have been lain bare by the sea along the present coast, and have yielded many fossils. The flora thus revealed was found on the whole to be practically the same as that living in the same part of England today.   None of the plants belong to the East Asiatic and American association, and only 5% were exotic or extinct.

At this point attention may be diverted for a while from the immediate theme, by letting our thoughts travel with incredible speed back through the equally incredibly long aeons, which separated the Carboniferous from the Pliocene. Throughout almost the whole of that great stretch of time Britain seems to have enjoyed the genial conditions of warm temperate or even sub-tropical climates. Geologically speaking therefore its present climate with mild summers and bleak winters is exceptional The fossil floras of the Pliocene, as well as the faunas of the newly born North Sea, tell of the gradual onset of this climate. But as already seen these changes proved to be merely the prelude to a sequence of climatic disasters.

Here and there, in proximity to the outcrop of the Cromer Forest beds, patches of peaty loam are exposed which were deposited originally in freshwater channels. Among the fossil plants which these yield are the remains of the Arctic Willow (*Salix polaris*), and the Arctic or Dwarf Birch (*Betula nana*); which today characterise the tundras that fringe the polar ice sheets. Evidently our climate had deteriorated still further, and had swung to the other extreme. All this is in harmony with the abounding geological evidence which shows that the state of affairs popularly known as 'The Great Ice Age' had now supervened.

One compact piece of evidence, illustrating the events that took place during that age, is provided by a series of deposits which were found exposed in a brickyard at Hoxne, Suffolk. Early in the final decade of last century it was shown that two sheets of boulder-clay were here present, one lying above the other. Between them, however, were 60 feet of deposits of which the lower two-thirds consisted of lacustrine clay and loam with three feet of peat in the middle. The upper third consisted of brick earth and glacial gravel. The kind of scene called to mind by the contemplation of these intervening deposits, is paralleled today in some parts of the Cheshire and North Shropshire plain. This area is clothed in hummocky boulder-clay. Nestling in the hollows may be seen, in the neighbourhood of Ellesmere, lakelets and meres partly occupied by peat-bogs and surrounded by peaceful wooded scenery (Plate XXIII*b*). If (may heaven forbid!) an ice age returned, this friendly scene would be changed to forbidding tundra; snowbound most of the year, and swept by biting winds that would kill every twig that peeped above the protective covering of snow. During the very brief summer the snow would melt; and water, carrying silt, would cover the peat-bog and fill the lake, or convert the moss-covered low ground into a soggy mess. On the better-drained rises of ground herbaceous plants would waken from their long winter sleep, and shooting up rapidly would beautify the scene with flowers. The dwarf birch and willow would put forth their leaves. Everywhere the scene would be enlivened by the hum of insects and the songs of migrant birds. As the climate deteriorated yet further the aerial music would cease; and the landscape become enshrouded in icefields, and buried under boulder clay. That such a sequence of events actually took place in East Anglia during the Pleistocene, is proved by the finding at Hoxne of fossil remains of temperate plants in the lower clay and peat; and of the arctic willow and dwarf birch in the upper loam.

In recent years interest in the study of Pleistocene deposits has been intensified by the increasing realisation of their value as a chronological basis for human prehistory. This has resulted in the discovery of many other fossiliferous Pleistocene sites. For example, while deep sewer trenches were being excavated north of Cambridge, other interglacial deposits were brought to light. An account of these, published in 1949 (Hollingworth), is an excellent example of the benefits to science accruing from good team-work involving many types of skill; from that of the observant labourer to that of the highly trained experts in the study of plant and animal remains and of geological deposits (Hollingworth, etc.). Careful treatment of the sediments found in the trenches resulted in the isolation of numerous plant fragments, more especially seeds and fruits. These were found to belong to about 30 different plants, including some aquatic types such as *Potamogeton* and *Naias*, which still live in Britain and other parts of the northern hemisphere, even as far afield as North Africa. This fact alone throws valuable light on the climatic conditions that existed during this interlude between two glaciations.

In addition a comparatively new technique (c.p. Plate XXIII*a*) was applied to some samples, by means of which minute pollen-grains of trees, as well as herbs, were separated out, identified and counted. This work, together with the evidence based on the study of the land and freshwater shells contained in the deposits, gave material for an even fuller picture, briefly described in the words of one expert who wrote:—'The land bordering the river was probably mixed grass-land and woodland and the climate was warm, possibly dry'.

Thus for a considerable length of time, almost certainly more than half a million years, the climate of Britain underwent a series of severe oscillations from warm temperate to intensely cold. For comparatively brief spells the presence of extensive icefields completely eliminated all forms of vegetation from much of the landscape. In between these were much longer spells during the passage of which tundra conditions merged through cold, then cool, and sometimes even into warm temperate conditions. Simultaneously the vegetation returned from sojourning elsewhere, and transformed the countryside once more into a home for many kinds of plants, animals and even man. These climatic happenings during the Pleistocene are so striking that there is a tendency to concentrate interest and attention upon them alone. They did not, however, descend upon our land like a bolt from the blue, but were foreshadowed by changes that had been going on throughout the Pliocene. These are reflected in the pro-gressive elimination of *Magnolia*, *Liriodendron* and other flowering trees that, as already seen, were present in Britain for a long time thus pointing to a genial and warm temperate climate.

Following the last glacial episode, which ended at least as long ago as 10,000 B.C. conditions ameliorated. Trees, bushes, herbs and grasses began to wander back slowly from their haven of refuge on the continent. The story of their return has been spelled out by the investigation layer by layer of the peat deposits that had meanwhile accumulated in fenny lowland and mossy moorland. After collecting identifiable fragments and seeds, recent workers have passed on to the isolation of pollen-grains. These had been carried by the wind from all quarters and, falling on the peat-bogs, have supplied evidence for the presence of many other types of flowering plants, of tall trees, tiny herbs and grasses that flourished on the landscape far from the borders of fen and moor. Out of this work has emerged a panoramic view of the processional return, in which dwarf birch and arctic willow led the way, followed by hazel and pine, and joined later by oak, ash, birch, alder and other familiar trees. There was, however, an important gap in the procession, for *Magnolia*, *Liriodendron* and their associates never returned, and consequently the present vegetation of Britain, beautiful as it is, is much impoverished compared with its counterpart throughout the greater part of Tertiary times.

This impoverishment was brought about mainly, though not entirely, by the southward shifting of climatic belts, in harmony with the growth and extension of the great icefields and glaciers, from polar into temperate latitudes. As the cool and then cold belts spread across Britain all the vegetation went on trek southwards. A like movement took place also in North America where, however, the mountains ran north and south and spacious lowlands lay to the south and gave refuge to the migrants. In Europe different geographical conditions prevailed, for here the lowlands were more limited in extent and were hemmed in on the south by the alpine and other mountain ranges and by the Mediterranean sea; both of which lay athwart the line of escape for these refugees.

Moreover the mountains themselves became cloaked in ice, and their flanks developed into tundras. Thus the refugee vegetation was imprisoned within lowlands of limited extent, under conditions in which the more tender plants perished. The annual return of summer was progressively delayed, and flowers remained unfertilised because the winds, still cold, confined the pollen-bearing insects to barracks; and late frosts killed off the young fruit, thus stultifying the reproductive functions. On the other hand the hardier plants survived. Even under the coldest conditions breezes continued to blow, and the wind-pollinated plants such as the willows, poplars, elms and oaks were fertilised and their generations renewed. When therefore the time for their return arrived these with a few hardy insect pollinated trees such as blackthorn, hawthorn and crab remained to set out for the homeland once more.

Though as a consequence of all this the British vegetation is an impoverished one, yet the pussy willows, the purple veil over the face of the elms, the golden tassels of the oaks, give to our springs and early summer landscapes a charming beauty of their own. But today man is taking a hand; he is painting this lily in public parks and garden suburbs, by bringing together colourful contributions from the ends of the earth, and by juggling with genes in laboratories and glass-houses.

CHAPTER 41

ORIGIN OF BRITISH
MAMMALIAN FAUNA

FOLLOWING the Oligocene there is, as already noted, a wide gap in the British record for the Mammalia. This covers the whole of the period known as the Miocene, during which terrestrial conditions were more widely spread over Europe. This continent was then openly connected with Asia and less openly linked with Africa. The enormous land mass thus created provided a vast living space within which evolution made great strides. Elephants, which had been evolving from lowly types in the Nile basin, now spread over the Old World. They had already advanced to the *Mastodon* stage with its long trunk, shortened jaws, elongated out-curving tusks, and large molars crowned with stout cross ridges.

Over much of this mighty expanse of land the rainfall did not suffice to support the growth of forests or even of open woodlands. But rolling savannahs and boundless grasslands provided food for all the mammals that surged hither and thither across these open spaces. Bulky browsing types such as the rhinoceroses became rapidly out-numbered by newly evolving grazing animals; with deeply crowned molars that could long withstand the grinding action required for a diet of dry grasses. Hosts of light-limbed swiftly running antelopes swarmed everywhere. Alongside these even-toed ungulates there arose those odd-toed forms which culminated in the horses; but as yet these had not advanced beyond the three-toed stage, in which the central toe was much larger than the two side toes. A new type of carnivore evolved out of the primitive creodont stock through *Miacis* and gave rise to the dogs and cats with their larger brains, more efficient teeth, and strongly constructed limb-joints. Probably these animals ranged into Britain but there is no direct evidence in the form of Miocene fossils. The presence of the remains of the three-toed horse *Hipparion*, in the nodule bed which underlies the Red Crag of East Anglia, however, indicates that some of them did in fact wander as far west as this country.

Other fossils, found in the same bed, and in the fluviomarine deposits known as the Norwich Crag, tell of the presence here in Pliocene times of a different type of fauna, which is interesting because it consisted of more highly evolved mammals and reflects a different environment. The warm temperate belt had by this time shifted southwards, and had been replaced by cooler moister conditions which, coming from the north, brought with them temperate woodlands and meadows and their associated faunas. In the rivers the water-rat or more correctly water-vole (*Arvicola*) splashed and the otter (*Lutra*) hunted for fish. The small beaver (*Castor europaeus*), which was followed later by the giant beaver (*Trogontherium*), felled the smaller trees, built their dams across the streams and produced artificial pools in which, because the surface level was constant, the beavers could erect their dwellings. In the larger rivers and minor freshwater lakes the hippopotamus whiled away its time and over the adjoining marshy flats the tapir wandered. The *Rhinoceros*, *Mastodon* and straight-tusked elephant (*Elephas antiquus*) crashed their way through the undergrowth. Gazelles (*Gazella anglia*), several species of deer (*Cervus*), and a species of the true one-toed horse (*Equis stenonis*). grazed in the meadows. Occasionally one of these was slaughtered by a lion (*Felis spelaeus*) and the remnants of its feast would be devoured by the striped hyaena (*H. striata*). All this indicates that during early Pliocene times the mammalian fauna of Britain had begun to develop a still closer resemblance to that existing today. Nevertheless, though a number of the genera are the same, only 3 or 4 out of the 41 species revealed by the fossils are alive today, the remainder became extinct.

Fossil shells, fossil plants, and fossil mammals from the pliocene deposits all combine in testifying to a continued deterioration of climate in Britain. The story of this change is carried a stage further by the mammalian remains from the Cromer Forest beds. Among these no less than 45 species have been recognised, of which more than half are alive today. Some of these such as the fox, wolf, marten, otter, red deer, roe deer, fallow deer and boar, live in Britain now or have become extinct only within historic times. Others, including the spotted hyaena (*H. crocuta*); glutton, bison (*Bonasus*); musk-ox

(*Ovibus*); and elk (*Alces latifrons*); still survive in other parts of the
world. The last two are particularly interesting for they are found
living only in the arctic tundras. The remainder were all large animals
and have become extinct. They include a horse (*Equus stenonis*);
several species of elephants (*Elephas antiquus, E. meridionalis* and *E. primigenius* which now made its first appearance) of rhinoceros (*R. magna,
etruscus* and *megarhinus*); and 10 species of deer. Here again as later
fossil records show, the mammoth (*E. primigenius*) was a tundra form
which was clothed in long hairy fur. The extinct *Machairodus* was a
highly specialised tiger-like type of carnivore, described as sabre-
toothed because it had very long curved dagger-shaped canines well
adapted for piercing and slashing the thick hides of large pachyderms.

At one time it was thought that the Cromer Forest beds were laid
down at the end of the Pliocene period, but the deposits which underlie
them have been shown to be of Pleistocene age. Consequently the
Forest beds themselves must belong to the first interglacial. This
would account for the fact that so many of the animals whose remains
are found in them, belong to the same species as those associated with
the present mild climate in Britain. Probably the tundra animals
reinvaded the scene when these interglacial conditions declined and
merged into the succeeding glaciation.

Though the Pleistocene period lasted less than one million years,
the fossil records of its mammalian fauna are much more copious and
much less fragmentary than those from any preceding time in Britain.
This is no doubt due largely to the fact that the deposits in which
they were found, are so recent in origin that they have not suffered
so much from the destructive action of geological agencies. Moreover
those that lay buried in caves had an additional advantage in being
placed in particularly well-protected sites. It is not surprising therefore that of the 49 Pleistocene species known no less than three-quarters
have been found in caves. No doubt some of these animals did from
time to time take shelter in the caves; but the fact that many of the
bones have their surfaces scored by the gnawing action of hyaena
teeth, shows that the caves were commonly used as hyaena dens,
to which corpses were dragged that had been scavenged from elsewhere. Here also primitive man sometimes dwelt and feasted on the
animals he had caught and slain in the chase including the cave bear
and young mammoth.

The great majority of these fossiliferous caves were no more than enlarged fissures in limestone excavated by the solvent action of underground water. The exploration for fossils of both caves and fissures was begun early in the nineteenth century, and a very comprehensive account of it was given by Buckland in his "Reliquiae Diluvianae," (1823). Owen in his 'British Fossil Mammals' (1846), describes or refers to 37 cave species. The remaining records came from alluvial deposits. These were no doubt the relics of animals that perished in floods but, drifting away from the main stream out across the plain, became buried in the newly forming alluvium. Of the animals thus salvaged only 8 are extinct:—*Machairodus*, cave bear, several species of deer including the reindeer (*Cervus. tarandus*), *Rhinoceros magna, Elephas antiquus, E. primigenius* (mammoth). It may be noted that all these are large animals more or less highly specialised. When the interglacial spells merged into glaciations much of the vegetation died out or migrated from the region thus the food resources became inadequate to satisfy the needs of these large beasts. On the other hand the smaller animals, which tended to be omnivorous, were more adaptable and found refuge in the periglacial lowland areas now extensively submerged in the British seas. There they eked out a precarious existence during the rigours of the later glaciations. Returning, when these had passed, they founded the present British fauna.

This brief summary of the origin of the British fauna is based mainly upon the finds made by early workers. It must not be supposed, however, that the evolution of these animals now came to a standstill. On the contrary the greater precision of present-day technical descriptions has led to the detection of slight changes which make it necessary, in a number of cases, to establish sundry new subspecies. Unfortunately our British fauna has suffered progressive depletion during historic times for in addition to deliberately destroying such animals as the wolf man has, in the process of adapting the landscape to his own needs, incidentally modified it extensively and laid waste their natural haunts.

CHAPTER 42

THE FIRST BRITONS

IN the foregoing chapters the word 'fossil' has been used to cover a wide range of objects. These have included the bones of vertebrates, the tests of sea-urchins, the carapaces of trilobites and of other arthropods; all of which were very intimately parts of the animal's body. At the other extreme they have included footprints, worm-tubes and castings, external and internal impressions of shells, in none of which is preserved even the tiniest fragment of the creature's body. Nevertheless these also throw some light upon the organism and also upon its habits and mode of life. This latter type of fossil evidence becomes supremely important in studying the story of early man in Britain.

Turning then to the rocks for light upon that story, we find that the actual remains of his skeleton are as scanty as those of the birds; for while these escaped disaster by using their wings, man escaped by using his wits, his gifts of foresight and intelligence. Nevertheless in using these he also made marks upon his surroundings, and modified the materials he found there upon a scale vastly exceeding that produced by any other organism. Today that scale has increased to such a degree that man is beginning to rival in effectiveness some of the normal geological agencies. Thus one Trent valley colliery may during the time of its existence shift as much material as the adjoining river itself. But at this point we begin to break into the precincts of geography. On the other hand the colliery shaft and tip-heaps when no longer in use are as truly fossil in their significance as a worm-burrow or casting found in the Permian rocks, or in the basal beds of the Cambrian.

In recent years the search for fossil records left by man has been so productive that this twig of the tree of geological knowledge has grown into the vigorous young science of Archaeology which is effectively combining the long-established techniques of geology with new ones of its own.

At the time when Lister and others were elucidating the true nature of 'figured stones', Conyers, a London apothecary endowed with the same type of interest picked up, from the gravels which were being excavated near Gray's Inn Lane, a flint which had been so carefully chipped into the shape of a flattened pear that there could be little doubt it had been produced by human craftmanship. At the time this flint was assumed to be a weapon that had been used by the ancient Britons, and is the first human tool known to have been found. Though discovered at the close of the seventeenth century no figure of it was published until 1715. During the next 200 years similar flints have turned up at many other places in Britain and on the continent.

While it was soon evident that these flints were indeed implements made and used by man, great difficulties arose out of the positions in which they were found; for these indicated that man must have lived upon the earth long before the date at which he was believed to have been created. Thus for example, at the close of the eighteenth century John Frere found similarly well-shaped stone implements at Hoxne, Suffolk, in those deposits which are now known to be of interglacial origin. These he considered to have been made by man before the use of metals had been discovered. To scientists generally at that time such a view seemed incredible. About the middle of the nineteenth century, however, Frere's view received strong support from discoveries made by Boucher de Perthes, in the terrace gravels of the Somme valley in France, of man-made implements dating from the far distant past. In 1859, the year when Darwin's 'Origin of Species' was published, several outstanding English scientists, including Sir Joseph Prestwich and John Evans, went to France and, after examining the evidence for themselves were convinced that de Perthes and Frere were right. Their example was followed by others and gradually the older view was discarded. The search for further evidence was then intensified.

Recent studies of primitive races living in the world today leave no doubt that early man could have used sticks for digging up roots; and stones, accidentally shaped by nature, for cutting wood, for missiles, and for killing or skinning animals caught in the chase. His wooden implements must soon have rotted away and perished, but the stones he used were practically imperishable. But even if the earliest of these were picked up today they would be unrecognisable, for they would bear no marks to show that they had been so used. Even when man began to shape the stones himself by chipping, his first efforts would be so crude that they could not be distinguished from stones accidentally chipped by such natural agencies as creeping soil or waves breaking on a stony beach. Some crudely chipped stones have been accepted by several collectors as human artefacts and classed as Eoliths (dawn stones). Of special interest are certain large flakes and crudely shaped blocks that have been found below the uppermost crags along the coast of Norfolk. If these flints should prove to be the products of human workmanship, they would carry the story of man as a maker of tools back beyond the opening of the Pleistocene, to the last pages of the Pliocene.

Clearly recognisable implements have been found in several types of Pleistocene and later deposits, in river terrace gravels, interglacial and cave deposits, in surface soils and earthworks. Careful geological fieldwork upon all these has made it possible to lay the foundations of a time-scale for these deposits and therefore for the implements they contain. Studying the latter in the order of their occurrence in time has led to the recognition of progressive stages in early man's technique of chipping stone.

Most of the earlier implements have come from river terrace gravels. In England some of the latter, lying alongside the lower Thames valley, have proved very productive. But it is the terraces of the Somme in France that have yielded a standard sequence. As might be expected, many of the earliest implements were made from flints that were about the size required. Later it became usual for man to start with a larger flint, which he reduced by coarse flaking to a suitable size. The core thus obtained was trimmed down by careful chipping on two faces, into one of two apparently standard forms, the ovate and the pear-shaped in outline. These were both somewhat flattened in section and had sharp cutting edges.

As the result of experiment and of observation on men at work in primitive societies today three stages in the development of the technique of trimming have been recognised. At first the flakes and chips were removed by smart blows systematically delivered by another stone at a suitable angle against the surface of the flint. In this case the flakes were thick and left deep concave scars on the core separated by prominent ridges. Along the line where the two faces met these scars intersected one another and produced a zigzag but sharp cutting edge. Implements showing these features are classed as Abbevillian (Chellean) and date from the early half of the Pleistocene.

In the next and later stage the blows were delivered indirectly by holding an elongated piece of wood or bone with one end at the appropriate angle against the surface of the flint and striking the other end sharply with a hammerstone. The impact thus delivered through the less rigid material produced thinner flakes, which left shallower concavities and less well-marked ridges. The cutting edge was correspondingly straighter. This grade is called the Acheulean (Plate XXIV). It lasted throughout the very long interglacial of mid-Pleistocene time into the third or late pleistocene interglacial; that is to say for about one quarter of a million years. In late Acheulean time the flakes were removed by pressure, and were so broad and thin that they looked like mere skimmings from off the surface, which consequently received a beautiful finish. These implements having chipped but not polished surfaces are classed as Palaeolithic.

Among the many sites where these early Old Stone age or Palaeolithic implements have been found, specific reference may be made to the '100-foot terrace' of the Thames at Swanscombe. Here a succession of gravels and sands had been built up on a rocky platform, which was part of the floor cut by the ancient Thames when the relative level of sea and land was 90 feet lower than it is now. On this floor, gravels were laid down and subsequently covered by loam. After a long time, during which extensive changes took place in this valley, this loam was buried under a second covering of gravels. Both lower and upper gravels have yielded implements, some of which fit into the technical sequence just outlined. Others, however, do not but exhibit features which illustrate some of the difficulties encountered in this effort to unravel the story of early man. Though the lower gravels at Swanscombe have yielded many artefacts, only one of these can be described as Acheulean; and that has had its features blunted, as the result of having been rolled along by running water from some distant and older site. All the others indicate a quite different industry or even culture from that described above. It is one in which, not merely the cores but the *flakes* were more usually trimmed and converted into implements. Such implements have been found at many

other places, especially in ancient deposits of the Thames that occur
at Clacton. Implements of this style are classed as Clactonian.

In the upper gravels which overlie the loam at Swanscombe only
a few clactonian tools occur, but they are associated with an abundance
of Middle Acheulean implements. With these have been found fragments of a human skull which, notwithstanding its great age, proved
to be remarkably like that of modern man. These are the earliest
traces of man himself that have been found in Britain. Other bones
from the same gravels show that the animals that shared the landscape
with him included an early type of mammoth, a straight-tusked elephant, a two-horned rhinoceros and a deer. This assemblage indicates
a temperate climate.

The later records of the presence of Old Stone Age or Palaeolithic
man in Britain have been preserved mainly in deposits that accumulated on the floors of caves. Though from the days of Buckland onwards
many caves have been explored, it must suffice for us to confine our
attention to those caves which occur in the Cresswell gorge. This is
situated just where the outcrop of the magnesian limestone crosses
the county boundary between Nottinghamshire and Derbyshire.
These caves were partially explored by Professor Boyd Dawkins with
others about the year 1875, but have been much more fully and carefully investigated in this century by Leslie Armstrong. A brief account
of his work will serve as an inset to the broad general picture built up
from the study of sites scattered over Britain as a whole.

The deposits in the Cresswell Caves may be as much as 20 feet
deep, and consist of fine yellow and red silts carried in by air currents
and on the feet of animals. The presence of the remains of such animals
as the horse, bison, red deer, and bear indicates that on the whole
a dry warm climate prevailed. This sequence is sealed in at the top
by a layer of travertine, or lime deposited from solution, and therefore indicative of moist or even wet conditions. Two similar layers
occur at deeper levels; but they contain angular blocks of stone
detached from the roof and walls by intense frost action, at times
when glacial conditions prevailed over the countryside around, during the latest phases of the Ice Age in Britain. This view receives
support from the presence of reindeer bones in proximity to these
stony layers.

Human artefacts are distributed throughout the deposits in such
a way as to indicate that the caves were not occupied continuously

by man, but served the purposes of a hunting lodge for wandering parties. Situated as they are, far from important centres of Middle and Upper Palaeolithic cultures in France, it is not to be expected that they would furnish a complete picture of those cultures. Nevertheless they do yield a remarkably good and well-dated summary of the sequence of cultural changes in later Pleistocene times.

From a level only a few inches above the upper layer of stony travertine downwards to the base of the deposits the cultural stage is that known as the Mousterian. On the continent this has been found associated with the actual remains of Neanderthal Man (*Homo neanderthalensis*); a short stocky race which left no descendants among the present population of the world. His technique was a development of the flake type influenced by contact with the Acheulean. Clactonian flakes occur in the lowest levels at Cresswell and are followed higher up by carefully trimmed or Mousterian flake-tools. From the lower traverine layer upwards, fascinating indications of an additional and a higher technical skill, occur in the form of bone tools, evidently used for piercing and then sewing skins together; and of finger-bones of the arctic hare with holes drilled through them so that they could be used as beads or as amulets. One long flat piece of bone with notched edges was shaped to serve as a 'bull roarer' for when fastened at the end of a long cord and whizzed round rapidly in the air it produced strange and weird noises. The presence of this among these prehistoric remains conjures up visions of magical rites and of feasts held in celebration of successful hunting expeditions.

A few inches above the upper stony layer, all traces of Mousterian man's activities are absent and an entirely new type of flint implement appears, made from long blade-shaped flakes. On the continent these are associated with the skeletal remains of a fine tall race known as Magdalenian man. He was essentially modern in character and referable to the species *Homo sapiens*. Early in the last century similar remains were found in a cave near Paviland, in the cliffs along the south coast of the Gower Peninsula. They were skeleton of a young man aged 25, who was evidently of such social standing that he had received a ceremonial burial.

The famous drawings which decorate the walls and the wonderful carvings on bone which are found in the French caves, were the handiwork of this magnificent race of men. At Cresswell this feature in their culture is reflected by the carving of a horse's head found by

Boyd Dawkins, and the drawing of a masked man executing a ceremonial dance found by Leslie Armstrong.

Though the Cresswell record is inferior in such respects to those
of the continent, it has yielded a remarkable sequence of implements
illustrating the evolution of the long blades of the Upper Palaeolithic
into the dwarf geometrical shapes known as the Mesolithic. Traces
of this are found on prehistoric outdoor camping sites scattered about
the countryside. These indicate a change to the more genial climate
which paved the way for the coming of the New Stone Age or Neolithic peoples; who, in addition to attaining yet higher degrees in the
techniques of chipping and polishing implements, brought with them
important new skills in agriculture, in pottery making and textile
weaving. These skills lay at the roots of a developing civilisation
which, notwithstanding its economic and other struggles, has provided
opportunities for sections of the population to cultivate purely cultural
interests. Among these may now be counted the study of fossils.

We have now come to the appointed end of our task, and it
remains only to glance back and try to fit this story into its overall
setting. Fragmentary as it may be, its pieces combine to produce a
panorama of great events commensurate with but even more deeply
significant than those involved in the growth of the physical uni-
verse. It is noteworthy that these events did not take place on some
mighty star but on a small planet in an otherwise unimportant solar
system.

This year (1958), in his annual address to the Geological Society of
London, the President (Dr. L. Hawkes), summarising a discussion of
living conditions said:—"In general the evidences regarding past
climates are in accord with a continuance throughout geological time
of a small range of temperatures; a range favourable to life as we know
it, although a few miles above and below the surface the temperature
alone would prohibit that life. This constant and favourable temperature maintained within an infinitesimal region of space for
milliards of years is one of the most impressive facts established by
geology."

Within this 'infinitesimal region' the creative influences moved
on to events of still greater significance than those described in the
above pages. There emerged, evolved, involved—or whatever you

will—life, consciousness and mind culminating in a spirit of fellowship based on faith, hope, love and willing sacrifice of which the human side of the story told in these pages is an example. The future of humanity and of the whole planet lies with the continued development of that fellowship.

BIBLIOGRAPHY
AND INDEX

BIBLIOGRAPHY

READERS who have no access to the library of a learned or scientific institution will sometimes find helpful books in the reference department of the local public library. These are often of long standing and in addition to series of scientific journals may contain even old and rare books. Help in reading and in field work may be gained by joining a local Naturalists' Society. 'The Geologists' Association' has branches in several parts of the country. The subscription is low. It has a library open to all its members and also publishes well illustrated Proceedings. It organises field excursions for days and for longer periods.

The list given below is necessarily short but further references will be found in many of the books mentioned.

ABBREVIATIONS

Biol. Rev.—Biological Reviews.
B.M.—British Museum (Natural History), catalogues and guides.
Geol. Mag.—Geological Magazine.
Geol. Surv.—Geological Survey, memoirs and handbooks.
Mon. Pal.Soc.—Monographs of the Palaeontographical Society.
P.G.A.—Proceedings of the Geologists' Association.
Phil. Trans. Roy. Soc.—Philosophical Transactions of the Royal Society.
P.Z.S.—Proceedings of the Zoological Society.
Q.J.G.S.—Quarterly Journal of the Geological Society.
Rep. B.A.—Report of the British Association for the Advancement of Science.
Trans. Roy. Soc. Edin.—Transactions of the Royal Society of Edinburgh.

GENERAL

DAVIES, A. M. (1920). 'An Introduction to Palaeontology', London, Murby.
NEAVERSON, E. (1955). 'Stratigraphical Palaeontology', Oxford.
SCOTT, D. H. (1913-23). 'Studies in Fossil Botany', London, A. & C. Black.
SWINNERTON, H. H. (1947). 'Outlines of Palaeontology', 3rd edit., London, Edward Arnold.
ZITTELL, K. A. von. (1913-1932). Edited by C. R. Eastman and A. S. Woodward, London, Macmillan.
Museums often issue useful and well-illustrated guides.

HISTORICAL AND BIOGRAPHICAL

CLARKE, J. W. and T. McK. HUGHES. (1890). 'The Life and Letters of the Reverend Adam Sedgwick', Cambridge.

COX, L. R. (1956). 'British Palaeontology—a retrospect', P.G.A. 67,209.

BUCKLAND, W. (1824). 'Reliquae Diluvianae', 2nd edit., London.
(Attests the action of a universal deluge. The earliest general account of mammals in caves.)

CONYBEARE, Revd. W. D. and W. PHILLIPS. (1822). 'Outlines of the Geology of England and Wales', London. Hollis & Carter.

FOTHERGILL, P. G. (1952). 'Historical Aspects of Organic Evolution', London.

GEIKIE, Sir ARCHIBALD. (1875). 'Memoirs of Sir Roderick Murchison', London, John Murray.
(1897). 'Founders of Geology', London.

GORDON, Mrs. E. O. (1894). 'The Life and Correspondence of William Buckland, D.D., F.R.S.', London.

LEEDS, E. THURLOW. (1956). 'The Leeds Collection of Fossil Reptiles', Oxford, Blackwell.

LISTER, MARTIN. (1678). 'Historiae Animalium Angliae Tres Tractatus'. London. (Portion of the last part deals with figured stones).

MILLER, HUGH. (1869). 'My Schools and Schoolmasters'. Edinburgh.
(1847). 'The Old Red Sandstone', Edinburgh.

OWEN, Revd. R. (1894). 'Life of Richard Owen'.

PARKINSON, JAMES. (1804-11). 'Organic Remains of a former World', London.

PHILLIPS, JOHN. (1844). 'Memoirs of William Smith, L.L.D., London.

PIDGEON, EDWARD. (1830). 'The Fossil Remains of the Animal Kingdom'.

RAVEN, CANON CHARLES E. (1950). 'John Ray, Naturalist, His life and work'. Cambridge.

SMILES, SAMUEL. (1875). 'Robert Dick, Baker of Thurso, Geologist and Botanist'. London.

SMITH, WILLIAM. (1815). 'Geological Map of England and Wales', and 'A Memoir to the Map and a delineation of the Strata of England and Wales'. London.
(1816). 'Strata identified by Organised Fossils'. London.
(1817). 'A Stratigraphical System of Organised Fossils'. London.

SOWERBY, J. and J. C. (1812-46). 'Mineral Conchology of Great Britain'. Vols. 1—6. Plates 604. London.

WATTS, W. W. (1939). 'The Author of the Ordovician System, Chas. Lapworth'. P.G.A. 50. 235.

WOODWARD, JOHN. (1695). 'Natural History of the Earth and of Terrestrial Bodies'. 3rd Edit., 1723.

ZITTEL, K. A. von. (1901). 'History of Geology and Palaeontology'. Trans. by Mrs. Ogilvie. London.
(Obituary notices of many other workers will be found in various Scientific Journals. Of especial interest is an article on Mary Anning by W. D. Lang in the 'Proceedings' of the Dorset Natural History Society, Vol. 60, 1938. See also remarks by De la Beche in his Presidential Address. Q.J.G.S. Vol. 4. 1848.)

ZOOLOGICAL

BARNARD, T. (1950). 'Foraminifera from the Lower Lias of the Dorset Coast'. Q.J.G.S. 105. 347.
BEER, G. de. (1958). 'Embryos and Ancestors'. Oxford.
BEIRNE, B. P. (1952). 'The Origin and History of the British Fauna'. London, Methuen.
BULMAN, O. M. B. (1933). 'Programme Evolution in the Graptolites'. Biol. Rev.
(1942). 'The Structure of Dendroid Graptolites.' Geol. Mag.
(1958). 'The Sequence of Graptolite Faunas'. Palaeontology. 1.
BISAT, W. S. (1924). 'The Carboniferous Goniatites of the North of England'. Proc. Yorks. Geol., Soc. 20.
CARRUTHERS, R. G. (1910). 'The Evolution of *Zaphrentis delanouei* in the Lower Carboniferous Times.' Q.J.G.S. 66.
DAVIES, W. S. and A. E. TRUEMAN. (1927). 'A Revision of the non-marine Lamellibranchs of the Coal Measures'. Q.J.G.S. 83.
DOWNIE, C. (1957). 'A Microplankton from the Kimmeridge Clay'. Q.J.G.S. 112.
ELLES, G. L. (1922). 'The Graptolite Faunas of the British Isles—a Study in Evolution'. P.G.A. 33.
HAWKINS, H. L. (1912). 'Classification, Morphology and Evolution of the Echinoidea Holectypoida'. P.Z.S.
(1919). 'The Morphology and Evolution of the Ambulacrum in the Echinoidea Holectypoida. Phil. Trans. Roy. Soc. 209.
(1943). 'Evolution and Habits among the Echinoidea'. Q.J.G.S. 99.
LANG, W. D. (1909). 'Growth Stages in the British Species of the Coral Genus *Parasmilia*. P.Z.S.
(1923). 'Trends in British Carboniferous Corals'. P.G.A. 34.
NEWTON, E. T. (1882). 'The Vertebrates of the Forest Bed Series of Norfolk and Suffolk'. Mem. Geol. Surv.
(1891). 'The Vertebrata of the Pliocene Deposits of Britain.' Mem. Geol. Surv.
(1891). 'The Vertebrata of the Pliocene Deposits of Britain. Mem. Geol., Surv.

OWEN, R. (1846). 'The Natural History of British Fossil Mammalia and Birds'. London.

ROWE, A. W. (1899). 'An Analysis of the Genus *Micraster*'. Q.J.G.S. 55.

SIMPSON, G. G. (1928). 'Mesozoic Mammalia'. B. M. Catalogue.

SPATH, L. F. (1938). 'The Ammonites of the Liassic Family Liparoceratidae.' B. M. Catalogue.

SPENCER, W. K. (1914–40). 'British Palaeozoic Asterozoa'. Mon. Pal. Soc. (1913). 'The Evolution of Cretaceous Asteroidea'. Phil. Trans. Roy. Soc. Series B. 204.

SWINNERTON, H. H. (1927). 'Earth Movements and Extinction.' Geol. Mag. 64.

TRUEMAN, A. E. (1922). The Use of *Gryphaea* in the Correlation of the Lower Lias'. Geol. Mag. 509.

VAUGHAN, A. (1905). 'The Palaeontological Sequence in the Carboniferous Limestone of the Bristol Area'. Q.J.G.S. 61.

WILLS, L. J. (1910). 'The Fossiliferous Lower Keuper Rocks of Worcestershire'. P.G.A. 21.

WATSON, D. M. S. (1926). 'Evolution and Origin of Amphibia'. Phil. Trans. Roy. Soc. Series B. 214.
(1937). 'The Acanthodian Fishes'. Phil. Trans. Roy. Roy. Soc. Series B. 228.

MITCHELL, E. (1949). 'The Zonal Value of Foraminifera in the Chalk of England'. P.G.A. 59.

WOOD, A. and BARNARD, T. (1946). '*Ophthalmidium*, a study in Nomenclature, Variation and Evolution in Foraminifera'. Q.J.G.S. 102.

WOODS, H. (1912). 'The Evolution of the genus *Inoceramus* in the Cretaceous Period'. Q.J.G.S. 68.

ZEUNER, F. E. (1940). 'Biology and Evolution of Fossil Insects'. P.G.A. 51.

'The Species Concept in Palaeontology'—A Symposium issued by The Systematics Association, London. 1956.

BOTANICAL

ARBER, E. A. N. (1921). 'Devonian Floras'. Cambridge.

BOWER, F. O. (1908). 'Origin of a Land Flora'. London.

CHANDLER, M. E. J. (1921). 'The Arctic Flora of the Cam Valley of Barnwell. Cambridge'. Q.J.G.S. 77.
(1925–26). 'The Upper Eocene Flora of Hordle, Hants'. Mon. Pal. Soc.

CROFT, W. N. and LANG, W. H. (1942). 'The Lower Devonian Flora of the Senni Beds of Monmouthshire and Breconshire'. Phil. Trans. Roy. Soc. Series B. 231.

Dix, E. (1937). 'The Succession of Fossil Plants in the South Wales Coalfield'. C. R. Congress Stratig. Carb.

Godwin, H. (1956). 'The History of the British Flora'. Cambridge.

Hollingworth, S. E. and Others. (1949). 'Interglacial Deposits from Histon Road, Cambridge'. Q.J.G.S. 105.

Kidston, R. and Lang, W. H. (1917–21). 'Old Red Sandstone Plants from The Rhynie Chert Bed, Aberdeenshire'. Trans. Roy. Soc. Edin. 51,52.

Reid, E. M. (1921). 'Two Preglacial Floras from Castle Eden and a Comparative Review of Pliocene Floras'. Q.J.G.S. 76.

Scott, D. H. (1922). 'The Early History of the Land Flora'. Nature, 110.
(1924). 'Extinct Plants and Problems of Evolution'. Cambridge.

Seward, A. C. (1931). 'Plant Life through the Ages'. Cambridge.

Thomas, H. H. (1925). 'Caytoniales a new Group of Angiospermous Plants from the Jurassic Rocks of Yorkshire'. Phil. Trans. Roy. Soc. Series B. 213.

INDEX

Numbers in heavy type refer to pages opposite which photographic illustrations will be found.